Kenneth R. Driessel

CONFERENCE ON INVERSE SCATTERING: THEORY AND APPLICATION

Conference on Inverse Scattering: Theory and Application

Edited by
J. Bee Bednar, Richard Redner,
Enders Robinson
University of Tulsa
and
Arthur Weglein
SOHIO Petroleum

siam Philadelphia
1983

Library of Congress Catalog Card Number: 83-51381
ISBN: 0-89871-190-8

Contents

PREFACE

Inverse, or system identification problems are fundamental to many areas of science. Whether one is trying to "hear the shape of a drum" from its acoustic signature, or determine the earth's subsurface acoustic impedance from surface reflection data, the underlying concepts are the same. Starting with a general structure consisting of an incompletely specified mathematical model, together with some constraints, and a set of observables related in some way to the model, the idea is to precisely specify the model. Questions concerning how well posed the problem is must be answered and understood before reliable progress toward inversion can be made. When the problem is well-posed, procedures for specifying the model from the data must be constructed. When ill-posed, methods for regularization must be developed. Stability in the presence of measurement error must also be considered and is usually attacked by constraining the size of the admissible data set.

With these general considerations in mind and motivated by recent interest in the geophysical community in the inverse techniques of the quantum physicist, J. Bee Bednar and A. B. Weglein began, in January of 1982, to discuss the possibility of organizing a conference which would bring together some of the leading researchers in scattering in an open atmosphere for discussion. This nucleus was increased with the addition of Richard Redner and E. A. Robinson. Within a brief period the foundations of the conference were outlined. There was to be a coherent series of reasonably expository lectures which would form the thread from which the conference would be sewn. Additional contributions from geophysical inversion and inverse problems in general would be organized into a unified whole. To provide a forum for intellectual exchange among participants, the agenda should allow the conference to develop at an unhurried pace. With the active support of the University of Tulsa, plans were solidified and the conference became a reality in Tulsa on May 16–18, 1983.

Roger Newton, Distinguished Professor of Physics at Indiana University, consented to provide the expository lectures and critical commentary during the course of the other presentations. As his article indicates, he did this superbly. He was admirably aided by the other speakers which included P. C. Sabatier, Reese Prosser, Sven Treitel, Enders Robinson, M. A. Hooshyar, Tom Banks, Patricia Daniel Lamm, Gregory Beylkin, Robert Carroll, L. R. Lines, Kenneth Driessel, Patrick Lailly, Weldon Wilson, S. Coen, M. Cheney, A. B. Weglein, Steven Johnson, R. H. Stolt, A. Tarantola, and Robert Phinney.

The majority of the comments of the aforementioned participants are collected together in this volume. To assist the reader, an introduction to the papers provides brief descriptions of their contents. The papers are also grouped into informal sections to provide easy access to specific areas of interest.

Contributions to the organization of the conference by Nick Sylvester, E. J. Douze, William Coberly, Milt Jarrett, Pat Hall, and the entire staff of the University of Tulsa's continuing education department are acknowledged and appreciated. Special additional thanks are due to Pat Hall for organizing a lovely conference banquet. The secretarial assistance of Sherry Graves and Terry Saunders is also acknowledged.

INTRODUCTION TO THE PAPERS

The purpose of this introduction is to provide a method by which readers with specific interests might better direct their attention to the contents of this volume. To achieve this goal, the papers were ordered into four vaguely defined categories. The first category is expository and contains only the paper by Roger Newton. The second category, consisting of the papers of Sabatier, Prosser, Beylkin, and Driessel and Symes, is largely theoretical. The third category consists of papers which are not directly concerned with reflection seismic applications. This category includes papers by Johnson et al., Hooshyar and Razavy, Wilson, Banks et al., and (Daniel) Lamm. The final category covers those applications which are directly related to reflection seismology and includes the works of Lailly, Coen et al., Carroll and Santosa, Treitel and Lines, and Robinson.

A brief discussion of the papers must begin with the excellent tutorial and exposition by Newton. As was the case for his lectures during the course of the conference, Professor Newton's remarks represent an enjoyable and comprehensive survey of the one-dimensional Marchenko and Gel'fand-Levitan inversion procedures and their extension to three dimensions.

A Darboux transformation based algorithm for solving the inverse problem for the one-dimensional Schrodinger equation with rational reflection coefficients is presented by P. C. Sabatier. Reese Prosser follows Sabatier's remarks with a discussion of the Born series approximation to the Gel'fand-Levitan equation from the point of view of quantitative estimation of the errors of these approximations. This algorithm is reminiscent of techniques for removing instabilities from analogue linear systems. Beylkin's paper considers the representation of a function in terms of the iterated spherical mean of its Fourier transform and reviews the applications of such a representation in diffraction tomography. The Born and Rytov approximations in inverse scattering theory are also considered. The theoretical aspects of the Cholesky decomposition and the Gel'fand-Levitan equation are discussed and applied to symmetric kernels in the paper by Driessel and Symes.

The first application section of the book begins with a procedure for construction of the shear modulus and the density profiles of a laterally homogeneous medium from known values of the logarithmic derivative of the surface torsional displacement at two distinct frequencies. This paper by Hooshyar and Razavy is novel because of the continued fraction development of the procedure. Johnson et al. present a method for solving the inverse scattering problem for the scalar, inhomogeneous exact,

Lippmann-Schwinger equation. Inverse scattering methods as they apply to the determination of the parameters for reservoir analysis are *discussed* by Wilson. This work leans heavily on the work of M. S. Howard (referenced in the paper by Wilson) on inverse scattering using the first-order equations of motion. Following Wilson, papers by Banks et al. and (Daniel) Lamm consider the computational and approximation theoretic aspects of parameter estimation in distributed systems. Because these two papers consider the parameter estimation problem from a least squares fit-to-data point of view, they serve as a kind of bridge to the seismic papers which conclude the volume. Specifically, they introduce least squares optimization methods which are similar in spirit to the techniques discussed by Lailly.

Lailly, using the least squares optimal control approach, shows that linearization of the inverse problem about a space varying reference medium leads to an iterative inverse procedure whose first step is interpretable as a "before stack migration." Subsequent iterations are residual before stack migrations. Coen, Cheney and Weglein consider the possibility that the subsurface is constant in one spatial horizontal direction, and Fourier transform the three-dimensional wave equation to yield a two-dimensional equation which can be attacked by the generalized Marchenko-Gel'fand-Levitan machinery developed by Cheney in her doctoral research. Carroll and Santosa study the inverse problem as a transmission rather than a reflection problem. They develop a formula for the spectral measure as the Fourier transform of an autocorrelation function and develop a generalized Gel'fand-Levitan equation for their seismic problem. Suggestions are made that some of the inverse theory may have links to statistical time series methods and concepts. Treitel and Lines consider seismic deconvolution within the Backus-Gilbert linear inverse theory and discuss its relationship to traditional Wiener shaping filters. Finally, Robinson concludes the volume with a discussion of the practical aspects of current processing steps in seismic inversion by least squares deconvolution.

The Marchenko and Gel'fand-Levitan Methods in the Inverse Scattering Problem in One and Three Dimensions

Roger G. Newton*

Abstract. This paper reviews the Marchenko and Gel'fand-Levitan approaches to inverse scattering problems in one and three dimensions. It also contains general remarks on the nature of inverse-scattering problems and an introduction to the differential equations considered as they arise in various physical contexts.

Preface. The purpose of this paper is not primarily to present formulas that may be useful for the physical application of inverse-scattering theory. First and foremost it is to give in a coherent manner, the underlying ideas that, at least in one way of looking at them, make the inversion procedures of Marchenko [1] and Gel'fand and Levitan [2] possible. Once these are properly understood in the one-dimensional case their transfer to three dimensions (or other dimensions) becomes almost obvious, though the proofs of the needed properties of the functions involved are not. About half of this paper therefore deals with the well-known one-dimensional inverse problem [3-13].

The three dimensional generalization that is discussed in this paper was given by the author in a series of papers [14-18] over the last four years. (For earlier approaches see [19-24].) These papers contain a number of errors that were later corrected, and false early leads that were later superseded. They also started out using a cumbersome notation that was changed in midstream. The present paper corrects all of these faults and I hope it will make the entire theory more accessible. It contains very few new results but ought to make those presented more coherent. Almost no proofs are given. For these I refer to the original papers.

The work on which this paper is based was supported in part by grants from the National Science Foundation.

*Physics Department, Indiana University, Bloomington, IN 47405

1980 Mathematics Subject Classification 35J10, 35R30, 81F05;
1983 PACS 03.65.Nk, 84.40.Mk, 91.90+p.

Table of Contents

1. Introduction. We are going to study inverse problems that have the following structure: A certain linear differential equation, or a system of such, that contains one or more (usually real-valued) functions is given; we shall call these functions schematically the forces. The equation may be that of electromagnetic or sound waves in media, or it may be the Schrödinger equation. (We shall always work in the frequency domain rather than the time domain.) The forces are then the index of refraction, the density, the velocity of sound, the impedance, moduli of elasticity, or the potential. The solution of the differential equation, with specified boundary conditions, leads to the determination of a set of quantities that are directly or indirectly connected with observations. These we shall call the data. They include such objects as scattering, reflection, and transmission amplitudes, and they are usually complex valued. The data may also include such other functions or numbers as turn out to be necessary.

The differential equation, with given boundary conditions, thus determines a map M from the forces to the data. The construction of this map and of its properties makes up the direct problem. To invert it, to find the forces from the data, is the inverse problem.

The data are usually not functions on the space on which the differential equation lives; they are functions of such variables as frequency or energy and angles that appear as parameters in the differential equation or in the boundary conditions. One of the important aspects of the direct problem is therefore the study of the functional dependence of the data on these parameters. The nature of this functional dependence determines the solution of the inverse problem.

In order to solve the direct problem one usually has to place restrictions on the force functions and work with a specified class F of forces. These restrictions may be partly technical and vary somewhat from one result to another, and partly fundamental. For example, the potential in the Schrödinger equation has to decrease to zero in some fashion at infinity in order for a scattering problem to make sense; the exact meaning of that "decrease" may however vary from one result to another.

Let us call D the image of the class F under M; D is the class of data that can be obtained from underlying forces F in the manner indicated. It is the class of admissible data.

The inverse problem has the following four separate components:

1) *Uniqueness*. The first question is whether the map M from F to D is one to one, or if perhaps several points in F have the same image. If M is not one to one then the inverse problem is ill-posed and our first task is to enlarge the number of quantities to be included as data until it becomes one to one, if that is possible. From a physical point of view this task is one of the most important aims of the solu-

tion of the inverse problem; it tells us what kind of information is required to infer the forces uniquely.

2) *Reconstruction*. Here we are given a set of data that is known to be the image of some member f of F, and the problem is to find a construction procedure to recover f, assuming that the uniqueness problem has been solved.

3) *Construction*. Suppose we are given data that are not known to be the image under M of some member of F. Then the first problem is to decide whether underlying forces exist, i.e., whether the data are admissible. We are thus led to the question of characterizing the admissible class D. Naturally we mean by this a characterization other than that D is the image of F under M: One wants to be able to recognize in some way if given data are admissible. In addition to the characterization, of course, as in the reconstruction we require uniqueness and a construction procedure. Since the characterization usually comes out of such a procedure, it is necessary to make sure that the constructed functions when used as forces are actually the pre-images of the given data under M.

The characterization problem is sometimes much simplified by enlarging the set F beyond what, perhaps for physical reasons, seems initially desirable, i.e., by embedding the inverse problem for M: $F \to D$ in one for M': $F' \to D'$, where $F \subset F'$, $D \subset D'$. It may be easier to characterize D' than D. One then finds the map M'^{-1}: $D' \to F'$, and if the solution to a particular problem is in F then one knows that the data were in D, provided that the uniqueness problem has been solved for M'.

In some instances the characterization problem is particularly severe because the data over-determine the forces, i.e., they are redundant. If a subset of the data can be identified as being sufficient the problem may be much simplified. The characterization problem is then replaced by a consistency problem. Since a part of the data determines the forces, the remainder is not independent and may not be compatible with the first part. An example of such a situation is the Schrödinger equation in three dimensions. The scattering amplitude, as a function of the angles and the energy, is redundant. If F is restricted to central potentials, the data for one angular momentum are sufficient. Instead of a difficult characterization problem one then has a compatibility problem (which is unsolved) for data of different angular momenta.

One other word of caution. The solution of the inverse problem must always rely on certain properties of the solution of the differential equation (with the given boundary condition). Sometimes it is convenient to start the logical chain with these properties, that is, to postulate them rather than to prove them. (Examples are the existence of the Povsner-Levitan representation with its famous triangular kernel and the Gel'fand-Levitan equation.) If this is done, both the resulting sets $\hat{F}$ and $\hat{D}$ require characterization, and the set $\hat{F}$ may be very small. There is particular danger if this procedure is used for an enlarged problem in which the one of interest is to be embedded; the intersetion of $\hat{F}'$ with F may be empty.

4) *Stability*. From a practical point of view it is of great importance to know if the inversion is stable with respect to small perturbations, i.e., if in some useful topology M^{-1} is continuous. Since real data always have errors an unstable procedure is of little use. Part of the stability problem is connected to the characterization problem. If the boundary of D is hard to recognize most small perturbations of all admissible data may make them inadmissible. This problem has received relatively little attention.

As a fifth component of the inverse problem we might mention one that in principle has great practical importance: Inversion from partial data (for example, band-limited data). Though uniqueness can in this case not be expected, one would like to know what restriction a knowledge of partial data places on the forces. Very little is known about this difficult problem.

2. The Equations. In a fluid medium a dilational stress wave of frequency ω is governed by the equation of motion

(2.1) $$-\omega^2\rho \underset{\sim}{W} = \underset{\sim}{\nabla} P ,$$

where $\underset{\sim}{W}$ is the displacement, P the isotropic stress, and ρ the density. The supplementary strain-stress relation, if linear and isotropic, is given by

(2.2) $$P = \rho\alpha^2 \underset{\sim}{\nabla}\cdot \underset{\sim}{W} ,$$

where α is the local velocity of sound. For vertical sound propagation in an elastic stratified medium for which ρ and α depend on z only, these equations simplify to

$$-\omega^2\rho W = dP/dz , \qquad P = \rho\alpha^2 dW/dz ,$$

in which $W = \underset{\sim}{W}_z$. The introduction of the propagation time

(2.3) $$\tau(z) = \int_0^z dz'/\alpha(z')$$

further simplifies these to

(2.4) $$-Z^2\omega^2 W = dP/d\tau , \qquad Z^2 dW/d\tau = P ,$$

where

(2.5) $Z^2 = \alpha\rho$

is the acoustical impedance.

The introduction of the new dependent variables $\Phi_1 = ZW$ and $\Phi_2 = -i\omega^{-1}Z^{-1}P$ leads to the system

$$\frac{d\Phi_1}{d\tau} = i\omega\,\Phi_2 + \left(Z^{-1}\frac{dZ}{d\tau}\right)\Phi_1$$

(2.6)

$$\frac{d\Phi_2}{d\tau} = i\omega\,\Phi_1 - \left(Z^{-1}\frac{dZ}{d\tau}\right)\Phi_2$$

which may be uncoupled:

(2.7) $$\frac{d^2\Phi_1}{d\tau^2} - V(\tau)\,\Phi_1 + \omega^2\,\Phi_1 = 0\ ,$$

where

(2.8) $V(\tau) = Z^{-1}\,d^2Z/d\tau^2$.

Study may now proceed either via that of the first-order system (2.6) or via the second-order Schrödinger equation (2.7). The restrictions needed on V in (2.7) place more severe constraints on the impedance than (2.6).

In seismology one seeks to solve (2.6) or (2.7) on the half-line $\tau \geq 0$, with the boundary condition that as $\tau \to \infty$ there should be no leftward (upward) travelling waves. If such a solution is normalized by the boundary condition $\phi_1(\tau = 0+) = 1$ then $\phi_2(\tau = 0+)$ for (2.6) and $\phi_1'(\tau = 0+)$ for (2.7) may constitute the data, considered as a function of ω. In the terminology used in the Introduction, the force is the impedance $Z(\tau)$. While it may be desirable to find both the density ρ and the sound velocity α, there is no way of determining both separately in the context of vertical propagation in a horizontally layered medium. (However, see [25,26].)

The propagation of electromagnetic waves in a medium of index of refraction n is governed by the equation

(2.9) $(\Delta + \omega^2 n^2)\phi = 0$.

If we write $V = \omega^2(1 - n^2)$ then (2.9) has the structure of (2.7), except that the potential V is proportional to ω^2, which very much complicates the inverse problem. If a finite scattering obstacle is placed in vacuum then outside its boundary n = 1, and hence V has compact support.

The equation (2.9) in one dimension may be simplified by a Liouville transformation similar to that used for (2.4). Defining

$$(2.10) \qquad \rho(x) = \int_{-\infty}^{x} dx'[n(x') - 1] + x$$

and setting $f = n^{\frac{1}{2}}\phi$ one obtains (2.7) with

$$(2.11) \qquad V(\rho) = n^{-\frac{1}{2}}\, d^2 n^{\frac{1}{2}}/d\rho^2 \ .$$

A similar trick works for the radial equation in two or three dimensions if n depends on the radial distance r only and (2.7) is separated in spherical coordinates [27]. Thus the factor ω^2 in the potential may be eliminated. If n is not rotationally invariant this cannot be done.

In one dimension the equation (2.7) also arises from an uncoupling of the first-order equations that govern electromagnetic propagation in a transmission line. If v is the voltage, j the current, L the inductance, and C the capacitance then

$$(2.12) \qquad \frac{dv}{dx} = i\omega Lj \ , \qquad \frac{dj}{dx} = i\omega Cv \ .$$

In this case the appropriate Liouville transformation is [28]

$$(2.13) \qquad \tau = \int_{a}^{x} dx'(LC)^{\frac{1}{2}} \ ,$$

$$v = Z^{\frac{1}{2}}\phi \ , \qquad Z = L/C \ ,$$

and the result is (2.7) with $V = Z^{\frac{1}{2}} d^2 Z^{-\frac{1}{2}}/dx^2$.

What constitutes relevant data will be discussed when we analyze equations (2.6) and (2.7). From the point of view of (2.7) the force is V. To solve an inverse problem for the force in (2.6) or (2.9) via (2.7) requires the solution of the question

$$(2.14) \qquad y'' = Vy \ ,$$

in which V is known, and in one case $y = n^{\frac{1}{2}}$ and in the other $y = Z$. If the problem is posed on the whole real line, such that $y \to 1$ as $\rho \to \pm\infty$, then (2.14) constitutes a quasi-eigenvalue problem, and for a given V that is the result of a construction from given data it will have a solution only under excpetional circumstances. The same remark applies to the radial equation if n is central, in which case the boundary conditions are $n(o) = 0$ and $n \to 1$ as $\rho \to \infty$. In the seismic case the boundary condition as $\rho \to \infty$ is $Z \to Z_\infty$, where Z_∞ is finite but may be unknown. In that case Z is uniquely determined if its value Z_o at $\rho = 0$ is known, and (2.14) always has a solution (provided that V is reasonable). Of course, if both Z_o and Z_∞ are known then we have a similar quasi-eigenvalue problem as in the electromagnetic case.

It is therefore important to realize that, even if there is no severe characterization problem in the inversion associated with (2.7), the final step to the impedance or the refractive index may impose strong restrictions on the admissible data, the nature of which may be far from transparent.

There is one further step needed in equation (2.9). Once $n(\rho)$ is found from (2.14), (2.10) has to be inverted. This, however, is trivially accomplished by

$$(2.15) \qquad x(\rho) = \int_{-\infty}^{\rho} d\rho' \left[\frac{1}{n(\rho')} - 1\right] + \rho .$$

As a final point of this section let us consider the question of eigenvalues or modes. If we are concerned with the Schrödinger equation (2.7) (or with its analog in R^3) directly, with no restrictions on V (other than decrease to zero, in some appropriate form, at large distance) then the equation may have eigenvalues, or bound states. However, in the acoustic and electromagnetic case these can be ruled out on the grounds of causality.

In the time domain any signal that vanishes for all negative times must give rise to a transmitted signal that also vanishes for all negative times. Fourier transformation implies that consequently in the frequency domain, any signal that has an analytic continuation into the upper half of the complex plane with no singularities there must give rise to a transmitted signal with the same property. Hence the transmission amplitude must also have that property. As we shall see, bound states give rise to poles of the transmission amplitude in the upper half-plane. Thus they are ruled out.

The causality argument is operative whenever the equation in the frequency domain originates from a hyperbolic equation in the time domain (or leads to one, as in the acoustic case). It fails for the time-dependent Schrödinger equation.

3. The Direct Problem for the Schrödinger Equation in One Dimension. *a. The scattering solution.* We shall first consider the direct problem for the Schrödinger equation

$$(3.1) \qquad Vy - \frac{d^2y}{dx^2} = k^2 y ,$$

where we have written k instead of ω to conform with most of the literature. Eq. (3.1) will be taken on the full line $-\infty < x < \infty$. For seismological applications one sets $V(x) \equiv 0$ for $x < 0$, which simplifies some results as we shall point out later.

The continuous spectrum of (3.1) has multiplicity two, corresponding to the solutions exp(ikx) and exp(-ikx) for V = 0. Therefore we form a two-component column vector ψ out of two solutions of (3.1) and replace the differential equation directly by an integral equation that incorporates the boundary conditions appropriate for scattering, the Lippmann-Schwinger equation:

$$(3.2) \qquad \psi(k,x) = \psi_0(k,x) - (i/2k) \int_{-\infty}^{\infty} dy e^{ik|x-y|} V(y)\, \psi(k,y)$$

where

$$\psi_0(k,x) = \begin{pmatrix} \exp(ikx) \\ \exp(-ikx) \end{pmatrix}$$

is the "free" solution. The solution ψ of (3.2) is characterized by the boundary condition that for large $|x|$ it differs from ψ_0 only by waves that travel away from the origin, i.e., towards $-\infty$ for $x < 0$, and towards $+\infty$ for $x > 0$. Introducing the matrices

$$I = \begin{pmatrix} 1 & 0 \\ 0 & -1 \end{pmatrix}, \qquad \overset{\circ}{1} = \begin{pmatrix} 1 \\ 1 \end{pmatrix}$$

we may write $\psi_0 = \exp(iIkx)\overset{\circ}{1}$.

Multiplying (3.2) by $|V(x)|^{1/2}$ we obtain the integral equation

$$(3.3) \qquad \xi(x) = \xi_0(x) + \int_{-\infty}^{\infty} dy\; K(x,y)\, \xi(y) ,$$

where $\xi(x) = |V(x)|^{1/2} \psi(k,x)$ and $K(x,y) = -(i/2k)|V(x)|^{1/2} V(y)|V(y)|^{-1/2} \exp(ik|x-y|)$. If $V \in L^1(R)$ then for all real $k \neq 0$ or $\mathrm{Im}k > 0$, K is in the Hilbert-Schmidt class with a finite trace and analytic Fredholm theory is applicable. As a result $\psi(k,x)$ exists and is found [7,8], for each x, to be a continuous function of k for all real $k \neq 0$, with an analytic continuation into C^+ (the upper half of the complex plane) that is meromorphic there. One also finds that as $|k| \to \infty$ for $\mathrm{Im}k \geq 0$

$$(3.4) \qquad e^{-iIkx}\psi(k,x) = \overset{\circ}{1} + O(|k|^{-1}) .$$

Eq. (3.2) leads to the asymptotic form as $|x| \to \infty$

(3.5) $\psi(k,x) = \psi_0(k,x) + e^{ik|x|} A(k,\varepsilon) + o(1)$

where $\varepsilon = x/|x|$ and

$$A(1) = \begin{pmatrix} T_\ell - 1 \\ R_r \end{pmatrix}, \qquad A(-1) = \begin{pmatrix} R_\ell \\ T_r - 1 \end{pmatrix}.$$

Here T_ℓ, T_r, R_ℓ, R_r are the transmission and reflection amplitudes for incidence from the left and right, respectively. That the components of $A(\varepsilon)$ have this significance is seen from the asymptotic behavior of the components of ψ:

$$\psi^{(1)} = \begin{cases} T_\ell e^{ikx} + o(1), & \text{as } x \to +\infty, \\ e^{ikx} + R_\ell e^{-ikx} + o(1), & \text{as } x \to -\infty. \end{cases}$$

Thus the first component of ψ describes a wave of unit amplitude impinging on the center from the left, being partially reflected and partially transmitted. Similarly for the second component, from the right:

$$\psi^{(2)} = \begin{cases} e^{-ikx} + R_r e^{ikx} + o(1), & \text{as } x \to \infty, \\ T_r e^{-ikx} + o(1), & \text{as } x \to -\infty. \end{cases}$$

It will be useful to form a square matrix A from the two row matrices $\tilde{A}(+1)$ and $\tilde{A}(-1)$, (the tilde will always denote the transpose):

$$A = \begin{pmatrix} T_\ell - 1 & R_r \\ R_\ell & T_r - 1 \end{pmatrix}.$$

From the Lippmann-Schwinger equation (3.2) and (3.5) one obtains the integral representation

(3.6) $A(k) = (1/2ik) \int_{-\infty}^{\infty} dx\, \bar{\psi}_0(k,x)\, V(x)\, \tilde{\psi}(k,x)$,

where the bar denotes the complex conjugate.

The Wronskian matrix

$$W(\psi,\tilde{\psi}) = \psi\tilde{\psi}' - \psi'\tilde{\psi}$$

(where the prime indicated the derivative) is independent of x. If we evaluate it as $x \to +\infty$ and as $x \to -\infty$ we find from the asymptotics of ψ that

$$W(\psi,\tilde{\psi}) = -2ik\, T_\ell \begin{pmatrix} 0 & 1 \\ -1 & 0 \end{pmatrix} = -2ik\, T_r \begin{pmatrix} 0 & 1 \\ -1 & 0 \end{pmatrix} .$$

Consequently $T_\ell = T_r = T$, and the S matrix is defined

(3.7) $$S = \mathbb{1} + A = \begin{pmatrix} T & R_r \\ R_\ell & T \end{pmatrix} ,$$

where $\mathbb{1}$ is the unit matrix. If we define

$$q = \begin{pmatrix} 0 & 1 \\ 1 & 0 \end{pmatrix}$$

then the equality of T_ℓ and T_r can be written as

(3.8) $$\tilde{S} = q\, S\, q ,$$

which is known as reciprocity.

The two components of the solution $\psi(k,x)$ are linearly independent and every solution of (3.1) must be expressible as a matrix-multiple of it. In particular the solution $\psi(-k,x)$ must be so expressible:

$$\psi(-k,x) = M\, \psi(k,x) .$$

We shall from now on always use the notation, for any function of k, $f^{\#}(k) = f(-k)$. This will simplify our formulas.

Comparison of the coefficients of e^{ikx} and e^{-ikx} as $x \to \pm\infty$ allows us to conclude that for all $k \in \mathbb{R}$ $M = qS^{\#}$, i.e.

(3.9) $$\psi^{\#} = qS^{\#}\psi .$$

This equation, together with (3.8) implies that

(3.10) $$S^{\#}\tilde{S} = \tilde{S}S^{\#} = 1 .$$

We note from (3.2) that for real k

(3.11) $$\psi(-k,x) = \bar{\psi}(k,x) ,$$

and therefore by (3.6) also $A^{\#} = \bar{A}$ and

(3.12) $S^{\#} = \bar{S}$.

These equations rely in an essential way on the reality of V, a property that had not been utilized until this point. Eqs. (3.10) and (3.12) imply that S is unitary. If V is not real, which would be the case for absorptive potentials or lossy transmission lines, for example, the unitarity of S breaks down, but (3.9) and (3.10) still hold.

For future reference we write the unitarity of S explicitly in terms of its elements:

(3.13a) $|R_\ell|^2 = |R_r|^2 = 1 - |T|^2$,

(3.13b) $\frac{R_\ell R_r}{|R_\ell R_r|} = - \frac{T^2}{|T|^2}$.

It also follows that the determinant of S is given by

(3.14) $\det S = T/\bar{T}$.

The Jost solution $f^{(1)} = \psi^{(1)}/T$ of (3.1) approaches exp(ikx) as $x \to \infty$. It therefore satisfies the integral equation

(3.15) $f^{(1)}(k,x) = e^{ikx} - k^{-1} \int_x^\infty dy \sin k(x - y)\, V(y)\, f^{(1)}(k,y)$.

The asymptotics of $f^{(1)}$ as $x \to \infty$ then lead to the integral representations

(3.16) $1/T = 1 + (i/2k) \int_{-\infty}^\infty dx\, e^{-ikx}\, V(x)\, f^{(1)}(k,x)$,

$R_\ell/T = -(i/2k) \int_{-\infty}^\infty dx\, e^{ikx}\, V(x)\, f^{(1)}(k,x)$.

Similarly $f^{(2)} = \psi^{(2)}/T$ must satisfy the equation

(3.15') $f^{(2)}(k,x) = e^{-ikx} + k^{-1} \int_{-\infty}^x dy \sin k(x - y)\, V(x)\, f^{(2)}(k,y)$,

which leads to

(3.17) $R_r/T = -(i/2k) \int_{-\infty}^\infty dx\, e^{-ikx}\, V(x)\, f^{(2)}(k,x)$.

These equations are useful in the limit as $k \to 0$:

$$f^{(1)}(0,x) = 1 - \int_x^\infty dy\,(x - y)\,V(x)\,f^{(1)}(0,y)$$

$$f^{(2)}(0,x) = 1 + \int_{-\infty}^x dy\,(x - y)\,V(y)\,f^{(2)}(0,y)$$

if we assume that $|x|V \in L^1(R)$. It follows from (3.16) and (3.17) therefore that in general T vanishes as $k \to 0$ [if $|x|^2 V \in L^1(R)$ then it does so exactly linearly], and R_ℓ and R_r approach $-1 + O(k)$:

(3.18) $$\lim_{k\to 0} S(k) = -q ,$$

where q is the matrix defined below (3.7). In that case we must also have $\psi^{(1)}(0,x) = \psi^{(2)}(0,x) = 0$. However, in exceptional cases this may not be so. If $\int dx\, Vf^{(1)}(0,x) = 0$ then (3.18) fails and (3.16), (3.17), (3.12), and (3.13a) imply that

(3.18') $$\lim_{k\to 0} S(k) = \mathbb{1} .$$

In this exceptional case there exists a solution of (3.1) with $k = 0$ that remains bounded both as $x \to -\infty$ and as $x \to +\infty$. We then have a "half-bound state." In one dimension there is never a bound state at $k = 0$.

If the Schrödinger equation originates from propagation of sound or electromagnetic waves, as described in Sec. 2, then the impedance (or the refractive index) is connected with V by (2.14). The boundary condition that Z should approach a constant as $x \to \infty$ then implies that $Z(x) = cf^{(1)}(0,x)$. In that case by (2.8)

$$\int_0^\infty dx\, V(x)\, f^{(1)}(0,x) = -c\, Z_0' ,$$

where Z_0' is the derivative of the impedance at the surface, $x = 0$. Therefore, if there is a homogeneous surface layer so that $Z_0' = 0$ then there is a half-bound state at $k = 0$ and $T(0) = 1$, but if $Z_0' \neq 0$ then $T(0) = 0$ and $R_\ell(0) = R_r(0) = -1$.

If $V(x) \equiv 0$ for $x < 0$ then

(3.19) $$d(k) = \frac{\psi^{(1)\prime}(k,0)}{\psi^{(1)}(k,0)} = ik\,\frac{1 - R_\ell}{1 + R_\ell} .$$

$\psi^{(1)}$ is a multiple of the solution of interest in seismology, because for $x \to \infty$ it contains right-ward traveling waves only. By the argument given in Sec. 2 (3.19) connects R_ℓ directly with the data d(k).

The properties of $\psi(k,x)$ and the integral representation (3.6) imply [7,8] that if $V \in L^1(R)$ and $|x|V \in L^1(R)$ then S(k) is continuous for real k and as $k \to \pm\infty$

(3.20) $$S(k) = \mathbb{1} + O(|k|^{-1}) .$$

Furthermore T(k) has an analytic continuation into C^+ that is meromorphic there, free of zeros, and as $|k| \to \infty$

(3.21) $$T(k) = 1 + O(|k|^{-1}) .$$

On the real axis by (3.15), $f^{(1)}(k,x) = \exp(ikx) + O(1/k)$ as $k \to \infty$. Therefore by (3.16) and (3.21)

(3.22) $$R_\ell(k) = -(i/2k)\,\tilde{V}(2k) + O(1/k^2) ,$$

where

$$\tilde{V}(k) = \int_{-\infty}^{\infty} dx\, e^{ikx}\, V(x) .$$

It follows that if $V \in L^2$ then $R_\ell \in L^1$, and similarly, $R_r \in L^1$.

One readily proves [7,8] from (3.15) and (3.15') that the column matrix f, whose components are $f^{(1)}$ and $f^{(2)}$, for each fixed x has an analytic continuation into C^+ that is holomorphic there. Therefore the poles of ψ in C^+ are due to the poles of T and of the same multiplicity. In fact, it can be shown that 1/T is the Fredholm determinant of (3.2).

b. The Jost function and the solution ϕ. Another column solution $\phi(k,x)$ of (3.1) may be defined by the boundary condition at x = 0

(3.23) $$\phi(0) = \begin{pmatrix}1\\1\end{pmatrix} \equiv \mathring{1} , \qquad \left.\frac{d\phi}{dx}\right|_{x=0} = ik\begin{pmatrix}1\\-1\end{pmatrix} .$$

It solves the Volterra equation $[\phi_o(k,x) = \exp(ikIx)\mathring{1} = \psi_o]$

(3.24) $$\phi(k,x) = \phi_o(k,x) + (1/k)\int_0^x dy\, \sin k(x-y)\, V(y)\, \phi(k,y)$$

and if $V \in L^1(R)$ then for each fixed x it and its x-derivative are entire analytic functions of k of exponential type $|x|$ [9]. There must exist a 2×2 matrix J such that

$$(3.25) \quad J(k)\ \psi(k,x) = \phi(k,x) .$$

Using (3.23) to calculate the Wronskian $W(\phi,\tilde{\phi})$ and using the Wronskian $W(\psi,\tilde{\psi})$ above (3.7) we find that

$$(3.26) \quad \tilde{J}^{-1} = T\, P\, J\, P , \qquad P = \begin{pmatrix} 0 & 1 \\ -1 & 0 \end{pmatrix} = Iq$$

and

$$(3.26') \quad J = (1/2ikT)\ W(\phi,\tilde{\psi})P .$$

Eq. (3.26) implies that

$$(3.27) \quad \det J = 1/T .$$

It follows (3.26') and the properties of ϕ, ψ, and T that for real $k \neq 0$ J(k) is continuous and that it has an analytic continuation into C^+ that is holomorphic there [9]. Furthermore, as $k \to \pm\infty$ and as $|k| \to \infty$ in C^+

$$(3.28) \quad J(k) = \mathbb{1} + O(1/|k|) .$$

As $k \to 0$, $J(k) = O(1/k)$ but in the generic case [i.e., when T(0) = 0] it follows from (3.26) that J^{-1} is continuous at k = 0. In the exceptional case when $T(0) \neq 0$, $J^{-1}(k) = ck^{-1} + o(k^{-1})$, $c \neq 0$ [9].

The boundary conditions (3.23) imply that

$$(3.29) \quad \phi^{\#} = q\ \phi .$$

Consequently (3.25) and (3.9) lead to the equation

$$(3.30) \quad J^{\#-1} = S^{-1}\ q\ J^{-1}\ q .$$

We note that the reality of V has not been used for the derivation of any of these equations [except for the unitary of S, which has not been used for (3.30)].

If $V \equiv 0$ for $x < 0$ a simple calculation using (3.26') shows that

$$(3.31) \quad J = \frac{1}{T}\begin{pmatrix} T & -R_\ell \\ 0 & 1 \end{pmatrix} .$$

However, in the general case, when $V \not\equiv 0$ for $x < 0$, there is no explicit solution of (3.30) that has the correct analytic and asymptotic properties. It should be noted that the point $x = 0$ plays a special role in the definition of J because the solution ϕ is defined by boundary conditions there. Therefore if $V \equiv 0$ for $x < a < 0$ but $V \not\equiv 0$ in $a < x < 0$, then J does not have the form (3.21) and in fact cannot be given explicitly.

Returning to the solution ϕ we note that because $\phi(k,x)$ is, at fixed x, an entire function of k of exponential type $|x|$, and on the real axis square integrable [as easily follows from (3.24)], it follows from the Paley-Wiener theorem that ϕ has the Povsner-Levitan representation [9]

$$(3.32)\qquad \phi(k,x) = e^{ikIx}\,\mathring{1} - \int_{-x}^{x} dy\, h(x,y) e^{ikIy}\,\mathring{1}\,.$$

Inserting this into (3.24) we find that $h(x,y)$ is not a matrix (i.e., it is a multiple of the 2×2 unit matrix) and that it must satisfy the integral equation

$$(3.33)\qquad h(x,y) = -\frac{1}{2}\int_{0}^{\frac{1}{2}(x+y)} dz\quad V(z) - \frac{1}{2}\int_{\Omega(x,y)} dt\, dz\, V(t)\, h(t,z)\,,$$

where the region Ω is the rectangle bounded by the lines $t = -z$, $t = y + x - z$, $t = z$, $t = x - y + z$. Eq. (3.33) implies that $h(x,y)$ is continuous. Furthermore, as $y \to -x$ and as $y \to x$ the area Ω shrinks to zero. Therefore, for $|y| \le |x|$,

$$(3.34)\qquad h(x,-x) \equiv \lim_{y \downarrow -x} h(x,y) = 0\,,$$

$$(3.35)\qquad h(x,x) \equiv \lim_{y \uparrow x} h(x,y) = -\frac{1}{2}\int_{0}^{x} dz\, V(z)\,.$$

The last equation implies that

$$(3.36)\qquad -2\frac{d}{dx} h(x,x) = V(x)\,.$$

Eq. (3.33) also leads to the partial differential equation for $h(x,y)$

$$(3.37)\qquad \left(\frac{\partial^2}{\partial x^2} - \frac{\partial^2}{\partial y^2}\right) h(x,y) = V(x)\, h(x,y)\,.$$

c. Bound states. The Fredholm determinant of (3.3) being equal to $1/T$, it follows that when $1/T = 0$, the homogeneous form of (3.3) has a nontrivial solution. For real k this cannot happen, because of

(3.13). If it occurs at a value κ of k for which Im $\kappa > 0$ then the corresponding solution of the homogeneous form of (3.2) is an eigenfunction of (3.1) with the eigenvalue κ^2. There cannot be two linearly independent eigenfunctions of the same eigenvalue; otherwise all solutions for that value of k would have to decrease exponentially. So there can be no degeneracy. If V is real then the operator in (3.1) is essentially self-adjoint and hence κ must lie on the imaginary axis. As T is meromorphic in C^+ the points κ are its poles. Their number must be finite if $(1 + x^2)V \in L^1(R)$ because then T tends to 1 as $|k| \to \infty$ and as $k \to 0$ it can at most vanish linearly. In the acoustic and electromagnetic cases there can be no bound states and T must be holomorphic in C^+.

Suppose then that κ, with Im $\kappa > 0$, is a zero of $1/T(k)$, $1/T(\kappa) = 0$. It follows from the Wronskian that therefore

$$(3.38) \qquad f^{(2)}(\kappa,x) = c\, f^{(1)}(\kappa,x)$$

and furthermore (again by the Wronskian)

$$(3.39) \qquad \frac{d}{dk}\,[1/T(k)]\Big|_{k=\kappa} = -i\, c \int_{-\infty}^{\infty} dx\, [f^{(1)}(\kappa,x)]^2 \; .$$

Since for purely imaginary κ $f^{(1)}$ is real the right-hand side cannot vanish, and hence the pole of T at κ is <u>simple</u>. The constant c is real.

At $k = \kappa$ the Jost function is a singular matrix: By (3.27) det $J(\kappa) = 0$. Therefore there must exist a vector r such that

$$(3.40) \qquad \tilde{\mathcal{J}}(\kappa) r = 0 \; .$$

As the pole of $\psi = Tf$ at $k = \kappa$ is simple it follows from (3.25) that $\tilde{r}\, \phi(\kappa,x)$ is finite and not identically zero:

$$(3.41) \qquad \tilde{r}\, \phi(\kappa,x) \equiv u(x) \; .$$

The boundary conditions (3.23) show that

$$(3.42) \qquad \frac{u'(0)}{u(0)} = i\kappa\, \frac{r_1 - r_2}{r_1 + r_2} \; .$$

Thus the components of the vector r determine the logarithmic derivative of the bound-state eigenfunction at the origin.

The constant c of (3.38), on the other hand, measures the ratio of of the asymptotic values of u on the left and right. Since $\phi(\kappa,x)$ is finite, and so is $f(\kappa,x)$, it follows from (3.25) and (3.38) that the vector ℓ which is such that

$$(3.43)\qquad J(\kappa)\ell = 0$$

is determined by $c = \ell_2/\ell_1$. Without loss of generality we may set $\ell_2 = 1$. We call the ray defined by ℓ the <u>character</u> of the bound state.

The normalization of the bound-state eigenfunction (3.41) is connected to the vectors r and ℓ by (3.39). If we define

$$(3.44)\qquad N^2 = \int_{-\infty}^{\infty} dx\; u^2(x)$$

then we obtain after some algebra (for $\ell_2 = 1$)

$$(3.45)\qquad N^2 = i(\tilde{r}\dot{J}\ell)r_1/J_{22}$$

where $\dot{J} = dJ/dk$ at $k = \kappa$ and J_{22} is the value of J_{22} at $k = \kappa$. Thus the Jost function contains all the bound-state information.

We now want to remove the bound state from J. That is, we define a reduced Jost function that has all the relevant properties of J except that it is not singular at $k = \kappa$. We define

$$(3.46)\qquad \Gamma(k) = \mathbf{1} - B + B\,\frac{k+\kappa}{k-\kappa}$$

where $B = \ell\tilde{\ell}/\tilde{\ell}\ell$ is a real orthogonal projection: $B = B^2 = \tilde{B}$. The reduced Jost function

$$(3.47)\qquad J^{red} = J\Gamma$$

is analytic in C^+, satisfies (3.28), and its determinant at $k = \kappa$ does not vanish. If we define

$$(3.48)\qquad S^{red} = q\Gamma^{-1}qS\Gamma^{\#}$$

then J^{red} is connected with S^{red} in the same way as J is with S, by (3.30)

$$(3.49)\qquad J^{red\#-1} = S^{red-1}\;qJ^{red-1}q$$

and S^{red} satisfies (3.8), (3.10), and (3.12). For more than one bound state we remove them one by one in the same manner. (Note, however, that each removal of a bound state changes the remaining ℓ.)

d. The Levinson theorem. For real k define δ as the phase of T:

$$T = |T|e^{i\delta} \tag{3.50}$$

so that by (3.14)

$$\det S = e^{2i\delta} . \tag{3.51}$$

Using (3.12), (3.21), and the meromorphic character of T in C^+ one then finds in the usual manner (see, for example, [29], p. 356) that if T(0) = 0 (which is the generic case) then

$$\delta(0) - \delta(\infty) = \pi(n - \tfrac{1}{2}) , \tag{3.52}$$

where δ has been defined to be continuous and n is the number of bound states. If $T(0) \neq 0$, so that we have a half-bound state at k = 0, then

$$\delta(0) - \delta(\infty) = \pi n . \tag{3.52'}$$

This is the reason for calling such a state a "half-bound state;" it enters as an extra ½ added to the number of bound states.

e. Completeness and the spectral function. As is well known, if V is real and $(1 + x^2)V \in L^1$ then each component of the solution ψ of (3.1) admits a generalized Fourier transform. For $f \in L^2(R)$, if there are no bound states

$$f(x) = (1/2\pi) \int_{-\infty}^{\infty} dk\ \hat{f}(k)\ \psi^{(i)}(k,x) , \tag{3.53}$$

$$\hat{f}(k) = \int_{-\infty}^{\infty} dx\ f(x)\ \psi^{(i)}(k,x) ,$$

which may be combined and written symbolically

$$(1/2\pi) \int_{0}^{\infty} dk\ (\psi(k,x),\ \psi(k,y)) = \delta(x - y) , \tag{3.54}$$

in which (3.11), and hence the reality of V has been used, and (,) denotes that inner product in the two-dimensional vector space. If there are bound states then

$$(1/2\pi) \int_{0}^{\infty} dk\ (\psi(k,x),\ \psi(k,y)) + \sum_n u_n(x)\ u_n(y) = \delta(x - y) , \tag{3.54'}$$

where $u_n(x)$ are the normalized eigenfunctions. Insertion of (3.23) in this completeness relation leads to

$$(3.55)\qquad \int (\phi(k,x),\ d\rho(k)\ \phi(k,y)) = \delta(x-y)\ ,$$

where the <u>spectral function</u> is given by $(E = k^2)$

$$(3.56)\qquad d\rho/dE = \begin{cases} (1/4\pi k)\ [J(k)\ J(k)^{\dagger}]^{-1}\ , & E > 0\ , \\ \sum_n M_n\ \delta(E - E_n)\ , & E < 0\ . \end{cases}$$

Here the dagger denotes the adjoint, $A^{\dagger} = \tilde{\bar{A}}$, E_n are the bound-state eigenvalues, and

$$(3.57)\qquad M_n = r_n \tilde{r}_n / N^2$$

where r_n and N are such that $\tilde{r}_n \phi(\kappa_n, x)/N$ is a normalized eigenfunction of eigenvalue $E_n = \kappa_n^2$. From (3.27) and the fact that for real V, $\phi(-k,x) = \bar{\phi}(k,x)$, it follows that ρ must satisfy the relation

$$(3.58)\qquad \bar{\rho} = q\rho q = \tilde{\rho}\ .$$

If $V \equiv 0$ for $x < 0$ then (3.31) leads to the simple expression

$$(3.59)\qquad (JJ^{\dagger})^{-1} = \begin{pmatrix} 1 & R_{\ell} \\ \bar{R}_{\ell} & 1 \end{pmatrix}\ .$$

4. <u>Solution of Inverse Problems for the Schrödinger Equation in one Dimension via the Gel'fand-Levitan Equation</u>. *a. The inverse spectral problem.* Let us write (3.32) in the symbolic form

$$(4.1)\qquad \phi = \omega\phi_0$$

where the kernel of $\omega = \delta - h$ is given by

$$(4.2)\qquad \omega(x,y) = \delta(x-y) - h(x,y)$$

and $h(x,y) = 0$ for $|y| > |x|$. Eq. (3.30) holds in the entire complex plane but we shall restrict it so that its range $\mathcal{R}(\omega)$ equals the span of the quasi-eigenfunctions (continuous spectrum) and the bound states (3.1). Its domain must then include a finite number of exponentials. Thus ω maps $L^2(R)$ augmented by the span of a finite number of exponentials onto $L^2(R)$.

We now construct the inverse of ω by an argument first given by [30,6]. The kernel of the right inverse of ω, $(\omega^{-1})_r = \delta - r$, must satisfy the Volterra equation

$$(4.3)\qquad r(x,y) = -h(x,y) + \int_{-x}^{x} dz\, h(x,z)\, r(z,y)\ ,$$

which has a unique solution and $r(x,y)$ vanishes when $|x| < |y|$. The kernel of the left inverse of ω, $(\omega^{-1})_\ell = \delta - \ell$, must satisfy the equation

$$(4.4)\qquad \ell(x,y) = -h(x,y) + \int_{|z|>|y|} dz\ \ell(x,z)\, h(z,y)\ .$$

The equation $\omega f = 0$ implies $f = 0$ because f must satisfy the homogeneous version of (4.3). Therefore the left inverse exists and (4.4) has a solution. Furthermore the solution of (4.4) must be unique, because otherwise its homogeneous form would have a nontrivial solution, which would imply that there must be an $f \varepsilon L^2$ such that $f\omega = 0$. But then a right inverse could not exist. Now for $|y| > |x|$ Eq. (4.4) becomes

$$\ell(x,y) = \int_{|z|>|y|} dz\ \ell(x,z)\, h(z,y)\ .$$

If this had a nontrivial solution the solution of (4.4) would not be unique. Consequently the unique solution of (4.4) must be "triangular," i.e., $\ell(x,y) = 0$ for $|y| > |x|$. Since left and right inverses of ω exist and are unique, they are equal.

Let us now explicitly indicate the potential to which ϕ belongs by a subscript and write (4.1) in the form $\phi_V = \omega_{VO}\phi_O$. Then $\phi_O = \omega_{VO}^{-1}\phi_V = \omega_{OV}\phi_V$, $\omega_{VO} = \delta - h_{VO}$, $\omega_{OV} = \delta - h_{OV}$, and both $h_{VO}(x,y)$ and $h_{OV}(x,y)$ vanish when $|y| > |x|$. We then have $\phi_W = \omega_{WO}\phi_O = \omega_{WO}\omega_{OV}\phi_V \equiv \omega_{WV}\phi_V$, $\omega_{WV} = \delta - h_{WV}$, where $h_{WV} = h_{WO} + h_{OV} - h_{WO}h_{OV}$, and $h_{WV}(x,y)$ vanishes for $|y| > |x|$. We also have $\omega_{WV} = \omega_{VW}^{-1}$.

The completeness relation (3.55) may be written in symbolic form

$$(4.5)\qquad \int(\phi_V, d\rho_V\phi_V) = \delta\ .$$

Since $\phi_V = \omega_{VW}\phi_W$ and $\omega_{VW}^{-1} = \omega_{WV}$, this leads to

$$\omega_{WV} = \int(\phi_W, d\rho_V \phi_V)\tilde{\omega}_{VW}$$

and also

$$\tilde{\omega}_{VW} = \int(\phi_W, d\rho_W \phi_W)\tilde{\omega}_{VW} .$$

Subtraction yields

$$\omega_{WV} - \tilde{\omega}_{VW} = \tilde{h}_{VW} - h_{WV} = \int(\phi_W, d(\rho_V - \rho_W)\phi_W)\tilde{\omega}_{VW} . \tag{4.6}$$

Similarly we obtain

$$\omega_{WV}\tilde{\omega}_{WV} - \delta = h_{WV}\tilde{h}_{WV} - h_{WV} - \tilde{h}_{WV} = \int(\phi_W, d(\rho_V - \rho_W)\phi_W) . \tag{4.7}$$

[Remember that h is not a matrix; $\tilde{h}(x,y)$ here means $h(y,x)$.]

Writing more explicitly

$$\nu_{VW}(x,y) = \int(\phi_W(k,x), d[\rho_V(k) - \rho_W(k)]\phi_W(k,y)) , \tag{4.8}$$

(4.6) reads for $|y| > |x|$

$$h_{VW}(y,x) = \nu_{VW}(x,y) - \int_{-y}^{y} dz\, \nu_{VW}(x,z)\, h_{VW}(y,z) , \tag{4.6'}$$

while (4.7) reads for $|y| > |x|$

$$h_{WV}(y,x) = -\nu_{VW}(x,y) + \int_{-x}^{x} dz\, h_{WV}(x,z)\, h_{WV}(y,z) . \tag{4.7'}$$

The first is the linear Gel'fand-Levitan equation, and the second is the nonlinear one. We shall not discuss (4.7') further. In the special case when the comparison potential is W = 0 we have $\phi_W(k,x) = (\exp ikIx)\, \overset{\circ}{1}$, $J_W = \mathbb{1}$, $M_n^{(W)} = 0$, and we shall drop the subscripts. We shall concentrate on this case.

If W = 0 then the exponential structure of ϕ_N implies that $\nu(x,y) = \nu(x + y,0)$, so that (4.6') for x = 0,

$$\nu(y,0) = h(y,0) + \int_{-y}^{y} dz\, \nu(z,0)\, h(y,z)$$

may be regarded as a Volterra equation for $\nu(y,0)$. It implies that, since h is continuous, so is ν, and $\nu(0,0) = 0$.

We now regard (4.6') as an integral equation for h in the region $-y \leq x \leq y$, in which $\nu(x,y)$ is given by means of (4.8) in terms of the spectral function ρ. The function ν being continuous, the solution h of (4.6') in L^2 can be proved to be unique and is continuous. The underlying potential V is connected to h by (3.35) and hence by (3.36). We have therefore solved the reconstruction problem in which the data are the spectral function ρ.

The result can be somewhat simplified as follows. Let us write the integral equation (4.6') for h symbolically

$$h_y = \nu_y - \mathcal{G}_y h_y \ ,$$

in which y is regarded as a parameter, and

$$h_y(x) = h(y,x), \quad \nu_y(x) = \nu(x,y), \quad \mathcal{G}_y(x,z) = \nu(x,z)\ \Theta(|y| - |z|)$$

where Θ is the Heaviside function. Then, denoting the Fredholm determinant by det,

$$\frac{d}{dy} \ell n \det(\mathbb{1} + \mathcal{G}_y) = \mathrm{tr}[(\mathbb{1} + \mathcal{G}_y)^{-1} \frac{d\mathcal{G}_y}{dy}] \ ,$$

where tr denotes the trace. But $d\mathcal{G}_y(x,z)/dy = \nu(x,z)\ [\delta(y+z) + \delta(y-z)]$. Therefore

$$\frac{d}{dy} \ell n \det(\mathbb{1} + \mathcal{G}_y) = h(y,y) + h(y,-y) \ ,$$

and by (3.34) and (3.36) [31]

$$(4.9) \qquad V(x) = -2 \frac{d^2}{dx^2} \ell n \det(\mathbb{1} + \mathcal{G}_x) \ .$$

Therefore all that is required for the reconstruction of V is the Fredholm determinant of the kernel of the GL equation (4.6').

Use of (4.8) and (4.1) in (4.6') together with (3.35) leads to the expansion

$$(4.10) \qquad \int_0^x dy\ V(y) = -2 \int [\phi_0(x), d(\rho - \rho_0)\phi(x)] \ .$$

In the special case when $V(x) = 0$ for $x < 0$ we obtain a simplification by substituting (3.59) and (3.56) in (4.8). The result is

$$(4.8') \qquad \nu(x,y) = (1/2\pi) \int_{-\infty}^{\infty} dk\ R_\ell(k) e^{-ik(x+y)}$$

if there are no bound states. This integral vanishes when $x + y < 0$.

Therefore (4.6') becomes

$$(4.6'') \quad h(y,x) = \nu(x + y,0) - \int_{-x}^{x} dz\, \nu(x + z,0)\, h(y,x) \;.$$

b. The inverse scattering problem. We shall give two ways to solve the inverse scattering problem. The first proceeds via the GL-equation. What is needed here is to find the Jost function from the S matrix. The key for this is Eq. (3.30) together with the analytic and asymptotic properties of J. We first assume that there are no bound states.

Consider the following Riemann-Hilbert problem H: Given a 2×2 matrix-valued functions $\sigma(k)$, $k \in R$, such that $(\sigma - \mathbb{1}) \in L^2(R)$ and $\sigma(-k) = q\sigma(k)^{-1}q$. Find a 2×2 matrix-valued function $f(k)$ such that $(f - \mathbb{1}) \in L^2(R)$, and such that $f(k)$ has an analytic continuation into C^+ that is holomorphic there, whose determinant nowhere vanishes there, furthermore $\lim_{|k|\to\infty} f(k) = \mathbb{1}$, and such that for $k \in R$

$$(4.11) \quad f(-k) = \sigma(k) q f(k) q \;.$$

It can be proved [32-34] that if this problem has a solution then this solution is unique. Therefore, if $f(k)$ solves it and if $\sigma(k) = S(k)^{-1}$, then $f(k) = J(k)^{-1}$ and we have found the Jost function.

In order to solve (4.11) we write it in the form

$$f^{\#} - \mathbb{1} = [\sigma - \mathbb{1}]q[f - \mathbb{1}]q + q[f - 1]q + \sigma - \mathbb{1}$$

and take Fourier transforms of both sides. Define

$$g(\alpha) = (1/2\pi) \int_{-\infty}^{\infty} dk\, e^{ik\alpha}[\sigma(k) - 1]q \;,$$

$$\eta(\alpha) = (1/2\pi) \int_{-\infty}^{\infty} dk\, e^{-ik\alpha}[f(k) - 1] \;,$$

both of which are well defined in the L^2-sense. Then (4.10) becomes

$$\eta = g{*}\eta^{\#}q + q\eta^{\#}q + gq \;,$$

where * denotes the convolution. Because $f(k) - 1$ is holomorphic in C^+ and vanishes as $|k| \to \infty$ there, $\eta(\alpha) = 0$ for $\alpha < 0$. Therefore for $\alpha \geq 0$, $\eta(\alpha) = g(\alpha)q + (g{*}\eta^{\#})(\alpha)q$, or in detail

$$(4.12) \quad \eta(\alpha) = g(\alpha)q + \int_{0}^{\infty} d\beta\, g(\alpha + \beta)\, \eta(\alpha)q \;.$$

This is the Marchenko equation. Thus, if

$$(4.13)\qquad g(\alpha) = (1/2\pi)\int_{-\infty}^{\infty} dk\, e^{-ik\alpha}[\tilde{S}(k) - \mathbb{1}]q$$

then the Fourier transform of $J^{-1} - \mathbb{1}$,

$$(4.14)\qquad \eta(\alpha) = (1/2\pi)\int_{-\infty}^{\infty} dk\, e^{-ik\alpha}[J(k)^{-1} - \mathbb{1}]$$

must satisfy (4.12) for $\alpha \geq 0$.

If $(1 + |x|)V \in L^1$ then one can prove [7,8,9] that both $S - \mathbb{1}$ and its derivative are in $L^2(R)$. It then follows that the kernel of (4.12) is Hilbert-Schmidt. Let us write (4.12) in operator form, on R_+

$$(4.12')\qquad \eta = gq + G\eta q\ .$$

where the operator G (which for real V is self-adjoint) has the kernel $G(\alpha,\beta) = g(\alpha + \beta)$. Iteration gives $\eta = gq + Gg + G^2\eta$. Therefore, if G has neither 1 nor -1 as eigenvalues then (4.11) has a unique solution. If V is real then the unitarity of S can be used to show that no eigenvalue of G can exceed 1 in magnitude (e.g. [16]). Therefore if (4.12) has a unique solution it is obtainable by iteration.

Furthermore it can be proved [18] that, because H has a solution, G cannot have the eigenvalues ±1. Thus J is always the matrix-inverse of the Fourier transform of the unique solution of (4.12).

If V produces bound states then we proceed as follows.

Suppose we are given the S matrix and for each bound state its character (see Sec. 3c). The eigenvalues are determined from the poles of T. We now pose a Riemann-Hilbert problem of the same form as earlier in this section, except that we require f(k) to be meromorphic in C^+, which simple poles at the points $k = \kappa_n$ (if κ_n^2 is an eigenvalue) and with residues (which are singular 2×2 matrices) there whose ranges are the given characters. This problem is reduced to the one posed earlier by the method indicated in Sec. 3c.

We define Γ as in (3.46) for a single bound state, and as a product successively for more than one. Then we define

$$(4.15)\qquad \sigma^{red} = \Gamma^{\#-1}\,\sigma q \Gamma q$$

and pose the Riemann-Hilbert problem H for σ^{red}. The solution f^{red} is obtained as given earlier in terms of the solution of (4.12). Then the solution f of the present problem is given by

$$f = \Gamma f^{red} \tag{4.16}$$

and the function sought is $J = f^{-1}$.

At this point we have constructed the Jost function from the S matrix and from the characters of the bound states. (The bound-state energies are not independent of the S matrix; they are determined by the analytic continuation of T as poles, and hence by the Fourier transform of T - 1.) Therefore the spectral function (3.56) is now given, and we may proceed to construct V by means of the Gel'fand-Levitan equation.

5. Solution of the Inverse Scattering Problem for the Schrödinger Equation in One Dimension via the Marchenko Equation. The following method for solving the inverse scattering problem is more direct than that given in the last section. The key to it is Eq. (3.9), $\psi(-k,x) = S(k)^{-1}q\,\psi(k,x)$. Let us define the function $\gamma(k,x) = \exp(-ikIx)\,\psi(k,x)$; then γ satisfies the relation [remember that $f^{\#}(k) = f(-k)$]

$$\gamma^{\#} = S_x^{-1}\, q\gamma\ , \tag{5.1}$$

where $S_x(k) = \exp(-ikIx)S(k)\exp(ikIx)$, i.e.,

$$S_x = \begin{pmatrix} T & R_r e^{2ikx} \\ R_\ell e^{-2ikx} & T \end{pmatrix}. \tag{5.2}$$

Furthermore, $\gamma(k,x)$ has an analytic continuation into C^+ that is meromorphic there, with simple poles at the bound states; by (3.4) $[\gamma(k,x) - \overset{\circ}{1}] \varepsilon\, L^2(R)$ as a function of k, and as $|k| \to \infty$ in C^+

$$\lim_{|k|\to\infty} \gamma(k,x) = \overset{\circ}{1}\ . \tag{5.3}$$

a. The case without bound states. Let us first consider the case without bound states. The problem of finding γ is closely related to the Riemann-Hilbert problem H posed in Sec. 4b. In fact, if H is solved with $\sigma = S_x^{-1}$ and f_x is its solution then $f_x\overset{\circ}{1} = \gamma(k,x)$ solves the present problem. It is important, then, to note that S_z given by (5.2) is the S matrix that would correspond to a potential $V_z(x) = V(x + z)$. This is easily seen from (3.2) and (3.6).

Therefore we know that there is a Jost function J_x corresponding to S_x, and thus a solution f_x to H exists. This solution must be unique [34]. (The immediate assurance of uniqueness depends on the requirement that the determinant of the solution nowhere vanish. It is therefore important that H is posed for solutions that are 2×2 matrices.) Therefore we also know that the operator in the Marchenko equation cannot have the eigenvalues ±1, and the equation is solvable by iteration, i.e., its Neumann series converges.

Explicitly, the Marchenko equation that needs to be solved for the solution of (5.1) is given by (for $\alpha > 0$)

$$\eta(\alpha,x) = g_x(\alpha)\overset{\circ}{1} + \int_0^\infty d\beta\, g_x(\alpha+\beta)\,\eta(\beta,x)\,, \tag{5.4}$$

where

$$g_x(\alpha) = (1/2\pi)\int_{-\infty}^{\infty} dk\, e^{-ik\alpha}[\tilde{S}_x(k) - \mathbb{1}]q\,, \tag{5.5}$$

and γ is obtained from η by

$$\gamma(k,x) = \overset{\circ}{1} + \int_0^\infty d\alpha\, e^{ik\alpha}\,\eta(\alpha,x)\,. \tag{5.6}$$

The Fourier transform of (3.2) leads to the following equation for $\eta(\alpha,x)$ in terms of V, for $\alpha > 0$

$$\eta^{(1)}(\alpha,x) = -\frac{1}{2}\int_{-\infty}^{x+\frac{1}{2}\alpha} dy\, V(y) - \frac{1}{2}\int_{-\infty}^{x+\frac{1}{2}\alpha} dy \int_0^{\alpha-|x-y|+(x-y)} d\beta\, \eta^{(1)}(\beta,y)\,V(y)\,, \tag{5.7}$$

$$\eta^{(2)}(\alpha,x) = -\frac{1}{2}\int_{x-\frac{1}{2}\alpha}^{\infty} dy\, V(y) - \frac{1}{2}\int_{x-\frac{1}{2}\alpha}^{\infty} dy \int_0^{\alpha-|x-y|-(x-y)} d\beta\, \eta^{(2)}(\beta,y)\,V(y)\,, \tag{5.8}$$

and therefore

$$\begin{aligned}\eta^{(1)}(0,x) &\equiv \lim_{\alpha\downarrow 0}\eta^{(1)}(\alpha,x) = -\frac{1}{2}\int_{-\infty}^{x} dy\, V(y)\,,\\ \eta^{(2)}(0,x) &\equiv \lim_{\alpha\downarrow 0}\eta^{(2)}(\alpha,x) = -\frac{1}{2}\int_{x}^{\infty} dy\, V(y)\,.\end{aligned} \tag{5.9}$$

These equations imply that

$$(5.10) \quad -2\frac{d}{dx}\eta(0,x) = I\,\mathring{1}\,V(x)\ .$$

We also obtain the partial differential equations from (5.7) and (5.8),

$$(5.11) \quad \left(\frac{\partial^2}{\partial x^2} - 2I\frac{\partial^2}{\partial\alpha\partial x}\right)\eta(\alpha,x) = V(x)\,\eta(\alpha,x)\ ,$$

and from (5.9) and (5.6) the expansions

$$\int_{-\infty}^{x} dy\, V(y) = -(1/\pi)\lim_{\alpha\downarrow 0}\int_{-\infty}^{\infty} dk\, e^{-ik(x+\alpha)}[\psi^{(1)}(k,x) - e^{ikx}]\ ,$$

$$\int_{x}^{\infty} dy\, V(y) = -(1/\pi)\lim_{\alpha\downarrow 0}\int_{-\infty}^{\infty} dk\, e^{ik(x-\alpha)}[\psi^{(2)}(k,x) - e^{-ikx}]\ .$$

It is of great practical interest to apply the Marchenko method in a somewhat different manner [4,7,8]. The Jost solution $f = (1/T)\psi$, whose components safisfy (3.15) and (3.15'), obeys the equation

$$f(-k,x) = \mathring{S}(k)qf(k,x)\ ,$$

where

$$\mathring{S} = \begin{pmatrix} T & -R_r \\ -R_\ell & T \end{pmatrix}.$$

Defining $\xi(k,x) = \exp(-ikIx)f(k,x) = (1/T)\gamma(k,x)$ we obtain

$$(5.12) \quad \xi^{\#} = \mathring{S}_x\, q\xi$$

instead of (3.9), with

$$\mathring{S}_x = \begin{pmatrix} T & -R_r e^{2ikx} \\ -R_\ell e^{-2ikx} & T \end{pmatrix}.$$

In the absence of bound states the analytic and symptotic properties of ξ are equal to those of γ. Therefore if we define

$$(5.13) \quad s(\alpha,x) = (1/2\pi)\int_{-\infty}^{\infty} dk\, [\xi(k,x) - \mathring{1}]e^{-ik\alpha}$$

then $s_x(x)$ vanishes for $\alpha \le 0$, and for $\alpha > 0$ it satisfies the Marchenko equation

$$(5.14)\qquad \overset{\circ}{s}(\alpha,x) = g_x(\alpha)\overset{\circ}{1} + \int_0^\infty d\beta\, g_x(\alpha+\beta)\, s(\beta,x) ,$$

where

$$g_x(\alpha) = (1/2\pi)\int_{-\infty}^{\infty} dk\, e^{ik\alpha}[\overset{\circ}{S}_x(k) - \mathbb{1}]q .$$

Now

$$[\overset{\circ}{S}_x - \mathbb{1}]q = \begin{pmatrix} -R_r e^{2ikx} & T - 1 \\ T - 1 & -R_\ell e^{-2ikx} \end{pmatrix}$$

and the Fourier transform of T - 1 vanishes for $\alpha > 0$ because of the analytic and asymptotic properties of T. Therefore (5.14) separates into two uncoupled equations, which may be written explicitly for $\alpha > 0$

$$(5.15)\qquad s^{(1)}(\alpha,x) = -\hat{R}_r(\alpha + 2x) - \int_0^\infty d\beta\, \hat{R}_r(\alpha+\beta+2x)s^{(1)}(\beta,x) ,$$

$$(5.16)\qquad s^{(2)}(\alpha,x) = -\hat{R}_\ell(\alpha - 2x) - \int_0^\infty d\beta\, \hat{R}_\ell(\alpha+\beta-2x)s^{(2)}(\beta,x) ,$$

where

$$\hat{R}_{r,\ell}(\alpha) \equiv (1/2\pi)\int_{-\infty}^{\infty} dk\, e^{ik\alpha} R_{r,\ell}(k) .$$

Taking the Fourier transform of (3.15) and (3.15'), and using (5.13), we obtain the following integral equations for $s^{(1)}$ and $s^{(2)}$ in terms of V, for $\alpha > 0$:

$$(5.17)\qquad s^{(1)}(\alpha,x) = \frac{1}{2}\int_x^\infty dy\, V(y) + \frac{1}{2}\Big[\int_x^{x+\frac{1}{2}\alpha} dy \int_{\alpha+2(x-y)}^{\alpha} d\beta + \int_{x+\frac{1}{2}\alpha}^{x} dy \int_0^\alpha d\beta\Big] V(y)s^{(1)}(\beta,y)$$

$$(5.18)\qquad s^{(2)}(\alpha,x) = \frac{1}{2}\int_{-\infty}^{x} dy\, V(y) + \frac{1}{2}\Big[\int_{-\infty}^{x-\frac{1}{2}\alpha} dy \int_0^\alpha d\beta + \int_{x-\frac{1}{2}\alpha}^{x} dy \int_{\alpha+2(y-x)}^{\alpha} d\beta\Big] V(y)s^{(2)}(\beta,y) .$$

These equations imply that

$$s^{(1)}(0,x) = \lim_{\alpha\downarrow 0} s^{(1)}(\alpha,x) = \frac{1}{2}\int_x^{\infty} dy\, V(y) ,$$

(5.19)

$$s^{(2)}(0,x) = \lim_{\alpha\downarrow 0} s^{(2)}(\alpha,x) = \frac{1}{2}\int_{-\infty}^{x} dy\, V(y) ,$$

which in turn lead to

$$-2 \frac{d}{dx} s^{(1)}(0,x) = V(x) ,$$

(5.20)

$$2 \frac{d}{dx} s^{(2)}(0,x) = V(x) ,$$

If $V(x) = 0$ for $x < 0$ then $\hat{R}_\ell(\alpha) = 0$ for $\alpha > 0$. Therefore in that case the upper limit on the integral in (5.16) becomes $2x - \alpha$, and $s^{(2)}(\alpha,x)$ vanishes when $\alpha > 2x$. Consequently (5.16) becomes an integral equation on the finite interval $0 < \alpha < 2x$, which is the same as Eq. (4.6"), and $s^{(2)}(\alpha,x) = -h(x,x-\alpha)$. This version of the Marchenko equation thus becomes identical to the Gel'fand-Levitan equation.

The same method that led to (4.9) can be used to show that if we denote the kernel of the integral equations (5.15) and (5.16) by G_r^x and G_ℓ^x, respectively, then

$$V(x) = -2 \frac{d^2}{dx^2} \ell n \det(\mathbb{1} + G_r^x)$$

(5.21)

$$V(x) = 2 \frac{d^2}{dx^2} \ell n \det(\mathbb{1} + G_\ell^x)$$

These results show that $V(x)$ may be reconstructed from either of the reflection coefficients by solving the Marchenko equation (5.15) or (5.16) and using (5.20), or else directly by calculating the Fredholm determinant of either (5.15) or (5.16). If $\hat{R}_\ell(\alpha)$, $\alpha\hat{R}_\ell(\alpha) \in L^2(R)$, respectively, $\hat{R}_r(\alpha)$, $\alpha\hat{R}_r(\alpha) \in L^2(R)$, then the kernels G_ℓ^x, resp. G_r^x, are Hilbert-Schmidt and for real V one can prove (by an argument similar to that on p. 2192 of [16]) that their spectra must be confined to the open interval (-1,1). Therefore the Marchenko equation has a unique solution that uniquely leads back to V.

A variant of this approach is obtained by noting that the equation $\psi^{(1)}(k,x) = f^{(2)}(-k,x) + R_\ell(k)f^{(2)}(k,x)$, which follows from (5.12), reads by (5.13)

$$\psi^{(1)}(k,x) = p(k,x) + \int_{-\infty}^{x} dy\; s^{(2)}(x - y,x)p(k,y) ,$$

where

$$p(k,x) = e^{ikx} + R_\ell(k)e^{-ikx} .$$

If $V(x) = 0$ for $x < 0$ then $s^{(2)}(x - y,x)$ vanishes for $y < -x$. In that case $p(k,x) = \psi^{(1)}(k,x)$ for $x < 0$, and for $x > 0$ $s^{(2)}(x - y,x)$ transforms the continued "free" function $p(k,x)$ into the solution of (3.1) that satisfies the same boundary condition at $x = 0$. Fourier transformation leads to functions that satisfy the hyperbolic equations

$$\left(\frac{\partial^2}{\partial x^2} - \frac{\partial^2}{\partial t^2}\right) U(x,t) = V(x)\; U(x,t) ,$$

$$\left(\frac{\partial^2}{\partial x^2} - \frac{\partial^2}{\partial t^2}\right) U_o(x,t) = 0 ,$$

and they are connected by

$$U(x,t) = U_o(x,t) + \int_{-x}^{x} dy\; s^{(2)}(x - y,x)\; U_o(y,t) ,$$

where by (5.6) $U(x,t) = \delta(x - t) + \eta^{(1)}(t - x,x)$ and $U_o(x,t) = \delta(x - t) + \hat{R}_\ell(x + t)$. For $x > t$ one then arrives at Eq. (5.16) with a time-domain interpretation [35].

Suppose now that we are given a 2×2 S matrix that satisfies (3.8), (3.10), (3.12), (3.18), (3.20), that is continuous on the real axis, and whose diagonal elements are boundary values of an analytic function holomorphic in C^+ that tends to 1 there at infinity. It has been proved [7,8] that if in addition one of the Fourier transforms $\hat{R}_{r,\ell}$ of $R_{r,\ell}$ satisfies certain weak conditions then an underlying potential V exists and is uniquely constructable by the Marchenko method.

b. The case with bound states. If there are bound states then we have to remove them from S_x and γ before solving the Riemann-Hilbert problem that is associated with (5.1). For a single bound state we begin with the fact that the residue of ψ at the bound-state pole is proportional to ℓ, as defined by (3.43). Therefore the residue of γ is proportional to $\ell_x = e^{-i\kappa Ix}\ell$, and we must set $B = \ell_x\tilde{\ell}_x/\tilde{\ell}_x\ell_x$. The matrix Γ is defined by (3.46), and it depends on x. (For more than one bound state the x-dependent becomes fairly complicated.)

We now pose the original Riemann-Hilbert problem

$$f^{\#} = S_x^{-1}qfq \tag{5.22}$$

for 2×2 matrix solutions f, and the reduced problem

$$f^{red\#} = S_x^{red-1}q\, f^{red}q\,, \tag{5.22'}$$

where S_x^{red} is related to S_x as in (3.48). In (5.22) f has poles in C^+, in (5.22') it is holomorphic. The vectors γ and γ^{red} are obtained from the solutions of these two problems by $\gamma = f\,\mathring{1}$ and $\gamma^{red} = f^{red}\,\mathring{1}$. Let

$$\eta^{red}(\alpha,x) = (1/2\pi)\int_{-\infty}^{\infty}dk\; e^{-ik\alpha}[f^{red}(k) - \mathbb{1}]$$

be the solution of the reduced Marchenko equation (4.12) for $\alpha > 0$, assuming that the operator G^{red} does not have the eigenvalues ±1. If we define

$$\Omega(\alpha,x) = (1/2\pi)\int_{-\infty}^{\infty}dk\; e^{-ik\alpha}[\Gamma(k) - \mathbb{1}] \tag{5.23}$$

then η^{red} and η are related by

$$\eta(\alpha,x) = \eta^{red}(\alpha,x) + \int_{\alpha}^{\infty}d\beta\;\Omega(\alpha-\beta,x)\,\eta^{red}(\beta,x)\,,\qquad \alpha > 0$$

$$\eta(\alpha,x) = \Omega(\alpha,x) + \int_{0}^{\infty}d\beta\;\Omega(\alpha-\beta,x)\,\eta^{red}(\beta,x)\,,\qquad \alpha < 0\,.$$

It has been proved [17] that the underlying potential is obtained in this case by

$$(5.24) \qquad I\,\overset{\circ}{1}\,V(x) = -2\,\frac{d}{dx}\,[\eta^{red}(0+,x) - \Omega(0-,x)]\ .$$

For the solution of the uncoupled scheme based on (5.12), when there are bound states, we refer to [7,8].

c. Discussion. Thus the reconstruction and construction problems in one dimension are completely solved. It should be noted that if a unitary S matrix is considered as the data and one proceeds to solve the Marchenko equation (5.4), then the fact that the same V appears as a result of each component as in (5.9) or (5.10), appears as a miracle. However, because (5.14) splits into the two uncoupled equations (5.15) and (5.16) it is possible to use partial data. The potential may be constructed from one reflection coefficient alone. That the other reflection coefficient leads to the same potentials now appears as a compatibility condition. The one-dimensional inverse scattering problem is rather special in that the compatibility can be established directly: The unitarity equations (3.13), together with the analyticity and asymptotics of T, and the bound-state eigenvalues, permit us to construct first T and then the other reflection coefficient. (The phase of T is determined from the logarithm of its modulus by a Hilbert transform [7].) Therefore for real potentials one reflection coefficient and the eigenvalues suffice for the construction of all of S. The characters of the bound states appear as additional free parameters both in the step that leads from S to J, and hence to ρ if the Gel'fand-Levitan approach is used, and in the step from S to ψ or f in the Marchenko approach. The characters and the norming constants are connected by (3.40), (3.41), (3.44), and (3.45).

We also note explicitly that the reflection coefficient R_ℓ, which is the seismologically relevant one, appears in Eq. (5.16) whose solution is the Fourier transform of the second component of f. From the equations below (3.17') it is clear that the limit of $f^{(2)}$ as $k \to 0$ in general increases without bounds as $x \to \infty$. Thus the $k = 0$ limit of the solution that emerges from (5.16) is generally not the solution of (2.14) needed for the construction of the impedance or the refractive index. For the same reason the solution of (5.16), when Fourier transformed, will not give the solution of (3.1) with the relevant boundary conditions. Instead it describes waves incident from the right (below). The Kay-method described at the end of Sec. 5b does lead to the physically interesting solution $\psi^{(1)}$, but as $k \to 0$ this function vanishes and will not lead to the impedance or refractive index. The same is true for $\phi(k,x)$; Eq. (3.24) shows that $\phi(0,x)$ grows linearly. Therefore the Gel'fand-Levitan equation also does not directly lead to an expression for the impedance. However, if one solution y, of (3.1) is known, then a linearly independent solution can be obtained by quadrature:

$$y_2(k,x) = c\, y_1(k,x) \int^x dx'/[y_1(k,x')]^2\ .$$

Therefore the impedance can be computed from a solution of the Marchenko equation or of the Gel'fand-Levitan equation by quadrature.

Explicit examples for which the inversion can be accomplished in closed form are given by S matrices that are rational functions. These lead to the so-called Bargmann potentials [35-39].

6. The First-Order Equations. *a. The direct problem.* We now want to deal with the first order system (2.6) [26,40,41]. Let us call the propagation time x and introduce as the dependent variable the two-component vector

$$(6.1) \qquad y = \begin{pmatrix} Z^{-1}P + i\omega ZW \\ Z^{-1}P - i\omega ZW \end{pmatrix} = i\omega \begin{pmatrix} \Phi_2 + \Phi_1 \\ \Phi_2 - \Phi_1 \end{pmatrix} .$$

Then the equations (2.6) read

$$(6.2) \qquad dy/dx = ikIy - Vqy .$$

where we now write $k = \omega$, $V = Z^{-1}dZ/dx$, and I and q are the matrices introduced earlier, $I = \begin{pmatrix} 1 & 0 \\ 0 & -1 \end{pmatrix}$, $q = \begin{pmatrix} 0 & 1 \\ 1 & 0 \end{pmatrix}$. We shall assume that Z is real and $V \equiv 0$ for $x < 0$.

It is of some interest that (6.2) lends itself to a very simple proof that there are no "modes," i.e., no square-integrable solutions for $\mathrm{Im}k \neq 0$. Integration by parts shows that

$$i(k - \bar{k}) \int_{-\infty}^{\infty} dx\, f^\dagger f = \int_{-\infty}^{\infty} dx\, [f^\dagger ikf + (ikf)^\dagger f]$$

$$= \int_{-\infty}^{\infty} dx\, \{f^\dagger (I \frac{d}{dx} + VIq)f + [(I \frac{d}{dx} + VIq)f]^\dagger f\} = 0$$

if f is a square integrable solution of (6.2) and $f^\dagger = \tilde{\bar{f}}$. Therefore $k = \bar{k}$, and k must be real [26].

It is convenient to define Jost solutions of (6.2) by the boundary conditions

$$(6.3) \qquad \lim_{x \to +\infty} e^{-ikx} f_\ell(k,x) = 1' , \quad \lim_{x \to -\infty} e^{ikx} f_r(k,x) = q1' ,$$

where $1' = \begin{pmatrix} 1 \\ 0 \end{pmatrix}$. They satisfy the integral equations

$$(6.4) \qquad f_\ell(k,x) = e^{ikIx}\, 1' + \int_x^\infty dy\, e^{ikI(x-y)} V(y) q f_\ell(k,y) ,$$

$$(6.4') \qquad f_r(k,x) = e^{ikIx} q1' - \int_0^x dy\; e^{ikI(x-y)} V(y) q f_r(k,y) ,$$

if $V(x) = 0$ for $x < 0$, as we shall assume in this Section. The first describes a wave coming in from the left, the second from the right, and they lead to the reflection and transmission amplitudes

$$(6.5) \qquad \begin{aligned} f_\ell(k,0) &= \lim_{x \to -\infty} e^{-ikIx} f_\ell(k,x) = \frac{1}{\mathring{T}} \begin{pmatrix} 1 \\ \mathring{R}_\ell \end{pmatrix} \\ &= \lim_{x \to +\infty} e^{-ikIx} f_r(k,x) = \frac{1}{\mathring{T}} \begin{pmatrix} \mathring{R}_r \\ 1 \end{pmatrix} . \end{aligned}$$

That the two transmission amplitudes are equal follows from an evaluation of the Wronskian

$$(6.6) \qquad W(f_r, f_\ell) \equiv \tilde{f}_r I q f_\ell ,$$

which is a constant. Similarly from the Wronskians $W(f_r, q\bar{f}_\ell)$, $W(f_r, q\bar{f}_r)$, and $W(f_\ell, q\bar{f}_\ell)$ we find that the matrix

$$(6.7) \qquad \underline{S} = \begin{pmatrix} \mathring{T} & \mathring{R}_\ell \\ \mathring{R}_r & \mathring{T} \end{pmatrix}$$

is unitary.

The solution f_ℓ is the one of interest to seismology as well as for transmission lines since for $x \to \infty$ it contains no leftward (upward) traveling waves. Relevant data may be considered to be $f_\ell^{(2)}(k,0)/f_\ell^{(1)}(k,0) = \mathring{R}_\ell(k)$. A comparison with (3.19) by means of (2.6) shows $\mathring{R}_\ell$ is connected with R_ℓ by

$$(6.8) \qquad R_\ell = -\frac{2ikZ_o \mathring{R}_\ell + Z_o'(1 - \mathring{R}_\ell)}{2ikZ_o + Z_o'(1 - \mathring{R}_\ell)} ,$$

where Z_o and Z_o' are the limits of the impedance and of its derivative as $x \to 0+$.

It is easily proved [26] by means of (6.4) and (6.4') that if $V \in L^1(0,\infty) \cap L^2(0,\infty)$ and $xV \in L^2(0,\infty)$, then f_ℓ and f_r are uniformly bounded continuous functions of k with analytic extensions that are holomorphic in C^+. Furthermore $[e^{-ikx} f_\ell(k,x) - 1'] \in L^2(R)$, $[e^{ikx} f_r(k,x) - q1'] \in L^2(R)$ as functions of k, and in C^+

$$\lim_{|k|\to\infty} e^{-ikx} f_\ell(k,x) = 1' ,$$

(6.9)

$$\lim_{|k|\to\infty} e^{ikx} f_r(k,x) = q1' .$$

From (6.5) and (6.3) we obtain

(6.10) $$1/\mathring{T} = 1 + \int_0^\infty dx\, e^{ikx} V(x) f_\ell^{(2)}(k,x) .$$

It follows from (6.9), the analytic and asymptotic properties of f_ℓ, and the unitarity of $\underline{S}$, that $\mathring{T}$ is continuous on R, has an analytic continuation that is holomorphic and without zeros in C^+, and is such that $[T(k) - 1] \in L^2(R)$ and

(6.11) $$\lim_{|k|\to\infty} \mathring{T}(k) = 1 .$$

That $\mathring{T}$ has no poles follows from the fact that if $1/\mathring{T}(k) = 0$ at $k = \kappa \in C^+$ then f_ℓ and f_r are linearly dependent and hence both would exponentially vanish as $|x| \to \infty$. But such square integrable solutions in C^+ are ruled out.

Now $q\bar{f}_r$ is a solution of (6.2); therefore it must be a linear combination of f_ℓ and f_r. The coefficients can be calculated by means of the Wronskians, with the result that

(6.12) $$q\bar{f}_r = \mathring{T} f_\ell - \mathring{R}_\ell f_r .$$

b. The inverse problem. The inverse problem can now be solved by the Marchenko method, using (6.12) together with the analytic and asymptotic properties of f_ℓ, f_r, and $\mathring{T}$, and the fact that $\bar{f}_r(k,x) =$

$f_r(-k,x)$ for real k (if Z is real). The Fourier transforms

$$\eta_\ell(\alpha,x) = (1/2\pi) \int_{-\infty}^{\infty} dk\ e^{-ik\alpha}[f_\ell(k,x)e^{-ikx} - 1']$$

$$(6.13) \qquad \eta_r(\alpha,x) = (1/2\pi) \int_{-\infty}^{\infty} dk\ e^{-ik\alpha}[f_r(k,x)e^{ikx} - q1']$$

$$t(\alpha) = (1/2\pi) \int_{-\infty}^{\infty} dk\ e^{-ik\alpha}[\mathring{T}(k) - 1]$$

all exist in the L^2-sense and vanish for $\alpha < 0$. Defining

$$(6.14) \qquad g(\alpha) = (1/2\pi) \int_{-\infty}^{\infty} dk\ e^{ik\alpha}\ \mathring{R}_\ell(k)$$

we therefore obtain by Fourier transformation of (6.12) for ($\alpha > 0$)

$$(6.15) \qquad \eta_r(\alpha,x) = -g(\alpha - 2x) - \int_0^{\infty} d\beta\ g(\alpha + \beta - 2x)q\ \eta_r(\beta,x) .$$

Since $V = 0$ for $x < 0$, in fact, $f_r(k,x)$ is an entire analytic function of k such that in C^- $[f_r(k,x)e^{ikx} - q1']e^{-2ikx}$ is uniformly bounded, as easily follows from (6.4'). Therefore $\eta_r(\alpha,x)$ vanishes not only for $\alpha < 0$ but also for $\alpha > 2x$. As a result (6.15) reads for $-x < \alpha < x$,

$$(6.15') \qquad \Omega_1(\alpha,x) = -g(\alpha - x) - \int_{-x}^{x} d\beta\ g(\alpha + \beta)\ \Omega_1(\beta,x)$$

where $\Omega_1(\alpha,x) = \eta_r(\alpha + x,x)$, and

$$(6.16) \qquad f_r(k,x) = e^{-ikx}\ q1' + \int_{-x}^{x} d\alpha\ e^{ik\alpha}\ \Omega_1(\alpha,x) .$$

The Fourier transform of (6.4') leads to the equation for $-x < \alpha < x$,

$$\Omega_1(\alpha,x) = -\tfrac{1}{2} V(\tfrac{1}{2}x - \tfrac{1}{2}\alpha) - \int_{\frac{1}{2}x-\frac{1}{2}\alpha}^{x} dy\ V(y)\ \Omega_2(\alpha - x + y,y)$$

$$\Omega_2(\alpha,x) = - \int_{\frac{1}{2}\alpha+\frac{1}{2}x}^{x} dy\ V(y)\ \Omega_1(\alpha + x - y,y) .$$

Therefore

(6.17) $$\Omega_1(-x,x) \equiv \lim_{\alpha\downarrow -x} \Omega_1(\alpha,x) = -\tfrac{1}{2} V(x) .$$

Eq. (6.15') can be proved [26] to have a unique solution obtainable by iteration (i.e., the Neumann series converges). The function V in (6.2) is then obtained from (6.17). Finally, Z has to be found such that $dZ/dx = VZ$. If the impedance Z_o at the surface is given then

(6.18) $$Z(x) = Z_o \exp \int_0^x d\tau\, V(\tau) .$$

Alternatively, if the impedance Z_∞ at $x \to \infty$ is known then

(6.18') $$Z(x) = Z_\infty \exp[- \int_x^\infty d\tau\, V(\tau)] .$$

It is important to note that this method leads to the impedance but not to the solution of (6.2) with the relevant boundary conditions. The Fourier transform of the solution of (6.15) is f_r, that is, the solution of (6.2) that describes waves incident from the right (below).

7. The Ubiquitous Riemann-Hilbert Problem. As we have seen in both one-dimensional inverse problems, at the heart of inverse scattering lies a Riemann-Hilbert problem, both in the Gel'fand-Levitan method and in the Marchenko method. In the first its solution leads from the S matrix to the Jost function, and in the second it leads directly to the solution of the initial differential equation and to the "potential." The same is true in higher dimensional generalizations. However,because the multiplicity of the spectrum of the Schrödinger equation in R^n, $n \geq 2$, is infinite, it is posed there not on a two-dimensional vector space but on an infinite dimensional one. The exact nature of the space depends on n. For $n = 2$ it has been proved that an L^2-space works [42]; for $n = 3$ an L^p-space, with $p > 4$, is needed [15]. (Unfortunately, $p = 2$ does not seem to work; a Hilbert space would simplify matters to some extent.) Therefore we will proceed on a Banach space that we shall call h. It is a space of functions on the unit sphere S^2 in R^3 and we shall denote points on S^2, i.e., unit vectors in R^3, by θ. Thus h consists of functions $f(\theta)$ such that $\|f\| = [\int d\theta |f(\theta)|^p]^{1/p} < \infty$.

By $\mathcal{B}$ we shall mean the space of bounded linear operators from h into h. An operator $A \in \mathcal{B}$ can be defined by its kernel $A(\theta,\theta')$, and we shall denote the operator whose kernel is $\bar{A}(\theta,\theta')$ by $\bar{A}$. The kernel $\tilde{A}(\theta,\theta') = A(\theta',\theta)$ defines the adjoint operator $A^\dagger$ on the dual $h^\dagger$ of h, which is the L^q-space over S^2, with $\frac{1}{p} + \frac{1}{q} = 1$. If $p \geq 2$ then $q \leq 2$

and $h^\dagger \supset h$. By $\tilde{A}$ we shall mean the restriction of $\bar{A}^\dagger$ to h. If $A \in \mathcal{B}$ then it does not necessarily follow that $\tilde{A} \in \mathcal{B}$. However, if both $A \in \mathcal{B}$ and $\tilde{A} \in \mathcal{B}$ then we shall say that $A \in \tilde{\mathcal{B}}$. The operator $\tilde{A}^{-1}$ will be denoted by A_*.

We will have to deal with operator-valued functions and use the following definitions. L^2 will denote the set of functions F: $R \to \tilde{\mathcal{B}}$, for which $\exists c$ and for all $f \in h$

$$\int_{-\infty}^{\infty} dk \ \|F(k)f\|_2^2 + \int_{-\infty}^{\infty} dk \ \|\tilde{F}(k)f\|_2^2 < c \ \|f\|_p^2 .$$

If $F \in L^2$ has an analytic continuation into C^+ that is holomorphic there and such that $\lim_{|k|\to\infty} \|F(k)\| = 0$, and if the same holds for $\tilde{F}$, then we say that $F \in H^+$; similarly we define H^-. If the analytic continuations of F and $\tilde{F}$ are meromorphic instead of holomorphic we say $F \in M^\pm$.

If zero is in the point spectrum of $F(k)$ then we shall say that F has a zero at k. If $F \in M^+$ (M^-, H^+, or H^-) and for no $k \in C^+$ (resp. C^-) it has a zero then we shall call it zero-free.

The operator Q is defined so that for all $f(\theta)$, $(Qf)(\theta) = f(-\theta)$. We also recall that for $k \in R$, $f^{\#}(k)$ means $f(-k)$.

Lemma 1: If $F \in L^2$ then its Fourier transform $\hat{F}$ exists in the mean and $\hat{F} \in L^2$.

Proof: Let $f \in h$. Then

$$h_K(s) = \frac{1}{2\pi} \int_{-K}^{K} dk \ e^{iks} \ F(k)f$$

converges in the mean to $h(s)$,

$$\lim_{K\to\infty} \int_{-\infty}^{\infty} ds \ \|h(s) - h_K(s)\|_2^2 = 0 ,$$

and by the generalized Plancherel theorem [43]

$$\int_{-\infty}^{\infty} ds \;\|h(s)\|_2^2 = \int_{-\infty}^{\infty} ds \int d\theta \;|h(s,\theta)|^2$$

$$= \int_{-\infty}^{\infty} dk \;\|F(k)f\|_2^2 < C \;\|f\|_p^2 .$$

Therefore for almost all s $h(s) \varepsilon L^2(S^2)$. The mapping $f \to h(s)$ defines the linear operator $\hat{F}(s)$, $h(s) = \hat{F}(s)f$, from $L^p(S^2)$ to $L^2(S^2)$ which we write

$$\hat{F}(s) = \frac{1}{2\pi} \int_{-\infty}^{\infty} dk \; e^{iks} \; F(k) \; .$$

If $\hat{F}$ is regarded as an operator $L^p(S^2) \to L^2(R \times S^2)$, then $\|\hat{F}f\|^2 < C \;\|f\|^2$ and hence $\hat{F}$ is bounded. The same holds for $\tilde{\hat{F}}$; thus $\hat{F} \;\varepsilon\; L^2$. q.e.d.

The Riemann-Hilbert problem that is of primary interest can be stated as follows:

Problem $H_0^1(\Omega)$: Suppose a function Ω, $R \to \tilde{\mathcal{B}}$, is given such that $(\Omega - \mathbb{1}) \varepsilon L^2$ and $\Omega^{\#} = Q\Omega^{-1}Q$. Find a function f, $R \to \tilde{\mathcal{B}}$, such that $(f - \mathbb{1}) \varepsilon H^+$ and on R

(7.1) $\quad f^{\#} = \Omega Q f Q$.

The homogeneous problem, in which we require that $f \;\varepsilon\; H^+$ and that it satisfy (7.1), will be denoted by $H_0^0(\Omega)$. We shall also write $H_0^1(\Omega_*) = H_{0*}^1(\Omega)$ and similarly for H_0^0.

The following has been proved [18]:

Lemma 2: (a) If H_0^1 has a solution then this solution is unique if and only if H_0^0 has only the trivial solution f = 0. (b) If H_0^1 has a unique solution then this solution is zero-free. (c) If H_0^1 has a zero-free solution f such that $(f^{-1} - \mathbb{1}) \varepsilon M^+$ then it is unique. (d) If H_0^1 has a unique solution f and $(f^{-1} - \mathbb{1}) \varepsilon M^+$ then H_{0*}^1 has the unique solution $g = f_*$, and f, g, $\tilde{f}$, and $\tilde{g}$ are all zero-free. (e) If H_0^1 and H_{0*}^1 have solutions f and g, respectively, then these solutions are unique, f, g, $\tilde{f}$, and $\tilde{g}$ are all zero-free, and $g = f_*$.

We note that most of this lemma becomes trivial if the Fredholm determinant of f exists. Otherwise, for example, from the fact that f is holomorphic and zero-free, it does not follow that f^{-1} is holomorphic.

The solution of $H_0^1(\Omega)$ is given by the following:

Theorem 1: Suppose that Ω has the properties assumed in $H_0^1(\Omega)$. Define

$$(7.2)\qquad G(\alpha) = (1/2\pi) \int_{-\infty}^{\infty} dk[\Omega(k) - \mathbf{I}]Qe^{ik\alpha}$$

and let $G(\alpha,\beta) \equiv G(\alpha + \beta)$ and $G_{\#}(\alpha,\beta) \equiv G(-\alpha-\beta)$ define the operators G and $G_{\#}$ on $L^2(R)\times h$, respectively. Suppose further that G, $\tilde{G}$, $G_{\#}$, and $\tilde{G}_{\#}$ are compact. Then

(a) The four problems $H_0^1(\Omega)$, $H_{0*}^1(\Omega)$, $H_0^1(\Omega^{\#})$, and $H_{0*}^1(\Omega^{\#})$ have solutions if and only if neither G^2 nor $G_{\#}^2$ has the eigenvalue 1.

(b) These solutions are unique and the solution of $H_0^1(\Omega)$ is given by

$$(7.3)\qquad f(k) = \mathbf{I} + \int_0^{\infty} d\alpha\ \lambda(\alpha)e^{ik\alpha}\ ,$$

where λ is the unique solution in L^2 of the integral equation for $\alpha > 0$

$$(7.4)\qquad \lambda(\alpha) = G(\alpha)Q + \int_0^{\infty} d\beta\ G(\alpha + \beta)\ \lambda(\alpha)Q\ .$$

The solutions of $H_{0*}^1(\Omega)$, $H_0^1(\Omega^{\#})$, and $H_{0*}^1(\Omega^{\#})$ are analogously given in terms of $G_{\#}$, $G^{\#}$, and $G_{\#}^{\#}$.

(c) If 1 is in one of the spectra of G^2 and $G_{\#}^2$ but not in both, then $H_0^1(\Omega)$ and $H_{0*}^1(\Omega)$ do not both have solutions, and neither do both $H_0^1(\Omega^{\#})$ and $H_{0*}^1(\Omega^{\#})$.

This theorem is proved in [18]. The procedure closely parallels that used in Sec. 4b for matrices.

Theorem 1 is the key to the solution of the inverse scattering problem by the Marchenko method in the absence of bound states. It is also one of the two key ingredients in the Gel'fand-Levitan method as it leads from the S matrix to the Jost function. In the presence of bound states one has to solve a more general Riemann-Hilbert problem which allows for simple poles in the solutions.

Problem $H^1_\Sigma(\Omega)$: Suppose a function Ω, $R \to \tilde{\mathcal{B}}$, is given such that $(\Omega - \mathbb{1}) \in L^2$ and $\Omega^\# = Q\Omega^{-1}Q$. Also given is a set Σ of n pairs, each consisting of a positive imaginary number κ_m and a finite dimensional subspace H_m of $L^2(S^2)$, m = 1, . . ., n. Find a function f, $R \to \tilde{\mathcal{B}}$, such that f satisfies Eq. (7.1) on R, and $(f - \mathbb{1}) \in M^+$ with simple poles at the points κ_m and residues I_m there such that Ran $I_m = H_m$. (Here Ran denotes the range of the operator, i.e., the space on which it maps its domain of definition.)

The corresponding homogeneous problem, in which $f \in M^+$ and Ran $I_m \subset H_m$, is denoted by $H^0_\Sigma(\Omega)$.

Parts (a) and (b) of lemma 2 are applicable to $H^1_\Sigma(\Omega)$.

The solution of H^1_Σ is accomplished by reducing it to H^1_0 as follows. Suppose first that n = 1, so that f is to have only one pole. We then construct a projection $B = B^2$ onto H and form

$$(7.5) \qquad \Gamma_1(k) = 1 - B + B\,\frac{k + \kappa}{k - \kappa}$$

as well as

$$(7.6) \qquad \Omega^{red} = \Gamma_1^{\#-1}\,\Omega Q \Gamma_1 Q\ .$$

The function Ω^{red} has all the properties postulated in $H^1_0(\Omega^{red})$ and we proceed to solve $H^1_0(\Omega^{red})$ by the method given in Theorem 1. If there is more than one bound state then the procedure of (7.5) and (7.6) has to be repeated for each of them, except that at each step the space on which B projects has to be modified. Let Γ_{m-1} be the operator constructed to "remove" the first m-1 poles. Then B_m is a projection onto $\Gamma^{-1}_{m-1}(\kappa_m)H_m$ and

$$(7.7) \qquad \Gamma_m(k) = \Gamma_{m-1}(k)\,[\mathbb{1} - B_m + B_m\,\frac{k + \kappa_m}{k - \kappa_m}]\ .$$

The reduced Ω is finally given by

$$(7.6') \qquad \Omega^{red} = \Gamma_n^{\#-1}\,\Omega Q \Gamma_n Q\ .$$

Suppose that $H^1_0(\Omega^{red})$ and $H^1_{0*}(\Omega^{red})$ have solutions and that f^{red}

solves $H^1_0(\Omega^{red})$. We then construct

$$f = \Gamma_n f^{red} . \tag{7.8}$$

Then f satisfies (7.1) with the originally given Ω. Furthermore $(f - \mathbb{1}) \varepsilon\, M^+$ with poles at the points κ_m, $m = 1, \ldots, n$. The residue of f at $k = \kappa_m$ is an operator of the form $\Gamma_{m-1}(\kappa_m)B_m A$, where A is invertable. By construction then the range of the residue is H_m. Finally one proves that f is the unique solution of $H^1_\Sigma(\Omega)$ [18].

8. The Schrödinger Equation in Three Dimensions. *a. The scattering solution and the S matrix.* We first consider the direct scattering problem for the Schrödinger equation with a potential without spherical symmetry:

$$\Delta y - Vy + k^2 y = 0 \tag{8.1}$$

in R^3. The problem in R^2 was studied by Cheney [42]. It will not be our aim to state needed results under assumptions that are as weak as possible; instead we will try to state them as simply as we can. Generally the assumptions on V are the following:

(i) Existence of a, c > 0 such that for all $y \varepsilon R^3$

$$\int d^3x |V(x)|^2 + \int d^3x |V(x)| \left(\frac{|x| + |y| + a}{|x - y|}\right)^2 < c .$$

(ii) Existence of a monotonely decreasing function $M_1 \varepsilon L^1(R_+) \cap L^2(R_+)$ and of $x_o \varepsilon R^3$ such that for all $x \varepsilon R^3$

$$|V(x + x_o)| < M_1(|x|) .$$

(iii) Existence of ℓ, C > 0 such that for all $x \varepsilon R^3$ and all $\theta \varepsilon R^3$, $|\theta| = 1$,

$$\int d^3y\, V^2(x + y)(1 + \theta \cdot \hat{y})^{-\ell} < C .$$

Here and everywhere in the following, $\hat{y} = y/|y|$, and the dot indicates the scalar product in R^3.

(iv) Existence of a monotonely decreasing function $M_2(t)$, $M_2 \varepsilon L^1(R_+)$, $t^n M_2 \varepsilon L^1(R_+)$, $5/2 < n$, and of some $x_o \varepsilon R^3$ such that for all $x \varepsilon R^3$

$$|\Delta V(x_o + x)| \leq M_2(|x|) .$$

Assumptions (i) - (iv) are satisfied, for example, if for some C, a, $\varepsilon > 0$, $|V(x)| \leq C(a + |x|)^{-3-\varepsilon}$ and $|\Delta V(x)| \leq C(a + |x|)^{-7/2-\varepsilon}$ for all x. For some purposes stronger assumptions are needed and we shall state them. We shall also assume that V is real.

A scattering solution of (8.1) will be defined by the Lippmann-Schwinger equation

$$(8.2) \qquad \psi(k,\theta,x) = E(k,\theta,x) - \int d^3y \, \frac{e^{ik|x-y|}}{4\pi|x-y|} V(y) \, \psi(k,\theta,y) .$$

Here, and in the following, θ denotes a point on S^2 or a unit vector in R^3, $E(k,\theta,x) = \exp(ik\theta \cdot x)$. This equation is converted into a Fredholm equation by multiplying it by $|V(x)|^{1/2}$. It is most convenient to define

$$(8.3) \qquad \gamma(k,\theta,x) = \psi(k,\theta,x)e^{-ik\theta \cdot x} .$$

On the assumptions (i) - (iii) one can prove [44] that if k = 0 is not an exceptional point, which we shall assume, on the real axis $\gamma(k,\theta,x)$ is, for each x, a continuous uniformly bounded function of k and θ, such that for all $x \in R^3$ and all $\theta \in S^2$

$$(8.4) \qquad \int_{-\infty}^{\infty} dk \, |\gamma(k,\theta,x) - 1|^2 < \infty .$$

It has an analytic continuation into C^+ that is meromorphic there, with simple poles at those points $k = i\kappa$ where $-\kappa^2$ is a bound-state eigenvalue, and furthermore

$$(8.5) \qquad \lim_{|k|\to\infty} \gamma(k,\theta,x) = 1 .$$

The scattering amplitude $A(k,\theta,\theta')$ is defined by the asymptotics of ψ for large $|x|$. The solution ψ is characterized by the fact that for large $|x|$ it differs from $E(k,\theta,x)$ by outgoing spherical waves only:

$$(8.6) \qquad \lim_{|x|\to\infty} |x|e^{-ik|x|}[\psi(k,\theta,x) - E(k,\theta,x)] = A(k,\hat{x},\theta) .$$

From (7.2) one readily obtains the representation

$$(8.7) \qquad A(k,\theta',\theta) = -(1/4\pi) \int d^3x \, \overline{E(k,\theta',x)} \, V(x) \, \psi(k,\theta,x) ,$$

and A is seen to have the symmetries

$$(8.8)\qquad A(-k,\theta,\theta') = \bar{A}(k,\theta,\theta') ,$$

$$(8.9)\qquad A(k,\theta,\theta') = A(k,-\theta',-\theta) .$$

For $k \to \pm\infty$, with $\tau = k(\theta - \theta')$ held fixed, A approaches the Born approximation [45,29]

$$(8.10)\qquad \lim_{k\to\pm\infty} A(k,\theta,\theta') = -(1/4\pi) \int d^3x\, V(x) e^{-i\tau\cdot x} .$$

The forward scattering amplitude $A(k,\theta,\theta)$, by (8.7), has the representation

$$A(k,\theta,\theta) = -(1/4\pi) \int d^3x\, V(x)\, \gamma(k,\theta,x) .$$

It therefore follows from the properties of γ that if V satisfies (i) to (iii) then $A(k,\theta,\theta)$ is, for each fixed θ, a continuous function of k with an analytic continuation into C^+ that is meromorphic there, with simple poles at the bound states. Asymptotically it is such that

$$(8.10')\qquad \lim_{|k|\to\infty} A(k,\theta,\theta) = -(1/4\pi) \int d^3x\, V(x) .$$

It will be very useful in the following and save us much cumbersome notation, if we consider ψ and γ, in their dependence upon θ, as members of a suitable normed linear space h. For many of our purposes we may take this space to be $L^2(S^2)$ so that we have an inner product too. However, we shall see that an important result requires that we take h to be an L^p-space with $p > 4$. Therefore h will be assumed to be a Banach space. We shall then simply write $\gamma(k,x)$, or we may not even indicate the x-dependence and write $\gamma(k)$. In the same vein we regard $A(k,\theta,\theta')$, for fixed k, as the kernel of an operator $A(k)$ on the space h. We then define the S matrix as the operator

$$(8.11)\qquad S(k) = \mathbb{1} - \frac{k}{2\pi i} A(k) ,$$

where $\mathbb{1}$ is the unit operator on h. Again adopting the convention used earlier, $f^{\#}(k) = f(-k)$, and using the operator Q which is such that $(Qf)(\theta) = f(-\theta)$ for $f \in h$, we may write (8.8) and (8.9)

$$(8.12)\qquad S^{\#} = \bar{S} , \qquad \tilde{S} = QSQ ,$$

where $\bar{S}$ is the operator whose kernel is $\bar{S}(k,\theta,\theta')$, and $\tilde{S}$ is the operator whose kernel is $\tilde{S}(k,\theta,\theta') = S(k,\theta',\theta)$. The S matrix is known to be unitary:

(8.13) $$S^\dagger S = SS^\dagger = \mathbb{1} ,$$

where $S^\dagger = \tilde{\tilde{S}}$.

The function $\psi(-k,\theta,x)$ solves (8.1) if $\psi(k,\theta,x)$ does, and the set of solutions $\psi(k,\theta,x)$ for θ ranging over the unit sphere is known to be complete in the space of solutions of (8.1). Therefore $\psi(-k,\theta,x)$ is a linear combination of $\psi(k,\theta,x)$: $\psi(-k,\theta,x) = \int d\theta' \, M(k,\theta,\theta') \psi(k,\theta',x)$. One finds [29] that $M(k,\theta,\theta') = S^{-1}(k,\theta,-\theta')$, or in operator notation,

(8.14) $$\psi^{\#} = S^{-1}Q\psi .$$

From the solution of the inverse scattering problem in one dimension we may expect that we will need the Fourier transform of $S - \mathbb{1}$ as a function of k. However, as (8.10) shows, $A(k,\theta,\theta)$ generally approaches a non-zero constant as $k \to \pm\infty$, and therefore by (8.11), $(S - 1)$ is of order k. Furthermore the Hilbert-Schmidt norm $\|S(k) - \mathbb{1}\|_{HS}$ is not square integrable, no matter what properties $V(x)$ has, as is easily proved for the Born approximation. Surprisingly it turns out that in a useful sense, nevertheless, $S(k) - \mathbb{1}$ is square integrable. We have

Lemma 3: Assume (i), (ii), (iv), and (v). The for all $p > 4$ there exists a constant C such that for all $f \in L^p(S)$

(8.15) $$\int_{-\infty}^{\infty} dk \, k^2 \, \|A(k)f\|_p^2 \leq C \, \|f\|_p^2 ,$$

where $\|\cdot\|_p$ denotes the L^p-norm.

Since there exists no published proof of this lemma we prove it in an appendix. We shall refer to the property of $kA(k)$ expressed in this lemma as strong square integrability on $L^p(S^2)$. As an immediate corollary it follows that for $p > 4$

$$\int_{-\infty}^{\infty} dk \, \|(S - \mathbb{1})f\|_p^2 \leq C \, \|f\|_p^2 .$$

Since for $L^2(S^2)$ and $L^p(S^2)$, $\|f\|_2 \leq C \, \|f\|_p$, it follows that

(8.16) $$\int_{-\infty}^{\infty} dk \, \|(S - \mathbb{1})f\|_2^2 \leq C \, \|f\|_p^2 .$$

Therefore by Lemma 1 the Fourier transform of $(S - \mathbb{1})f$ exists.

b. The Jost function and the solution ϕ. In order to generalize the Gel'fand-Levitan procedure we need a generalization of the solution ϕ which in one dimension is defined by a boundary condition at a point. This method has no known generalization to R^3. Instead we have to define a Jost function by solving a Hilbert problem, and then define ϕ by means of it.

Assume first that there are no bound states and that both the Riemann-Hilbert problems $H_0^1(S^{-1})$ and $H_0^1(\tilde{S})$, as defined in Sec. 7, have solutions. [Note that (8.12) and (8.13) imply that $\tilde{S}_* = S^{-1}$.] Theorem 1 requires that the self-adjoint operators whose kernels are $G(\alpha + \beta)$ and $G(-\alpha - \beta)$ be compact. This has been proved [16] on the assumptions (i), (ii), and (iv). Let f solve $H_0^1(S^{-1})$. The solution f is therefore unique; by Lemma 1, it is zero-free and its inverse is holomorphic in C^+. We set $J = f^{-1}$. It satisfies the equation

$$(8.17) \qquad J^{\#} = QJQS$$

on R; it is holomorphic in C^+, and

$$(8.18) \qquad \lim_{|k|\to\infty} \|J(k) - \mathbb{1}\| = 0 \; .$$

Having thus constructed J, if it exists, we now define the solution

$$(8.19) \qquad \phi(k,x) = J(k)\, \psi(k,x) \; .$$

This function has the property

$$(8.20) \qquad \phi(-k,x) = Q\, \phi(k,x)$$

by (8.17) and (8.14). Furthermore it is such that for any $f \in L^p(S^2)$, the function

$$\Phi(k,x) = \int d\theta\, f(\theta)[\phi(k,\theta,x) - E(k,\theta,x)]$$

is square integrable as a function of k and $\|\Phi\|_2^2 \le C\,\|f\|_p^2$. Also $\phi(k,x)$ has analytic continuations into C^+ and C^- that are holomorphic there and $\exp(ik|x|)\,\Phi(k,x)$ is bounded in C^+ while $\exp(-ik|x|)\,\Phi(k,x)$ is bounded in C^-. Therefore the Fourier transform of $\Phi(k,x)$ exists as an L^2 function and its support lies in the interval $(-|x|,|x|)$, such that

$$\Phi(k,x) = \int_{-|x|}^{|x|} d\alpha\; e^{ik\alpha}\, \hat{\Phi}(\alpha,x) ,$$

$$\int_{-|x|}^{|x|} d\alpha\; |\hat{\Phi}(\alpha,x)|^2 \le C\; \|f\|_p^2 .$$

In that sense we have the Povsner-Levitan representation

$$(8.21)\qquad \phi(k,\theta,x) = E(k,\theta,x) - \int_{-|x|}^{|x|} d\alpha\; e^{ik\alpha}\; w(\alpha,\theta,x) .$$

The solution ϕ is an entire function of k, of exponential type $|x|$. It is the appropriate generalization of the solution which in one dimension is defined by boundary conditions at $x = 0$. Its existence, however, depends on the existence of a solution to the Riemann-Hilbert problem.

The definition (8.19) of ϕ, together with the Lippmann-Schwinger equation (8.2) leads to the integral equation

$$(8.22)\qquad \begin{aligned} \phi(k,\theta,x) &= \int d\theta'\; J(k,\theta,\theta')e^{ik\theta'\cdot x} \\ &\quad - \int d^3y\, \frac{e^{ik|x-y|}}{4\pi|x-y|}\, V(y)\; \phi(k,\theta,y) \end{aligned}$$

for ϕ. Subjecting this equation to Fourier transformation with respect to k, we obtain the following equation for $-|x| < \alpha < |x|$,

$$(8.23)\qquad \begin{aligned} w(\alpha,\theta,x) &= \xi(\alpha,\theta,x) - \int d\theta'\; \zeta(\alpha - \theta'\cdot x,\theta,\theta') \\ &\quad - \int d^3y\, \frac{V(y)}{4\pi|x-y|}\, w(\alpha - |x-y|,\theta,y) , \end{aligned}$$

where the last integral runs over the region in which $-|y| < \alpha - |x-y| < |y|$, and

$$\zeta(\alpha,\theta,\theta') = (1/2\pi) \int_{-\infty}^{\infty} dk\; e^{-ik\alpha}[J(k,\theta,\theta') - \delta(\theta,\theta')] ,$$

$$\xi(\alpha,\theta,x) = \int d^3y\, \frac{V(y)}{4\pi|x-y|}\, \delta(|x-y| + \theta\cdot y - \alpha) .$$

The function ξ has a step-like discontinuity at $\alpha = \theta\cdot x$. For $\alpha < \theta\cdot x$ it vanishes, while

$$\lim_{\alpha\downarrow\theta\cdot x} \xi(\alpha,\theta,x) = \frac{1}{2}\int_0^{\infty} dr\; V(x - \theta r) .$$

The two other terms in (8.23), on the other hand, are continuous at this point. As a result w has the discontinuity

$$w(\theta\cdot x+,\theta,x) - w(\theta\cdot x-,\theta,x) = \frac{1}{2}\int_0^\infty dr\ V(x - \theta r) ,$$

from which it follows that

(8.24) $$2\theta\cdot\nabla[w(\theta\cdot x+,\theta,x) - w(\theta\cdot x-,\theta,x)] = V(x) .$$

In a weak sense one also obtains the partial differential equation

(8.25) $$(\Delta - \frac{\partial^2}{\partial\alpha^2})w = Vw$$

in the region $|\alpha| < |x|$.

We also note that (8.20) and (8.21) together imply that w must have the symmetry

(8.26) $$w(-\alpha,-\theta,x) = w(\alpha,\theta,x) .$$

Now let us define the spherical-harmonic projections of $\phi(k,\theta,x)$ for fixed k and x:

(8.27) $$\phi_\ell^m(k,x) = \int d\theta\ Y_\ell^m(\theta)\ \phi(k,\theta,x) ,$$

where $Y_\ell^m(\theta)$, $-\ell \le m \le \ell$, are the spherical harmonics of order ℓ. It has been proved [17] that if the potential decreases exponentially, i.e., if $\exists$ a > 0 such that

(8.28) $$\int d^3x|V(x)|e^{a|x|} < \infty ,$$

then in general near k = 0

(8.29) $$\phi_\ell^m(k,x) = O(k^\ell) .$$

The words "in general" here indicate that the existence of exceptional cases has not been ruled out. If the potential is central, i.e., $V(x) = f(|x|)$, then (8.29) is well known and its proof does not require exponential decrease of the potential.

Since $\phi(k,\theta,x)$ is an analytic function of k holomorphic at k = 0, it may be expanded in a convergent Taylor expansion

(8.30) $$\phi(k,\theta,x) = \sum_0^\infty k^n\ C_n(\theta,x) .$$

The result (8.29) implies that

$$(8.31) \qquad \int d\theta \; \phi^{(n)}(0,\theta,x) \; Y_\ell^m(\theta) = 0$$

for all $\ell > n$, if $\phi^{(n)}$ denotes the nth derivative of ϕ with respect to k. Eqs. (8.27), (8.30), and (8.31) together imply that ϕ is an analytic function of each component of the vector $K = k\theta \in R^3$.

While the function w is the Fourier transform of $E - \phi$ regarded as a function of k, it will be more useful for later purposes to define the three-dimensional Fourier transform of $E - \phi$ regarded as a function of $K = k\theta$:

$$(8.32) \qquad h(x,y) = (1/2\pi)^3 \int_0^\infty dk \; k^2 \int d\theta \; e^{-ik\theta\cdot y}[E(k,\theta,x) - \phi(k,\theta,x)] \; .$$

It is extremely unlikely that this object can be defined as a function, because of the extra factor of k^2. This Fourier transform, in contrast to (8.21), has to be defined as a distribution.

In a weak sense one obtains, from (8.1), the partial differential equation

$$(8.33) \qquad (\Delta_x - \Delta_y) \; h(x,y) = V(x) \; h(x,y) \; ,$$

to be satisfied by h in the region $|y| \leq |x|$. In place of (8.24) one also finds [16]

$$(8.34) \qquad -2\hat{x}\cdot\nabla_x[h(|x|\hat{x}, |x|\hat{y})|x|^2] = \delta(\hat{x},\hat{y}) \; V(x) \; .$$

Here and above Δ_x, Δ_y, ∇_x are the Laplacians with respect to x and y, and the gradient with respect to x.

If w and h are defined by (8.21) and (8.32) then if follows that $w(\alpha,\theta,x)$ is the Radon transform of $h(x,y)$:

$$(8.35) \qquad w(\alpha,\theta,x) = \int d^3y \; h(x,y) \; \delta(\alpha - \theta\cdot y) \; .$$

The question now is whether the fact that the support of $w(\alpha,\theta,x)$ as a function of α is in the interval $(-|x|,|x|)$ implies that the support of $h(x,y)$ in its dependence upon y is contained in the ball $|y| < |x|$. A sufficient condition, applicable to distributions, for this to be true is that w satisfy (8.26) and (8.31) [49]. The second has been established "in general" for potentials that obey (8.28), and the first follows from (8.20). In general we therefore have the generalized Povsner-Levitan representation

$$(8.36) \qquad \phi(k,\theta,x) = E(k,\theta,x) - \int_{|y|<|x|} d^3y\, h(x,y)\, E(k,\theta,y) \ ,$$

where $E(k,\theta,x) = \exp(ik\theta\cdot x)$.

The procedure of Sec. 4a shows that we will need an inverse of (8.36), in the sense that

$$(8.37) \qquad E(k,\theta,x) = \phi(k,\theta,x) + \int d^3y\, \ell(x,y)\, \phi(k,\theta,y) \ .$$

The argument given there is equally applicable here, and it leads to the conclusion that such an inverse exists (as a distribution) and that the support of $\ell(x,y)$ is contained in the ball $|y| < |x|$.

We also note that the inverse of (8.35) is given by

$$(8.38) \qquad h(x,y) = -(1/8\pi^2)\, \Delta_y \int d\theta\, w(\theta\cdot y,\theta,x) \ ,$$

where Δ_y denotes the Laplacian with respect to y.

c. Bound states. The modified Fredholm determinant $\Delta(k)$ of the Lippmann-Schwinger equation (8.2) has an analytic continuation into C^+ that is holomorphic there [29]. The squares of those values κ of k for which $\Delta = 0$ are eigenvalues of (8.2) in L^2. We shall assume that $\Delta(0) \neq 0$. [See [44] for detailed discussion of $k = 0$ as an exceptional point.] Let $u(x)$ be a normalized eigenfunction of eigenvalue $\kappa^2 < 0$. Its asymptotic form for large $|x|$ is given by

$$(8.39) \qquad u(x) = -(e^{-|\kappa||x|}/4\pi|x|)\, Y(\hat{x}) + o(e^{-|\kappa||x|}/|x|)$$

where we have arbitrarily fixed the normalization of Y. Both u and Y may be chosen to be real. (If V is central, Y is a spherical harmonic.) Assume for the moment that to each eigenvalue there corresponds only one eigenfunction (i.e., no degeneracy).

The Green's function of (8.1) has a simple pole at $k = \kappa$ and its principal part that is

$$(8.40) \qquad G(k,x,y) = \frac{u(x)u(y)}{2\kappa(k-\kappa)} + \ldots .$$

Similarly the solution ψ of (8.2) and the forward scattering amplitude have simple poles there with principal parts

$$(8.41) \qquad \psi(k,\theta,x) = \frac{Y(-\theta)u(x)}{2\kappa(k-\kappa)} + \ldots .$$

$$(8.42) \qquad A(k,\theta,\theta) = \frac{R(\theta)}{k-\kappa} + \ldots ,$$

where

$$(8.43) \quad R(\theta) = -(1/8\pi\kappa)\, Y(\theta)\, Y(-\theta)\ .$$

The approach of $A(k,\theta,\theta)$ to its Born approximation (8.10') is sufficiently fast that the difference is square integrable [15]. Thus the Fourier transform exists in the mean and for $t > 0$

$$(8.44) \quad \int_{-\infty}^{\infty} dk\, e^{ikt}\, [A(k,\theta,\theta) + (1/4\pi)\overline{V}] = 2\pi i \sum_n e^{-|\kappa_n| t}\, R_n(\theta)$$

if κ_n is the nth eigenvalue, and $\overline{V} = \int d^3x\, V(x)$.

It is useful to employ the differential rotation operator about the axis p:

$$(8.45) \quad M_\theta^p = (\theta p \nabla_\theta)\ ,$$

where (abc) is the triple product of the three vectors a, b, c. For any differentiable function of $a\cdot\theta$ we have

$$M_\theta^p f(a\cdot\theta) = f'(a\cdot\theta)\ (\theta p a)\ ,$$

where f' is the derivative of f. If V decreases sufficiently rapidly as $|x| \to \infty$, $A^{(1)}(k,\theta,\theta) = \lim_{\theta'\to\theta} M_\theta^p A(k,\theta,\theta')$ is meromorphic in C^+ with a simple pole at the bound state and principal part

$$(8.46) \quad A^{(1)}(k,\theta,\theta) = \frac{R^{(1)}(\theta)}{k - \kappa} + \ldots .$$

where

$$(8.47) \quad R^{(1)}(\theta) = -(1/8\pi\kappa)\, Y^{(1)}(\theta)\, Y(-\theta)$$

and $Y^{(1)}(\theta) = M_\theta^p\, Y(\theta)$.

If there is degeneracy (i.e., several linearly independent eigenfunctions of the same eigenvalue) then these statements have generalizations [15]. The poles in C^+, however, are always <u>simple</u> (if V is real). We shall refer to the space spanned by the functions Y at a given eigenvalue as the <u>character</u> of that eigenvalue. (For central potentials specifying the character is equivalent to specifying the angular momentum.)

If the scattering amplitude is given then the eigenvalues may be obtained by (8.44) from the forward amplitude. Eqs. (8.42), (8.43), (8.46), and (8.47) allow us to set up the differential equation for Y,

$$Y^{(1)} = Y\, R^{(1)}/R \ ,$$

in which $R^{(1)}$ and R known. For each direction p this is an ordinary differential equation of first order and it is solvable for Y, up to its scale. The scale of Y is finally fixed by (8.42) and (8.43). In the case of degeneracy the situation is more complicated, but the function Y may still be determined from the scattering amplitude [15]. Thus both the eigenvalues and their characters are determined by A.

In order to obtain the Jost function we now pose the Riemann-Hilbert problem $H^1_\Sigma(S^{-1})$, in which the set Σ consists of the positive imaginary numbers κ_m, m = 1, . . ., n whose squares are the eigenvalues, and of the spaces $\mathcal{H}_m$ which are obtained by letting Q act on their characters. As discussed in Sec. 7 this problem is reduced to $H^1_0[(S^{-1})^{red}]$ and solved, if a solution exists, by the method of Theorem 1.

Suppose then that f solves $H^1_\Sigma(S^{-1})$ uniquely. We form $J = f^{-1}$. It satisfies (8.17) and (8.18) and it is holomorphic in C^+. If κ is one of the κ_m in Σ then the operator $J(\kappa)$ has a nullspace that equals the range of the residue of f at κ: For every Y in the character of κ we have

(8.48) $\quad J(\kappa)QY = 0 \ .$

Assuming for the moment that the character is one-dimensional, we define the vector X so that

(8.49) $\quad J^+(\kappa)X = 0 \ .$

If we choose the normalization of X such that

(8.50) $\quad (1/2\kappa)(X,\dot{J}QY) = 1 \ ,$

where (,) is the inner product on $L^2(S^2)$ and $\dot{J} = dJ/dk\big|_{k=\kappa}$, then we get from (8.19) and (8.41)

(8.51) $\quad (X,\phi(\kappa,x)) = u(x) \ .$

We may therefore write

$$(8.52) \quad u(x)u(y) = (\phi(\kappa,x), M\phi(\kappa,y)) ,$$

where the operator M has the integral kernel

$$(8.53) \quad M(\theta,\theta') = X(\theta)\, \bar{X}(\theta') .$$

In the case of n-fold degeneracy there will be n linearly independent vectors Y_a and n linearly independent vectors X_b such that X_b and $(1/2\pi)\dot{J}QY_a$ for a bi-orthonormal system and

$$(8.52') \quad \sum_b u_b(x)\, u_b(y) = (\phi(\kappa,x), M\phi(\kappa,y)) ,$$

$$(8.53') \quad M(\theta,\theta') = \sum_b X_b(\theta)\, \bar{X}_b(\theta') .$$

Note that (8.48) and (8.49) are independent of the scale or normalizations of the vectors X and Y. However, the normalization requirement of u(x) fixes the scale of Y by (8.39), and once J is known (8.50) fixes the scale of X.

d. The Levinson theorem. The scattering amplitude is the integral kernel of a trace-class operator. Therefore we can define the Fredholm determinant of the S matrix and because of unitarity

$$(8.54) \quad \det S = e^{2i\delta} ,$$

where δ is real and may be defined to be continuous for $0 < k < \infty$. It is connected with the modified Fredholm determinant Δ of the Lippmann-Schwinger equation by [44]

$$(8.55) \quad \Delta(-k)/\Delta(k) = \det S(k) \exp(ik\bar{V}/2\pi) .$$

As the zeros of Δ on the imaginary axis correspond to bound states (with their multiplicity equal to the degeneracy) one can prove [44] that if k = 0 is not an exceptional point then

$$(8.56) \quad \delta(0) - \lim_{k\to\infty} [\delta(k) + k\bar{V}/4\pi] = \pi n ,$$

where n is the number of bound states, each counted as many times as their degeneracy indicates.

e. Completeness and the spectral function. If there are no bound states the scattering functions are known (under very general conditions on the potential) to admit a generalized Fourier transform. For $f \in L^2(R^3)$ we have for almost all $x \in R^3$ in the mean

$$\begin{aligned} f(x) &= (1/2\pi)^3 \int_0^\infty dk\, k^2 \int d\theta\, \hat{f}(k,\theta)\, \psi(k,\theta,x) , \\ \hat{f}(k,\theta) &= \int d^3x\, f(x)\, \bar{\psi}(k,\theta,x) , \end{aligned} \tag{8.57}$$

which may be combined symbolically into the completeness relation

$$(1/2\pi)^3 \int_0^\infty dk\, k^2 \int d\theta\, \bar{\psi}(k,\theta,x)\, \psi(k,\theta,y) = \delta(x - y) . \tag{8.58}$$

If there are bound states the normalized bound-state eigenfunctions $u_n^b(x)$ (which may be chosen to be real) have to be included:

$$\begin{aligned} &(1/2\pi)^3 \int_0^\infty dk\, k^2 \int d\theta\, \bar{\psi}(k,\theta,x)\, \psi(k,\theta,y) \\ &\quad + \sum_{n,b} u_n^b(x)\, u_n^b(y) = \delta(x - y) . \end{aligned} \tag{8.58'}$$

Insertion of (8.19) and (8.52') in this gives us the completeness relation for ϕ, which we write in the more compact vector and operator notation

$$\int (\phi(k,x),\, d\rho(k)\, \phi(k,y)) = \delta(x - y) , \tag{8.59}$$

where the parenthesis indicated the inner product on $L^2(S^2)$, and the <u>spectral function</u> is given by

$$d\rho/dE = \begin{cases} (k/16\pi^3)\, [J(k)\, J(k)^\dagger]^{-1} , & E > 0 , \\ \sum_n M_n\, \delta(E - E_n) , & E < 0 ; \end{cases} \tag{8.60}$$

here $E = k^2$. When the potential vanishes we simply have the Fourier theorem

$$\int (E(k,x),\, d\rho_0(k)\, E(k,y)) = \delta(x - y) , \tag{8.59'}$$

and

$$d\rho_0/dE = \begin{cases} (k/16\pi^3)\, \mathbb{1} , & E > 0 , \\ 0 , & E < 0 . \end{cases} \tag{8.60'}$$

9. <u>Solution of Inverse Problems for the Schrödinger Equation in Three Dimensions via the Gel'fand-Levitan Method</u>. *a. The inverse spectral problem.* We now have all the ingredients and proceed as in

Sec. 4a. The crux of the matter is the generalized Povsner-Levitan representation (8.36) with the "triangular" kernel h(x,y). The completeness relation (8.59) then leads to a generalized Gel'fand-Levitan equation, exactly as (4.6) was obtained from (3.55) and (3.32). For $|x| > |y|$

$$h(x,y) = \nu(x,y) - \int_{|z|<|x|} d^3z\, h(x,z)\, \nu(z,y) , \tag{9.1}$$

where

$$\nu(x,y) = \int (E(k,x), d(\rho(k) - \rho_0(k))\, E(k,y)) \tag{9.2}$$

in terms of the spectral functions (8.60) and (8.60'). Similarly, and in complete analogy with (4.6), for an arbitrarily given comparison potential.

Eq. (9.1) is to be regarded as an integral equation for h(x,y) in which ν(x,y) is given. One can prove [15], as in the one-dimensional case, that the homogeneous form of (9.1) has no nontrivial solutions in L^2. However, for distributional solutions such a proof is lacking.

One may also obtain a generalized Gel'fand-Levitan equation for w instead of h. This is done by subjecting Eq. (9.1) to partial Radon transformation, as it holds for $|y| < |x|$ only. The result is somewhat cumbersome and we shall not give it here [17].

Once the solution h(x,y) of (9.1) is obtained the solution ϕ of the corresponding Schrödinger equation is given by (8.36). In order to obtain the potential one first computes the Radon transform (8.35). The resulting function w should satisfy the integral equation (8.23) and therefore have a step-like discontinuity at $\alpha = \theta \cdot x$ whose derivative in the θ-direction leads to the potential by (8.24).

Eq. (8.24) exhibits a remarkable property: Whereas its left-hand side appears to depend upon θ, the right-hand side does not. If the inverse problem is solved from given spectral data and (9.1) is solved, the θ-independence of (8.24) appears as a miracle. However, if an underlying potential is known to exist, this miracle is guaranteed to happen and (8.24) reconstructs V. If such a potential is not known to exist and the miracle fails to happen then no potential exists. We note that the kernel of the spectral function depends on five real variables, while V(x) is a function of only three. It is therefore to be expected that the inverse spectral problem generally has no solution. The resulting characterization problem is still unsolved.

A three-dimensional analog of the nonlinear Gel'fand-Levitan equation (4.7') has also been given but we shall not list it here [17].

b. The inverse spectral problem for central potentials. If $V(x) = V_c(|x|)$ then the three-dimensional Gel'fand-Levitan procedure may be formally reduced to the well-known radial equations as follows [17].

Since the solution $\psi(k,\theta,x)$ can depend on the direction of x only relative to θ if V is central, we may expand it as

$$(9.3) \qquad \psi(k,\theta,x) = (1/k|x|) \sum_{\ell,m} i^{\ell}\, \psi_{\ell}(k,|x|)\, \bar{Y}_{\ell}^{m}(\theta)\, Y_{\ell}^{m}(\hat{x}) \ ,$$

where it is understood that ℓ runs from 0 to ∞ and m from $-\ell$ to $+\ell$. Similarly for the Jost function:

$$(9.4) \qquad J(k,\theta,\theta') = \sum_{\ell,m} f_{\ell}(k)\, Y_{\ell}^{m}(\theta)\, \bar{Y}_{\ell}^{m}(\theta') \ .$$

As a result (8.19) leads to the expansion for ϕ,

$$(9.5) \qquad \phi(k,\theta,x) = \sum_{\ell,m} \frac{(ik)^{\ell}}{|x|(2\ell+1)!!}\, \phi_{\ell}(k,|x|)\, \bar{Y}_{\ell}^{m}(\theta)\, Y_{\ell}^{m}(\hat{x}) \ ,$$

where

$$(9.6) \qquad \phi_{\ell}(k,|x|) = (2\ell+1)!!\, k^{-\ell-1}\, f_{\ell}(k)\, \psi_{\ell}(k,|x|) \ .$$

Also

$$(9.7) \qquad E(k,\theta,x) = \sum_{\ell,m} \frac{(ik)^{\ell}}{|x|(2\ell+1)!!}\, \phi_{\ell}^{(0)}(k,|x|)\, \bar{Y}_{\ell}^{m}(\theta)\, Y_{\ell}^{m}(x) \ .$$

The expansion coefficients ψ_{ℓ}, f_{ℓ}, and ϕ_{ℓ} are the conventional radial scattering solution, Jost function, and regular solution, respectively. If we also expand

$$(9.8) \qquad h(x,y) = (1/|x|\,|y|) \sum_{\ell,m} Y_{\ell}^{m}(\hat{x})\, \bar{Y}_{\ell}^{m}(\hat{y})\, K_{\ell}(|x|,|y|)$$

then the Povsner-Levitan representation (8.36) leads to the representation

$$(9.9) \qquad \phi_{\ell}(k,r) = \phi_{\ell}^{(0)}(k,r) - \int_0^r ds\, K_{\ell}(r,s)\, \phi_{\ell}^{(0)}(k,r) \ .$$

The generalized Gel'fand-Levitan equation (9.1) together with the expansions for h and ν,

$$(9.10) \quad \nu(x,y) = (1/|x||y|) \sum_{\ell,m} g_\ell(|x|,|y|)[(2\ell+1)!!]^{-2}\, Y_\ell^m(\hat{x})\, \bar{Y}_\ell^m(\hat{y}) ,$$

in which

$$(9.11) \quad g_\ell(r,s) = \int \phi_\ell^{(0)}(k,r)\, d(\rho_\ell - \rho_\ell^{(0)})\, \phi_\ell^{(0)}(k,s) ,$$

gives the well-known Gel'fand-Levitan equation [46,29], for $s < r$

$$(9.12) \quad K_\ell(r,s) = g_\ell(r,s) - \int_0^r du\, K_\ell(r,u)\, g_\ell(u,s) .$$

The formula (8.34) together with (9.8) leads to the conclusion that

$$(9.13) \quad -2\frac{d}{dr} K_\ell(r,r) = V(r) ,$$

where $K_\ell(r,r) \equiv \lim_{u\uparrow r} K_\ell(r,u)$.

We note that in this case the miracle expresses itself in the fact that the right-hand side of (9.13) is independent of ℓ. The potential can here be reconstructed from the spectral function for a single value of ℓ, i.e., from partial data, and the miracle becomes a compatibility condition for spectral functions of different ℓ-values.

c. The inverse scattering problem. Just as in the one-dimensional case the inverse scattering problem in three-dimensions may be solved via the Gel'fand-Levitan method. The idea is to construct the spectral function from the S matrix and then to solve the inverse spectral problem. The vehicle for this is the Jost function. As Eq. (8.60) indicates, the spectral function ρ is explicitly expressible in terms of $J(k)$ and the bound states and their characters. There is an a priori uniqueness theorem that is not available in one dimension, and it will be discussed in the next section.

The construction of the Jost function from the S matrix was explicitly discussed in Sec. 8b in terms of the solution of one of the Riemann-Hilbert problems stated and solved in Sec. 7. Therefore the inverse scattering problem, at least as far as its reconstruction aspect is concerned, is completely solved by the Gel'fand-Levitan method, provided that the Jost function exists and we are not in one of the accidental situations for which (8.31) might not hold.

This procedure has the disadvantage that it requires first the construction of J via the generalized Marchenko equation, and then, in addition, the solution of the Gel'fand-Levitan equation. A more direct method will be given in the next section.

10. Solution of the Inverse Scattering Problem in Three Dimensions via the Marchenko Method. *a. Uniqueness.* Before proceeding to the solution method, it is important to note a significant difference between the situation in one dimension and that in higher dimensions. As was stated in Sec. 8a, when $k \to \pm\infty$ with $\tau = k(\theta - \theta')$ fixed, the scattering amplitude $A(k,\theta,\theta')$ approaches its Born approximation, (8.10). But this Born approximation, considered as a function of τ, is just the Fourier transform of V, and as $k \to \pm\infty$ the upper bound $|\tau|_{max} = 2|k|$ on τ also tends to infinity. Therefore the large-$|k|$ limit of A determines the entire Fourier transform of V. (Note that for a given k, as θ and θ' vary τ sweeps out the ball $|\tau| < 2|k|$.) It follows that $A(k,\theta,\theta')$ uniquely determines V almost everywhere. In fact, it is sufficient to know $A(k,\theta,\theta')$ for $|k| > c$, for any c, which clearly is a consequence of the redundant nature of the data contained in A.

Alternatively the Born approximation limit may be expressed as [47]

$$(10.1) \qquad \lim_{k\to\infty} k^2(E(k,x),\ A(k)\ E(k,x)) = -2\pi \int d^3y\ V(y)|x - y|^{-2}$$

and V may be uniquely determined from the right-hand side of this relation [48].

We note explicitly that the uniqueness theorem includes the case of bound states. As was shown in Sec. 8 all the bound-state information needed for inversion is contained in $A(k,\theta,\theta')$. This should therefore come as no surprise. (It does not contradict the well-known fact that for central potentials and a single angular momentum the scattering and bound-state data are, except for the Levinson theorem, independent. If $A(k,\theta,\theta')$ is given the central potential may be uniquely reconstructed from a phase shift of a sufficiently high angular momentum for which there are no bound states. For local potentials it does support the old Heisenberg contention that the S matrix contains all the information needed to determine the dynamics.) The situation is, in this regard, quite different from that in one dimension, where there is no such uniqueness theorem and the norming constants are independent of the S matrix.

Since the Fourier transform of the potential is directly obtainable from the large-k asymptotics of A, one may regard the inverse scattering problem as solved. While this is, in principle, correct, there are practical disadvantages in an exclusive reliance on high-energy (high-frequency) data. It therefore still serves a useful purpose to find inversion methods that depend less sensitively on the data at large k.

b. The Marchenko method without bound states. The basis of the inversion procedure is Eq. (8.14), $\psi^{\#} = S^{-1}Q\psi$, for the scattering solution, together with its analyticity in C^+ and its asymptotics as given by (8.4) and (8.5) in terms of the function $\gamma(k,\theta,x) = \psi(k,\theta,x)\exp(-ik\theta\cdot x)$. (It is worth remarking that the data are actually obtained from the asymptotic formula (8.6) and not from (8.14), but it is via (8.14) that they enter the inversion. The connection between (8.6) and (8.14) is not very direct.)

Let us write (8.14) as an equation for γ

$$(10.2) \qquad \gamma^{\#} = S_x^{-1} Q\gamma \; .$$

where S_x is the operator whose kernel is

$$(10.3) \qquad S_x(k,\theta,\theta') = S(k,\theta,\theta')e^{ik(\theta - \theta')\cdot x} \; .$$

One easily finds from (8.2) and (8.7) that S_z is the S matrix that corresponds to a shifted potential $V_z(x) = V(x + z)$.

Eq. (10.2) together with the requirement that $\gamma(k)$ be holomorphic (if there are no bound states) in C^+ and have the asymptotics (8.5) constitutes a Riemann-Hilbert problem similar to $H_0^1(S_x^{-1})$ in the terminology of Sec. 7. The only difference is that here we are looking for solutions that are vectors in h rather than linear operators. However, if f solves $H_0^1(S_x^{-1})$ then the vector $f\hat{1}$ solves the present problem, if $\hat{1}$ is the vector given by the function on S^2 that is identically equal to 1. We can therefore rely completely on the results given in Sec. 7.

We define the Fourier transform

$$(10.4) \qquad G(\alpha) = \frac{i}{(2\pi)^2} \int_{-\infty}^{\infty} dk \; kQA_x(k)e^{-ik\alpha} \; ,$$

where we have used (8.12) and (8.13), or more explicitly,

$$(10.4') \qquad G(\alpha,\theta,\theta') = [i/(2\pi)^2] \int_{-\infty}^{\infty} dk \; kA(k,-\theta,\theta')e^{-ik[\alpha + x\cdot(\theta + \theta')]} \; .$$

The sense in which this Fourier transform exists has been established in Sec. 8a. The generalized Marchenko equation now reads

$$(10.5) \qquad \eta(\alpha) = G(\alpha)\hat{1} + \int_0^{\infty} d\beta \; G(\alpha + \beta) \; \eta(\beta)$$

for $\alpha > 0$. The self-adjoint operators G and $G_{\#}$ defined by $G(\alpha + \beta)$

and $G(-\alpha - \beta)$ have been proved [16] to be compact if V satisfies the conditions (i) - (v) of Sec. 8; in fact, their squares are Hilbert-Schmidt. [Note that (8.9) implies that $\tilde{G}(\alpha) = G(\alpha)$, and (8.8) implies $\overleftarrow{G}(\alpha) = G(\alpha)$.] Therefore by Theorem 1 of Sec. 7, if neither G^2 nor $G^2_{\#}$ have the eigenvalue 1 then (10.5) has a unique solution, and the Fourier transform

$$(10.6) \qquad \gamma(k,x) = \hat{1} + \int_0^\infty d\alpha\ \eta(\alpha)e^{ik\alpha}$$

of the solution $\eta(\alpha)$ of (10.5) is holomorphic in C^+, and it satisfies (10.2), (8.4), and (8.5).

The x-dependence is exhibited more clearly if we write these equations explicitly. Define

$$(10.4'') \qquad g(\alpha,\theta,\theta') = [i/(2\pi)^2] \int_{-\infty}^{\infty} dk\ kA(k,-\theta,\theta')e^{-ik\alpha} ,$$

which is independent of x. Then the function $\lambda(\alpha,\theta,x) = \eta(\alpha - \theta\cdot x,\theta,x)$ is the solution of the integral equation for $\alpha > \theta\cdot x$

$$(10.5') \qquad \begin{aligned} \lambda(\alpha,\theta,x) &= \int d\theta'\ g(\alpha + x\cdot\theta',\theta,\theta') \\ &+ \int d\theta' \int_{x\cdot\theta'}^{\infty} d\beta\ g(\alpha + \beta,\theta,\theta')\ \lambda(\beta,\theta',x) , \end{aligned}$$

and

$$(10.6') \qquad \Psi(k,\theta,x) = e^{ik\theta\cdot x} + \int_{\theta\cdot x}^{\infty} d\alpha\ \lambda(\alpha,\theta,x)e^{ik\alpha}$$

satisfies (8.14).

The x-dependence of all the functions involved has played no role up to this point. However, Fourier transformation of (8.2) together with (10.5) or (10.5') gives us the integral equation for $\eta(\alpha,\theta,x)$ in terms of V, for $\alpha > 0$,

$$(10.7) \qquad \begin{aligned} \eta(\alpha,\theta,x) &= \sigma(\alpha,\theta,x) \\ &- \int_{\Omega(\alpha,\theta,x)} d^3y\ \frac{V(y)}{4\pi|x - y|}\ \eta(\alpha - |x-y| + \theta\cdot(x-y),\theta,y) , \end{aligned}$$

where as in (8.23)

$$(10.8) \qquad \sigma(\alpha,\theta,x) = -\int d^3y\ \frac{V(y)}{4\pi|x - y|}\ \delta(|x-y| + \theta\cdot(y-x) - \alpha) ,$$

and the integral in (10.7) runs over the region Ω bounded by a paraboloid which is determined by $\alpha - |x-y| + \theta\cdot(x-y) > 0$. As $\alpha\downarrow 0$, $\Omega \to 0$ and

$$\lim_{\alpha\downarrow 0} \sigma(\alpha,\theta,x) = -\tfrac{1}{2} \int_0^\infty dr\, V(x - \theta r) .$$

Consequently

$$(10.9) \quad \lim_{\alpha\downarrow 0} \eta(\alpha,\theta,x) = -\tfrac{1}{2} \int_0^\infty dr\, V(x - \theta r)$$

and hence

$$(10.9') \quad -2\theta\cdot\nabla\, \eta(0+,\theta,x) = V(x) ,$$

and

$$(10.9'') \quad -2\theta\cdot\nabla\, \lambda(\theta\cdot x+,\theta,x) = V(x) .$$

Equations (10.9') or (10.9") again exhibit the "miraculous" property that their left-hand sides appear to depend on θ, but their right-hand sides do not. If for the given $A(k,\theta,\theta')$ an underlying potential exists then the miracle is guaranteed to happen, and the potential is reconstructed by (10.9') or (10.9"). The reconstruction problem is therefore solved. On the other hand, if an arbitrarily given function $A(k,\theta,\theta')$ with all the appropriate needed properties is given then the solution (10.5') will generally not lead to the miracle. In that case an underlying potential does not exist. [The fact that $A(k,\theta,\theta')$ depends on five real variables and $V(x)$ on three should lead us to expect that for almost no functions A a potential exists. The miracle is thus appropriately named.]

The appropriate properties of A that are needed are the following:

(i) A satisfies (8.8) and (8.9).

(ii) For all θ and θ', $A(k,\theta,\theta')$ is a continuous function of k for all $k \in R$.

(iii) In the absence of bound states A must be such that $S = \mathbf{1} - (k/2\pi i)A$ is unitary and satisfies the appropriate Levinson theorem (see Sec. 8d), namely $\exists$ c such that

$$\log \det S(0) = \lim_{k\to\infty} [\log \det S(k) + ikc]$$

where det denotes the Fredholm determinant.

(iv) $A(k)$ is strongly square integrable in the sense defined in Sec. 8a.

(v) The operators G and $G_{\#}$ defined below (10.5) are compact and their squares are Hilbert-Schmidt.

(vi) Neither G^2 nor $G_{\#}^2$ has the eigenvalue 1.

It has been shown [16] that if a scattering amplitude is given that has the properties (i) to (vi), and if the solution of (10.5') is miraculous, i.e., the left-hand side of (10.9") is independent of θ, then the function ψ defined by (10.6') satisfies the Schrödinger equation with the potential V given by (10.9"), ψ satisfies (8.14) with the S matrix corresponding to the given scattering amplitude, and ψ has the asymptotic large-$|x|$ behavior of (8.6). Thus the construction problem is solved and properties (i) to (vi) together with the miracle are sufficient conditions for the existence of a potential, that is, they serve to <u>characterize</u> the functions that are admissible as scattering amplitudes. They do not give a complete characterization because they do not determine the class of potentials; specifically, they do not tell us if V satisfies the conditions (i) to (v) stated at the beginning of Sec. 8. Therefore the circle is not completely closed.

As a simple exercise we may check (10.4"), (10.5'), and (10.9") with the Born approximation. If V is replaced by εV, the scattering amplitude A is formally expanded in a power series in ε (the Born series), and this series is formally used in (10.5), then equating the linear terms on both sides leads to the equation, by (10.9"), (10.5'), and (10.4"),

$$V(x) = (i/2\pi^2)\ \theta\cdot\nabla \int d\theta' \int_{-\infty}^{\infty} dk k\ e^{-ikx\cdot(\theta+\theta')} A_B(k,-\theta,\theta')$$

where A_B is the Born approximation, given by (8.10). The right-hand side of this equation reads

$$(1/2\pi)^3 \int d^3y\ V(y) \int d\theta' \int_{-\infty}^{\infty} dt\ t^2(1+\theta\cdot\theta') e^{it(\theta+\theta')\cdot(y-x)} .$$

If we use the vector $k = t(\theta + \theta')$ as variable of integration in R^3 and spherical polar coordinates with the z-axis along θ we find that $d\theta' dt\ t^2(1 + \theta\cdot\theta') = d^3k$. The angle ϑ' between θ' and θ is related to the angle ϑ between $\theta + \theta'$ and θ by $\vartheta' = 2\vartheta$. As ϑ' varies between 0 and π, ϑ varies between 0 and $\frac{1}{2}\pi$, which covers the upper hemisphere of k if $t > 0$. The lower hemisphere is covered by $t < 0$. Therefore we obtain

$$\int d^3y\ V(y)(1/2\pi)^3 \int d^3k\ e^{ik\cdot(y-x)} = V(x) ,$$

which verifies the miracle for the Born approximation.

c. The Marchenko method with bound states. If there are bound states then the solution γ of Eq. (10.2) has poles and we must solve the Riemann-Hilbert problem $H^1_\Sigma(S_x^{-1})$, in the terminology of Sec. 7. Here the set Σ consists of the numbers κ_m, m = 1, . . . , n, whose squares are the eigenvalues, and of the spans of the residues of γ at its poles. The κ_m and their characters are computable from the scattering amplitude, as shown in Sec. 8c. As seen from (8.41) these characters H_n are the spans of the residues of $\psi(k,\theta,x)$. Since $\gamma(k,\theta,x) = \psi(k,\theta,x) \exp(-ik\theta\cdot x)$ the spaces H^x_m that enter into Σ are given by $H^x_m = E(-\kappa_m,x)H_m$.

The problem $H^1_\Sigma(S_x^{-1})$ is solved, as in Sec. 7, by reducing it to $H^1_0[(S_x^{-1})^{red}]$. Thus we must solve a generalized Marchenko equation (7.4) in which G^{red} is calculated as in (7.2) with

$$(10.10)\quad \Omega = \Gamma^{\#-1}\, \tilde{S}^{\#}_x\, Q\Gamma Q$$

and Γ is obtained as in Sec. 7 from H^x_m. Let $\eta^{red}(\alpha,x)$ be the solution of

$$(10.11)\quad \eta^{red}(\alpha,x) = G^{red}(\alpha)\hat{1} + \int_0^\infty d\beta\, G^{red}(\alpha+\beta)\, \eta^{red}(\beta,x)$$

for $\alpha > 0$. (Note that Γ and G depend on x.) Then it has been shown [17] that the potential is found from η^{red} by

$$(10.12)\quad V(x) = -2\theta\cdot\nabla\, [\eta^{red}(0+,\theta,x) - \Lambda(\theta,x)]\ ,$$

where

$$(10.13)\quad \Lambda(\theta,x) = \lim_{\alpha\downarrow 0}\, (1/2\pi) \int_{-\infty}^{\infty} dk \int d\theta'\, e^{ik\alpha}\, [\Gamma(\theta,\theta',k) - 1]\ ,$$

in which $\Gamma(\theta,\theta',k)$ is the integral kernel of $\Gamma(k)$.

This solves both the reconstruction and the construction problem with bound states. The needed properties of A are the same as those stated in Sec. 10b, except that the appropriate Levinson theorem is now that given in Sec. 8d, and the bound-state eigenvalues and characters must be connected with A as in Sec. 8c.

d. Remark on the miracle. The fact that the characterization of admissible amplitudes includes the miracle, a condition that cannot be checked directly but only after solving the generalized Marchenko equation, is very inconvenient from the point of view of applications and the construction of models. It would, for example, be of great interest to construct explicitly solvable cases analogous to the Bargmann potentials, which correspond to rational S matrices in one dimension and for central potentials. No such cases that are solvable in closed form are known in three dimensions and one does not even know how to write down explicitly a class of admissible amplitudes.

The miracle also has disturbing implications for stability. If we begin with an admissible amplitude we do not know how to perturb it infinitesimally and still stay in the admissible class. The nature of the class D of admissible data mentioned in Sec. 1, and of its boundary, is unknown. All given data have natural errors attached, and one expects that, in some suitable norm, being near admissible data implies being near a miracle. However, this has not been proved and the needed norm is unknown.

11. Open Questions and Problems. There are a number of open problems in the area of the Marchenko and Gel'fand-Levitan methods. The most bothersome have to do with the miracle, of course. Take first the problem without bound states.

Consider the Marchenko method in one dimension. Forward analyticity (by which I mean analyticity of T in C^+ together with its asymptotics) allows us to uncouple the equations, as in the Kay-Moses-Faddeev method, and then to prove compatibility of the uncoupled equations if S is unitary. This therefore leads to the miracle. Similarly, unitarity and forward analyticity allow us to construct all of S directly from R_ℓ. They are thus sufficient conditions for the miracle to occur. It is not clear, however, how the Marchenko equation (in the coupled version) utilizes these properties of S.

In three dimensions the situation is much less clear. Are unitarity and forward analyticity (i.e., analyticity of the forward scattering amplitude in C^+, together with its asymptotics) sufficient for the miracle to occur? That's unlikely. In contrast to the situation in one dimension they are not sufficient to construct all of S directly from a part of it. Possibly there are other properties of S that lead to the miracle which have not yet been discovered. The role of forward analyticity is quite obscure in three dimensions.

When there are bound states the situation in three dimensions is as follows. Each bound state has three attributes: the eigenvalue $-\kappa_n^2$, the character, and a scale variable (which corresponds in the central case and in one dimension to the norming constant). In the Gel'fand-Levitan method a knowledge of all three is required. In the Marchenko method one needs only the eigenvalues and the characters.

This apparent contradiction is cleared up as follows.

In order to utilize the Gel'fand-Levitan method for the solution of the inverse scattering problem we must first construct the Jost function. This is done by a Marchenko procedure and requires only the eigenvalues and characters of the bound states. The scale constants are then determined by J. Therefore both procedures require only the eigenvalues and characters for the solution of the inverse scattering problem. In fact, however, all of the bound-state information is contained in the S matrix and the entire solution of the inverse scattering problem is uniquely determined (if it exists) by S (for positive k^2) alone. That's again due to forward analyticity.

Note that forward analyticity implies that the Jost function contains all the needed information. This is in contrast to the case for a central potential, where the Jost function does not contain information on the norming constants. But the solution of the inverse scattering problem in that case does not utilize forward analyticity! The important role of forward analyticity certainly merits further study.

Suppose A is an admissible scattering amplitude. What is the nature of small perturbations of A that ensure admissibility of the perturbed function? If we stay in the admissible class, is there a topology in which the mapping from D to F is continuous? What is the needed norm? Is there a topology that permits us to go outside D, such that near any A in a larger class there is an admissible function?

There are no noncentral potentials for which the Schrödinger equation is known to be solvable in closed form. It would be of great interest for the construction of models to have some cases in which the Marchenko equation could be explicitly solved, as for example in the one-dimensional and in the central three-dimensional case of rational S matrices, leading to the Bargmann potentials. We do not even know any explicit amplitudes that are admissible.

Another problem whose solution would be interesting is that of the Marchenko equation (in one or three dimensions) in which the starting point is an arbitrary comparison potential for which everything is assumed to be known. The Gel'fand-Levitan procedure easily lends itself to the use of such comparison potentials, as we have seen. However, no analog of that is known for the Marchenko method.

Another open question is: What happens if the kernel of the generalized Marchenko equation has eigenvales ±1? Can that actually happen, or is it ruled out as in one dimension? Are there as yet unknown reasons why the generalized Marchenko equation in three dimensions, just as in one dimension, always has a solution (for a reasonable class of S matrices)? In other words, does the three dimensional Jost function always exist?

There are several open questions in connection with the Gel'fand-Levitan method in three dimensions. The first is that of a direct definition of the solution ϕ. That would lead to a direct definition of J and ensure its existence. A proof of the properties of ϕ that ensure the three-dimensional Povsner-Levitan representation without the assumption of exponential fall-off of the potential is lacking but ought to be possible. Can exceptions to (8.29) really occur, for reasonable potentials?

A detailed study of the distributional nature of the three-dimensional Fourier transform h of ϕ - E would be very useful, and so would be a study of the Volterra equation that leads to the inverse of $\mathbb{1} - h$.

Finally, and perhaps most importantly, there is the question of what happens if the miracle does not occur. It would be of great interest to embed the inverse problem in a setting in which inversion would still make sense even if the miracle did not happen. Many of the questions mentioned earlier might then be answered.

Appendix. *Proposition*: If V satisfies assumptions (i), (ii), (iv), and (v) of Sec. 8 then for all $p > 4$ there exists a constant C such that for all $f \in L^p(S^2)$

$$\int_{-\infty}^{\infty} dk\, k^2 \, \|A(k)f\|_p^2 \leq C \, \|f\|_p^2 ,$$

where A(k) is the scattering amplitude and $\|\cdot\|_p$ denotes the L^p-norm.

Proof: We write A as the sum of four terms:

$$A(k,\theta,\theta') = \sum_1^4 B_n(k,\theta,\theta') .$$

The B_n are given as follows:

$$B_1(k,\theta,\theta') = \int d^3x\, V(x) e^{ikx\cdot(\theta' - \theta)} = \hat{V}[k(\theta' - \theta)]$$

$$B_2(k,\theta,\theta') = \int d^3x\, V(x) e^{ikx\cdot\theta'} \, \Gamma(k,x,\theta)$$

$$\Gamma(k,x,\theta) = \int d^3y \frac{V(y)}{|x - y|} e^{ik(|x-y| - \theta\cdot y)}$$

$$B_3(k,\theta,\theta') = \int d^3x\, V(x)\, \Gamma(k,x,-\theta')\, \Gamma(k,x,\theta)$$

$$B_4(k,\theta,\theta') = \int d^3x \int d^3y\, V^{\frac{1}{2}}(x) e^{-ikx\cdot\theta} L(k,x,y)\, |V|^{\frac{1}{2}}(y)\, \Gamma(k,y,-\theta')$$

where $L = (\mathbb{1} - K)^{-1} K^2$, $K = |V|^{1/2} G^0 V^{1/2}$, $V^{1/2} = V|V|^{-1/2}$.

Let us first prove the following four auxiliary results:

Lemma A: If $|\hat{V}(k)| \leq C(\mu^2 + |k|^2)^{-3/4}$ then

$$F(k,\theta) = \int d\theta' \; \hat{V}[k(\theta' - \theta)] \; f(\theta') ,$$

where $f \in L^p(S^2)$, is such that for $p > 4$

$$\int_{-\infty}^{\infty} dk \; k^2 \; \|F(k)\|_p^2 < C \; \|f\|_p^2 .$$

Proof: For fixed k and θ consider $v(\theta') = \hat{V}[k(\theta' - \theta)]$ as a vector in L^q, $q > 4/3$. Then by Hölder's inequality, $|F(k,\theta)| \leq \|f\|_p \|v\|_q$, $\frac{1}{p} + \frac{1}{q} = 1$, and

$$\|v\|_q^q = \int d\theta' \; |\hat{V}[k(\theta' - \theta)]|^q \leq C \int d\theta' \; [\mu^2 + 2k^2(1 - \theta\cdot\theta')]^{-\ell}$$

$$= 2\pi \; C \int_{-1}^{1} \frac{du}{[\mu^2 + 2k^2(1 - u)]^{\ell}} \leq \frac{C'}{a^2 + k^2} .$$

where $\ell = 3q/4$ and we have used the hypothesis and the fact that $\ell > 1$. Therefore $\|v\|_q \leq C(a^2 + k^2)^{-1/q}$. As a result

$$\|F(k)\|_p^p = \int d\theta \; |F(k,\theta)|^p \leq C \int d\theta \; \|f\|_p^p \; \|v\|_q^p$$

$$\leq C' \; \|f\|_p^p \; (a^2 + k^2)^{-p/q}$$

and consequently

$$\int_{-\infty}^{\infty} dk \; k^2 \; \|F(k)\|_p^2 \leq C \; \|f\|_p^2 \int_{-\infty}^{\infty} dk \; k^2 (a^2 + k^2)^{-2/q} .$$

If $p > 4$ then $2 - 4/q < -1$ and the integral converges. (Note that assuming a stronger decrease of $\hat{V}$ is of no help.) q.e.d.

Lemma B: If $|\Gamma(k,x,\theta)| \leq C(a^2 + |k|)^{-1}$ and $\int d^3x \; |V(x)| \, |x|^{-1/2} < \infty$ then for $f \in L^2$ and each $\theta \in S^2$

$$\int dk \; k^2 \; |(B_2(k)f)(\theta)|^2 < C \; \|f\|_2^2 .$$

Proof: Defining $h(k,x) = \int d\theta\ f(\theta)e^{ik\theta\cdot x}$ we have

$$(B_2(k)f)(\theta) = \int d^3x\ V(x)\ \Gamma(k,x,\theta)\ h(k,x)\ ,$$

$$|(B_2(k)f)(\theta)||k| \le C \int d^3x\ |V(x)||h(k,x)|\ .$$

Therefore

$$\int_{-\infty}^{\infty} dk\ k^2\ |B_2(k)f|^2$$

$$\le C' \int d^3x \int d^3x'\ |V(x)||V(x')| \int_{-\infty}^{\infty} dk\ |h(k,x)||h(k,x')|$$

$$\le C' \{\int d^3x\ |V(x)|[\int dk\ |h(k,x)|^2]^{\frac{1}{2}}\}^2\ .$$

But

$$\int dk\ |h(k,x)|^2 = \int dk \int d\theta d\theta'\ f(\theta)\ f^*(\theta')e^{ikx\cdot(\theta - \theta')}$$

$$= (2\pi/|x|) \int_{-1}^{1} du\ |\int_0^{2\pi} d\phi\ f(\theta)|^2 \le (2\pi/|x|)\ \{\int_0^{2\pi} d\phi\ [\int_{-1}^{1} du\ |f(\theta)|^2]^{\frac{1}{2}}\}^2$$

$$\le [(2\pi)^2/|x|] \int_0^{2\pi} d\phi \int_{-1}^{1} du\ |f|^2 = [(2\pi)^2/|x|]\ \|f\|_2^2\ ,$$

where $u = \hat{x}\cdot\theta$. Therefore

$$\int_{-\infty}^{\infty} dk\ k^2\ |B_2(k)f|^2 \le C''\ \|f\|_2^2\ [\int d^3x\ |V(x)||x|^{-\frac{1}{2}}]^2$$

$$\le C'''\ \|f\|_2^2$$

by assumption. q.e.d.

Lemma C: If Γ satisfies the same assumption as in lemma B, and $V \in L^1(R^3)$ then for each θ and $\theta' \in S^2$

$$\int_{-\infty}^{\infty} dk\ k^2\ |B_3(k,\theta,\theta')|^2 < \infty\ .$$

Proof: By assumption

$$|B_3(k,\theta,\theta')| = |\int d^3x\ V(x)\ \Gamma(k,x,-\theta')\ \Gamma(k,x,\theta)|$$

$$\leq C \int d^3x\ |V(x)|\ (a^2 + k^2)^{-2}$$

and the result follows. q.e.d.

Lemma D: If Γ obeys the same assumptions as in lemma B and V satisfies assumptions (i) and (ii) then for each θ and $\theta' \in S^2$

$$\int_{-\infty}^{\infty} dk\ k^2\ |B_4(k,\theta,\theta')|^2 < \infty .$$

Proof:

$$|B_4(k,\theta,\theta')| \leq C(a^2 + |k|)^{-1} \int d^3x d^3y\ |V(x)\ V(y)|^{\frac{1}{2}} |L(k,x,y)|$$

$$\leq C(a^2 + |k|)^{-1} \int d^3x\ |V(x)|\ \|L(k)\|_2$$

where $\|\cdot\|_2$ denotes the Hilbert-Schmidt norm. For each $k \neq 0$, $(\mathbb{1} - K)^{-1}$ is a bounded operator and $\|(\mathbb{1} - K)^{-1}\| \to 1$ as $k \to \pm\infty$. Therefore for all $|k| \geq k_o > 0$, $\|L(k)\|_2 \leq C\ \|K(k)^2\|_2$ and

$$\int_{|k|\geq k_o} dk\ k^2\ |B_4(k,\theta,\theta')|^2 \leq C' \int_{|k|\geq k_o} dk\ \|K(k)\|_2^2 < \infty$$

by the corollary to lemma 2.1 of [15]. The singularity of $k = 0$, if that is an exceptional point, was proved in to be $O(1/k)$. Therefore the integral may be extended to zero.

Now if $\Delta V \in L^1(R^3)$ then $k^2\ \hat{V}$ is uniformly bounded. Therefore (v) implies that $\exists\ \mu$, c such that $|\hat{V}| \leq C(\mu^2 + |k|^2)^{-1}$. Furthermore

$$|\Gamma(k,x,\theta)| = \left|\int d^3y\ \frac{V(x+y)}{|y|}\ e^{ik(|y| - \theta\cdot y)}\right|$$

$$\left|\int_0^{\infty} d|y|\,|y|\,e^{ik|y|} \int d\hat{y}\ V(x+y)e^{-ik\theta\cdot y}\right| .$$

Integration by parts (see Appendix 4 of [15]) gives

$$k \int d\hat{y}\ V(x+y)e^{ik\theta\cdot y} \equiv \mathring{V}(k,x,|y|,\theta)$$

$$= (2\pi i/|y|)[e^{-ik|y|}V(x + \theta|y|) - e^{ik|y|}\ V(x - \theta|y|)]$$

$$- i \int d\hat{y}\; V'(x,y,\theta) e^{ik\theta\cdot y} ,$$

where

$$V'(x,y,\theta) = \frac{(\theta - \hat{y}\theta\cdot\hat{y}) \cdot \nabla V(x+y)}{1 - (\theta\cdot y)^2} .$$

Therefore

$$|\overset{\circ}{V}| \le (2\pi/|y|)\,[\,|V(x + \theta|y|)| + |V(x - \theta|y|)|\,]$$

$$+ \int dy \frac{|\Delta V(x + y)|}{[1 - (\theta\cdot\hat{y})^2]^{1/2}}$$

$$\le (4\pi/|y|)\, M_1(|x| - |y|) + \int d\hat{y} \frac{M_2(|x + y|)}{[1 - (\theta\cdot\hat{y})^2]^{1/2}} \equiv \overline{\overline{V}}(x,|y|)$$

and $|\Gamma| \le |k|^{-1} \int_0^\infty dss\, \overline{\overline{V}}(x,s)$. Since Γ is continuous at $k = 0$ it follows that assumptions (ii) and (iv) imply that $|\Gamma(k,x,\theta)| \le C(a^2 + |k|)^{-1}$. Therefore all the assumptions made in lemmas A - D follow from (i) - (v).

The results of lemmas A - D imply that for each n, $\int dk\, k^2 \; \|B_n f\|_p^2 < C\,\|f\|_p^2$ for $p > 4$. Since $A = \Sigma B_n$ the proposition follows.

REFERENCES

[1] V.A.MARCHENKO, The construction of the potential energy from the phases of the scattered waves, Dokl. Akad. Nauk SSSR 104 (1955), pp. 695-698 [Math. Rev. 17, p. 740].

[2] I.M. GEL'FAND and B.M. LEVITAN, On the determination of a differential equation from its spectral function, Isvest. Akad. Nauk SSSR 15 (1951), p. 309 [Am. Math. Soc. Transl. 1, pp. 253-304].

[3] I. KAY, The inverse scattering problem, New York Univ. Res. Rep. No. EM-74 (1955), reprinted in Inverse Scattering Papers: 1955-1962, I. Kay and H.E. Moses, eds., Math. Sci. Press, Brookline, Mass., 1982, pp. 37-64.

[4] I. KAY and H.E. MOSES, The determination of the scattering potential from the spectral measure function, III. Calculation of the scattering potential from the scattering operator for the one-dimensional Schrödinger equation, Nuovo Cimento 3 (1956), pp. 276-304.

[5] L.D. FADDEEV, On the relation between S matrix and potential for

the one-dimensional Schrödinger operator, Dokl. Akad. Nauk SSSR 121 (1958), pp. 63-66 [Math. Rev. 20, p. 773].

[6] L.D. FADDEEV, The inverse problem in the quantum theory of scattering, Usp. Mat. Nauk 14 (1959), p. 57 [Transl. J. Math. Phys. 4 (1963), pp. 72-104].

[7] L.D. FADDEEV, Properties of the S matrix of the one-dimensional Schrödinger equation, Trudy Mat. Inst. Steklov 73 (1964), p. 314 [Am. Math. Soc. Transl. 2, pp. 139-166].

[8] P. DEIFT and E. TRUBOWITZ, Inverse scattering on the line, Commun. Pure Appl. Math. 32 (1979), pp. 121-251.

[9] R.G. NEWTON, Inverse scattering.I. One Dimension, J. Math. Phys. 21 (1980), pp. 493-505.

[10] R.G. NEWTON, Inversion of reflection data for layered media: a review of exact methods, Geophys. J. R. astr. Soc. 65 (1981), pp. 191-215.

[11] R.G. NEWTON, Note on inversion of reflection data for layered media, Geophys. J. R. astr. Soc. 69 (1982), pp. 571-572.

[12] G.N. BALANIS, Inverse scattering: determination of inhomogeneities in sound speed, J. Math. Phys. 23 (1982), pp. 2562-2568.

[13] S.H. GRAY, Inverse scattering for the reflectivity functions, J. Math. Phys. 24 (1983), pp. 1148-1151.

[14] R.G. NEWTON, New result on the inverse scattering problem in three dimensions, Phys. Rev. Lett. 43 (1970), pp. 541-542.

[15] R.G. NEWTON, Inverse scatterin.II. Three dimensions, J. Math. Phys. 21 (1980), pp. 1698-1715; 22 (1981), p. 631; 23 (1982), p. 693.

[16] R.G. NEWTON, Inverse scattering.III. Three dimensions, continued, J. Math. Phys. 22 (1981), pp. 2191-2200; 23 (1982), p. 693.

[17] R.G. NEWTON, Inverse scattering.IV. Three dimensions: Generalized Marchenko construction with bound states, J. Math. Phys. 23 (1982), pp. 594-604.

[18] R.G. NEWTON, On a generalized Hilbert problem, J. Math. Phys. 23 (1982), pp. 2257-2265.

[19] I. KAY and H.E. MOSES, The determination of the scattering potential from the spectral measure function, V. The Gel'fand-Levitan equation for the three-dimensional scattering problem, Nuovo Cimento 22 (1961), pp. 689-705.

[20] I. KAY and H.E. MOSES, A simple verification of the Gel'fand-Levitan equation for the three-dimensional scattering problem, Commun. Pure Math. 14 (1961), pp. 435-445.

[21] L.D. FADDEEV, Inverse problem of quantum scattering theory II, Itogi Nauki i Tekhniki, Sov. Prob. Mat. 3 (1974), pp. 93-180 [Transl. J. Soviet Math. 5 (1976), pp. 334-396].

[22] R.G. NEWTON, The Gel'fand-Levitan Method in the Inverse Scattering Problem, in Scattering Theory in Mathematical Physics, J.A. Lavita and J.-P. Marchand, eds., D. Reidel Publ. Co., Dortrecht, 1974, pp. 193-225.

[23] R.G. NEWTON, The three-dimensional inverse scattering problem in quantum mechanics, invited lectures at 1974 Summer Seminar on Inverse Problem, Am. Math. Soc., U.C.L.A., August, 1974, unpublished.

[24] R.T. PROSSER, Formal solution of inverse scattering problems, J. Math. Phys. 10 (1969), pp. 1819-1822; II, ibid 17 (1976), pp. 1775-1779; III, ibid 21 (1980), pp. 2648-2653; IV, ibid 23 (1982), pp. 2127-2130.

[25] S. COEN, Inverse scattering of the permittivity and permeability profiles of a plane stratified medium, J. Math. Phys. 22 (1981), pp. 1127-1129.

[26] M. HOWARD, Inverse scattering for a layered acoustic medium using the first-order equations of motion, Geophysics 48 (1983), pp. 163-170.

[27] C. EFTIMIU, Direct and inverse scattering by a sphere of variable index of refraction, J. Math. Phys. 23 (1982), pp. 2140-2146.

[28] I. KAY, The inverse scattering problem for transmission lines, in Mathematics of Profile Inversion, L. Colin, ed., NASA TM X-62, 150, 6-2 to 6-17.

[29] R.G NEWTON, Scattering Theory of Waves and Particles, Second ed., Springer Verlag, New York, 1982.

[30] I. KAY and H.E. MOSES, The determination of the scattering potential from the spectral measure function, I. Continuous spectrum, Nuovo Cimento 2 (1955), pp. 917-961; . . . II. Point eigenvalues and proper eigenfunctions, ibid 3 (1956), pp. 66-84.

[31] H. CORNILLE, Connection between the Marchenko formalism and N/D equations: Regular interactions, J. Math. Phys. 8 (1967), pp. 2268-2281.

[32] J. PLEMELJ, Ein Ergänzungssatz zur Cauchyschen Integraldarstellung analytischer Funktionen, Randwerte betreffend, Monatsh. f. Math. u. Phys. XIX (1908), pp. 205-210.

[33] J. PLEMELJ, Riemannsche Funktionenscharen mit gegebener Monodromiegruppe, Monatsh. f. Math. u. Phys. XIX (1908), pp. 211-245.

[34] N.I. MUSKELISHVILI, Singular Integral Equations, Noordhoff Publ., Leyden, 1977.

[35] I. KAY, The inverse scattering problem when the reflection coefficient is a rational function, Commun. Pure Appl. Math. XIII (1960), pp. 371-393.

[36] V. BARGMANN, On the connection between phase shifts and scattering potential, Rev. Mod. Phys. 21 (1949), pp. 488-493; also unpublished.

[37] T. FULTON and R.G. NEWTON, Explicit non-central potentials and wave functions for given S-matrices, Nuovo Cimento 3 (1956), pp. 677-717.

[38] W.R. THEIS, Explizete Potentiale zu gegebenen Streufunktionen geladener Teilchen mit Absorption, Z. Naturf. 11a (1956), pp. 889-891.

[39] P.C. SABATIER, these Proceedings.

[40] V.E. ZAKHAROV and A.B. SHABAT, Exact theory of two-dimensional self-focusing and one-dimensional self-modulation of waves in nonlinear media, Zh. Eksp. Teor. Fiz. 61 (1971), pp, 118-134 [Transl. Soviet Physics JETP 34 (1972), pp. 62-69].

[41] V.E. ZHAKHAROV and A.B. SHABAT, Interactions between solitons in a stable medium, Zh. Eksp. Teor. Fiz. 64 (1973), pp. 1627-1639 [Transl. Soviet Physics JETP 37 (1973), pp. 823-828].

[42] M. CHENEY, Quantum mechanical scattering and inverse scattering in two dimensions, Ph.D. thesis, Indiana University, 1982, unpublished.

[43] E.M. STEIN, Singular Integrals and Differentiability Properties of Functions, Princeton University Press, 1970, p. 46.

[44] R.G. NEWTON, Noncentral potentials: The generalized Levinson theorem and the structure of the spectrum, J. Math. Phys. 18 (1977), pp. 1348-1357.

[45] C. ZEMACH and A. KLEIN, The Born expansion in non-relativistic quantum theory, Nuovo Cimento X (1958), pp. 1078-1087.

[46] R. JOST and W. KOHN, On the relation between phase shift energy levels and the potential, Kgl. Danske Videnskab. Sels., mat.-fys. Medd. 27 (1958), no. 9, pp. 1-19.

[47] Y. SAITO, Some properties of the scattering amplitude and the inverse scattering problem, Osaka J. Math. 19 (1982), pp. 527-547.

[48] Y. SAITO, An inverse problem in potential theory and the inverse scattering problem, J. Math. Kyoto University 22 (1982), pp. 307-327.

[49] D. LUDWIG, The Radon transform on Euclidean space, Commun. Pure Appl. Math. 19 (1966), pp. 49-81.

Rational Reflection Coefficients in One-Dimensional Inverse Scattering and Applications

Pierre C. Sabatier*

Abstract. The Inverse Scattering Problem for the Schrödinger equation on the line can be solved in closed form for reflection and transmission coefficients that satisfy usual regularity conditions and are rational functions of k. This well-known result, and its consequences, is rederived here in a very simple and compact way, which makes easy to review the various approaches to the subject. After this review is done, the author gives his point of view on the subject, which is in his opinion a remarkable example of how a potential can be progressively stripped of its bound states and resonances. Noticing that this undressing can be done through reversible steps by means of Darboux transformations, it is possible to construct a new algorithm for solving the inverse problem of the Schrödinger Equation on the line with rational reflection coefficients. This algorithm is interesting from the theoretical and from the practical point of view altogether. Generalizations applying to geophysical problems are suggested.

1. Introduction. After a brief technical introduction, this lecture contains three other sections. The section II is a review of the inverse scattering on the line for the Schrödinger equation in the case of rational reflection coefficients. In the section III, we present our point of view on the problem, which leads us to derive a new algorithm. In the section IV, we discuss generalizations, and, in particular, we comment on the case of a medium where jump discontinuities are added to a background yielding rational reflection coefficients.

Let us first briefly recall notations and main results on the problem. We start with the equation

$$(1.1)\quad \left[-\frac{d^2}{dx^2}+V(x)\right]\varphi(k,x)=k^2\,\varphi(k,x)$$

where V belongs to the set L^1_p, defined by

$$(1.2)\quad V\in L^1_p\ :\ \int_{-\infty}^{+\infty}dx\,\left[1+|x|^p\right]|V(x)|<\infty$$

*Physique Mathématique et Théorique, CNRS : ERA 153; RCP 264
Universite Montpellier II 34060 Montpellier Cedex France

at least for $p = 1$. With this assumption, and for real k, we can define the "Jost solutions" of (1.1), say $f_{\pm}(k,x)$, respectively asymptotic to $\exp[\pm ikx]$ as x tends (resp.) to $\pm\infty$. Since (1.1) is a 2nd order differential equation, we can write down

$$(1.3) \quad T(k)\, f_{\mp}(k,x) = f_{\pm}(-k,x) + R_{\pm}(k)\, f_{\pm}(k,x)$$

The formula (1.3) can also be considered as a relation between the progressive waves which are obtained by Fourier-transforming the Jost solutions. Thus it clearly describes a scattering problem in which T is a transmission coefficient $R_{\pm}$ a reflection coefficient (resp. on the right and on the left). Setting

$$(1.4) \quad F_{\pm}(k,x) = \exp[\mp ikx]\, f_{\pm}(k,x)$$

we see that the equation (1.1), completed by the convenient asymptotic conditions, is equivalent to the following (Volterra) integral equations :

$$(1.5) \quad F_{\pm}(k,x) = 1 - \int_{-\infty}^{+\infty} dy\, L_{\pm}(x,y)\, F_{\pm}(k,y)\, V(y)\, \theta[\pm(y-x)]$$

where θ is the Heaviside function, and

$$(1.6) \quad L_{+}(x,y) = L_{-}(y,x) = -k^{-1} \sin[k(y-x)] \exp[ik(y-x)]$$

The iterated series $\sum_{0}^{\infty} F_{\pm}^{(n+1)}$ solving (1.5) is constructed through the algorithm :

$$(1.7) \quad F_{\pm}^{(n+1)}(k,x) = -\int_{-\infty}^{+\infty} dy\, L_{\pm}(x,y)\, F_{\pm}^{n}(k,y)\, V(y)\, \theta[\pm(y-x)]$$

Setting

$$(1.8) \quad I(x) = J(-x) = 1 + |x|\,\theta(x)$$

we notice that for $y \geq x$, $y-x$ is smaller than $I(x)\,J(y)$. Using it, we obtain for $y \geq x$ the inequalities

$$\begin{matrix}(1.9a)\\ \\ (1.9b)\end{matrix} \quad |L_{+}(x,y)V(y)| \leq 2\,|V(y)| \exp[(y-x)\sigma(k)] \begin{cases} |k|^{-1} \\ I(x)J(y) \end{cases}$$

where $\sigma(k) = |\mathrm{Im}k| - \mathrm{Im}k$, and similar inequalities for $x \geq y$ and L_{-}. All these bounds can be written in the form $\alpha(x)\,\beta(y)$. If this is used in (1.7), one obtains as a majorant of F_n the nth term of the series expansion of

$$(1.10) \quad 1 + a(x) \int_{x}^{\infty} du\, \beta(u) \exp\left[\int_{x}^{u} \alpha(t)\beta(t)\,dt\right]$$

For $V \in L_1^1$, the formula (1.10) yields absolute majorants for the F_n's in the half-plane Im k ≥ 0. The majorant of $\bar{F}_n$ is the nth term of a convergent numerical series expansion. Since it also follows from (1.7) that the F_n's are entire functions of k, we conclude that $F_\pm(k,x)$ is a holomorphic function of k in Im k ≥ 0, continuous as Im k $\to 0$, and such that :

$$(1.11) \qquad |F_\pm(k,x)-1| = O(|k|^{-1}) \qquad |k| \to \infty, \quad \text{Im } k \geq 0$$

Thus we can define, at least in L_2, the so called "transformation kernels", $K_\pm$, by the Fourier transforms :

$$(1.12)\, K_\pm(x,y) = (2\pi)^{-1} \int_{-\infty}^{+\infty} dk \, \exp[\mp ik(y-x)] \, \{F_\pm(k,x)-1\}$$

We can show that K_+ (resp. K_-) vanishes for $y < x$ (resp. $y > x$), by closing the contour of the integral (1.12) by a circle in the upper half plane. Hence, $K_\pm(x,y)$ can be written as well in the form $K_\pm(x,y)\theta[\pm(y-x)]$. The inverse Fourier transform yields the formula

$$(1.13) \quad F_\pm(k,x)-1 = \int_{-\infty}^{+\infty} dy \, \exp[\pm ik(y-x)] \, K_\pm(x,y) \, \theta[\pm(y-x)]$$

which holds at least in L_2. Actually, it is easy to derive more refined behaviors and to use them in order to prove the uniform convergence of formulas (1.12) and (1.13). Besides, by substituting (1.5) into (1.2), then using (1.13) to eliminate $F_\pm$ in favor of $K_\pm$, and performing the Fourier transforms, we obtain the integral equations

$$(1.14a)\; K_+(x,y) = \frac{1}{2} \int_{\frac{1}{2}(x+y)}^{\infty} ds \{V(s)+2 \int_0^{\frac{1}{2}(y-x)} dr \, V(s-r)K_+(s-r,s+r)\} \quad (y>x)$$

$$(1.14b)\; K_-(x,y) = \frac{1}{2} \int_{-\infty}^{\frac{1}{2}(x+y)} ds \{V(s)+2 \int_{\frac{1}{2}(y-x)}^{0} dr V(s-r)K_-(s-r,s+r)\} \quad (y<x)$$

$K_\pm$ can be constructed from V by solving these Volterra equations. Since the kernels $K_\pm$ are generators for the Jost solutions, the solutions of (1.14a,b) completely solve the direct problem. In turn, V is trivially obtained from $K_\pm$, since it follows from (1.14) that

$$(1.15) \qquad \lim_{y \to x_\pm} K_\pm(x,y) = \frac{1}{2} \int_{-\infty}^{+\infty} ds \; V(s) \; \theta[\pm(s-x)]$$

The result (1.15) can also be obtained by comparing the first orders of $F_\pm(k,x)$ as a function of V in the formulas (1.5) and (1.13). Let us also notice that the integral equation (1.14a) (resp. 1.14b) is equivalent for $y > x$ (resp. $y < x$) to the partial differential equation

$$(1.16) \qquad \left[\frac{\partial^2}{\partial x^2} - \frac{\partial^2}{\partial y^2} - V(y)\right] K_{\pm}(x,y) = 0$$

completed by the boundary condition (1.15) and the asymptotic condition :

$$(1.17) \qquad K_{\pm}(x, \pm\infty) = 0$$

For "solving" the inverse problem, it is sufficient to construct $K_{\pm}$ from the "scattering data", i.e. T and $R_{\pm}$. Now it follows from (1.16) and the analytical properties of $F_{\pm}(k,.)$ that the Cauchy formula holds

$$(1.18) \qquad F_{\pm}(k,x)-1 = \lim_{\epsilon \to 0^+} \frac{1}{2\pi i} \int_{-\infty}^{+\infty} dk' \frac{F_{\pm}(k',x)-1}{k' - k - i\epsilon}$$

It can be transformed by making $k' \to -k'$ and by inserting (1.3) into the result, obtaining

$$(1.19) \quad F_{\pm}(k,x)-1 = (2\pi i)^{-1} \lim_{\epsilon \to 0^+} \{\int_{-\infty}^{+\infty} dk' \frac{1-T(k')F_{\mp}(k',x)}{k'+k+i\epsilon}$$

$$+ \int_{-\infty}^{+\infty} dk' \frac{R_{\pm}(k')\, F_{\pm}(k',x) \exp[\pm 2ik'x]}{k'+k+i\epsilon}$$

in which the scattering data appear as the input of an equation yielding the Jost solutions. So as to go further, let us notice that the relation (1.3) implies for $T(k)$ the formula

$$(1.20) \qquad T(k) = 2ik\, \{W[f_-(k,.), f_+(k,.)]\}^{-1}$$

where W stands for the "wronskian". Since f_- and f_+ are holomorphic in $\mathrm{Im}\, k \geq 0$, so is W. W vanishes if (iff) $f_-(k,x)$ and $f_+(k,x)$ are proportional - say, $f_- = C_-\psi_-$, $f_+ = C_+\psi$, where C_- and C_+ are numbers, and ψ is conveniently standardized. Now this cannot occur for real non vanishing k, because $\psi^*(k,x)$ would be a solution of (1.1) with $\psi(k,x)$, and their wronskian would be equal to $2ik|C_-|^2$ and to $-2ik|C_+|^2$. For $\mathrm{Im}\, k > 0$, $f_+(k,x)$ and $f_-(k,x)$ exponentially go to zero respectively as $x \to +\infty$ and $x \to -\infty$. Thus, if k is a pole of $T(k)$, $\psi(k,x)$ belongs to $L_2(\mathbb{R})$. These poles are therefore the eigenvalues of the "discrete spectrum" of the differential operator in (1.1). They are simple (the wronskian of two different eigenfunctions would be zero). They are purely imaginary (use (1.1) to calculate $[W[\psi,\psi^*]]_{-\infty}^{+\infty}$). Besides, they are not present in many cases, and in particular in most geophysical applications. Then $T(k)$ is holomorphic in the upper half plane. One can close the contour in $\text{Im } k > 0$, and, taking into account (1.20) and (1.11), together with the holomorphic properties of $F_{\mp}$, one readily shows that the first integral in (1.19) vanishes. Fourier-transforming the remaining integral, we obtain the so-called Marchenko equation (written here "with no discrete spectrum") :

$$(1.21)\quad K_{\pm}(x,y) + M_{\pm}(x,y) + \int_{-\infty}^{+\infty} dz\ \theta(\pm(z-x))M_{\pm}(y+z)K_{\pm}(x,z) = 0$$

where

$$(1.22)\quad M_{\pm}(x) = (2\pi)^{-1}\int_{-\infty}^{+\infty} dk\ R_{\pm}(k)\exp[ikx]$$

So as to close the descriptive part of our problem, let us also notice that some simple calculations yield from Eq. (1.3) the formulas

$$(1.23)\quad R_{\pm}(k) = \pm\frac{W[f_{\pm}(-k,.),f_{\mp}(k,.)]}{W[f_{-}(k,.),f_{+}(k,.)]}$$

$$(1.24)\quad R_{+}(k)\,T(-k) + R_{-}(-k)\,T(k) = 0$$

$$(1.25)\quad R_{+}(k)\,R_{+}(-k) + T(k)T(-k) = R_{-}(k)\,R_{-}(-k) + T(k)\,T(-k) = 1$$

Because of the reality of $V(x)$, we have in addition, for real k

$$(1.26)\quad R_{\pm}(-k) = [R_{\pm}(k)]^* \qquad T(-k) = [T(k)]^*$$

Actually, the formulas (1.23)-(1.24)-(1.25) generally hold only for real k. However, if R and T can be continued analytically in the k plane, the formulas can be too.

The machinery which is described in the equations (1.1) to (1.22) is due to the efforts of several authors. Kay [17] introduced it in the case of potentials that vanish on the half-line, and Faddeyev [9] studied it completely in the general case, but with a few errors in the inequalities on f_+ and f_-. The presentation we give here is Faddeyev's, revised and simplified by Atkinson [2] and ourselves [33].

The result above gives us every reason to guess that a knowledge on $\mathbb{R}$ of $R_+(k)$ (respectively $R_-(k)$) is sufficient to construct $K_+(x,y)$) (respectively $K_+(x,y)$) and hence $V(x)$. Deift and Trubowitz

[8] have given conditions on R_+, R_- and T sufficient to guarantee that a potential V yielding no discrete spectrum exists and is unique in L_2^1, where it can be constructed by the Marchenko equation, and yields R_+, R_-, and T in the scattering problem. These conditions are

C/1 $T(k)$, $R_+(k)$, $R_-(k)$ satisfy on the real axis the equations (1.24), (1.25) and (1.26).

C/2 $T(k)$ is holomorphic in $\text{Im } k > 0$, and continuous down to the real axis

C/3 $T(k)-1 = O(|k|^{-1})$ $(\text{Im } k \geq 0)$
$R_\pm(k) = O(|k|^{-1})$ $(k \in \mathbb{R})$

C/4 $|T(k)| > 0$ $(\text{Im } k \geq 0,\ k \neq 0)$

either $|T(k)| > 0$ $(\text{Im } k \geq 0)$ or there exists $\dot{T}(0)$ and ρ_+ such that $T(k) = k\,\dot{T}(0° + O(k)$, $\text{Im } k \geq 0$, and $1+R_\pm(k) = k\rho_\pm + O(k)$, $(k \in \mathbb{R})$

C/5 $M_\pm(x)$ is absolutely continuous , and there exists $c(a)$ finite such that $\int_{-\infty}^{+\infty} dx\ \theta[\pm(x-a)]\ M_\pm(x)\ (1+x^2) \leq c(a)$.

Starting from this potential, it is possible to get potentials having the some reflection coefficient and a discrete spectrum either by Crum transformations (see Deift and Trubowitz [8] or by solving the Marchenko equation (1.21) with a conveniently modified kernel $M(x+y)$.

2 . Rational coefficients. When the potential $V(x)$ vanishes on one side of the line, the Jost solution which has its asymptotic condition on this side is trivial there. The bounds obtained from (1.10) for the terms (1.7) of this Jost solution involve only finite integrals, so that they converge even in $\text{Im } k < 0$, and the Jost solution is an entire function of k. It follows from (1.23) that the corresponding reflection coefficient is holomorphic in $\text{Im } k > 0$, and conversely one can show from Marchenko's equation that such a coefficient produce a cut potential. Now, the inverse problem on the line was first studied in electromagnetic problems, where $V(x)$ vanishes on one side of the line. Thus, it is not surprising to see that $R(k)$ holomorphic in $\text{Im } k > 0$, and meromorphic in $\text{Im } k < 0$, was the "natural" working assumption in the first studies. Before going through this litterature, let us first derive, in a modern way, the results which can be obtained for "rational" reflection coefficients. We first assume that
(1) $T(k)$ is a rational fraction, goes to 1 as $|k| \to \infty$, vanishes on the upper half plane at $k = 0$ only, where it has a simple zero, has no pole in the upper half plane (no "discrete spectrum"), and satisfies (1.26).

(2) $R_{\pm}(k)$ are rational fractions, $O(|k|^{-2})$ as $|k| \to \infty$, go to -1 as $|k| \to 0$, and satisfy (1.24), (1.25), (1.26), this implies (in particular) that for each pole outside of the imaginary axis, there exists another pole symmetric with respect to the imaginary axis, with antisymmetric residues.
(3) either $R_+(k)$ or $R_-(k)$ is given, consistent with assumption C1.

It is easy to see that the assumptions C1-C5 are satisfied, so that there exists a unique potential $V(x)$ in L_2^1 which can be constructed either from $R_+(k)$ or from $R_-(k)$.

If R_+, R_- and T are rational fractions, the relations (1.24) and (1.25) partly determine two of them from the other. Indeed, suppose $R(k) = P(k)/D(k)$ is a rational fraction, with all zeros and poles outside of the real axis, except possibly a simple zero at $k = 0$. Suppose we hnow $R(k)\,R(-k)$. Then there exists a unique (up to a factor ± 1 which here is fixed by other conditions) irreducible rational fraction $R_S(k)$ such that all its zeros and poles are in $\mathrm{Im}\, k \leq 0$, and that

$$(2.1) \quad R(k) = \frac{P_S(k)}{D_S(k)} \, \frac{P_N(-k)}{P_N(k)} \, \frac{P_D(k)}{P_D(-k)} = R_S(k)\, R_N(-k)\, R_D(k)$$

where $P_N(k)$ and $P_D(k)$ are two polynomials with zeros in $\mathrm{Im}\, k < 0$. We shall call R_N and R_D the phase factors, R_S the reduced form. We assume that the fraction P_D/P_N has been completely reduced, but P_D resp. P_N may contain factors belonging also to P_S, resp. D_S. If this decomposition is applied to R_+, R_- and T, in our case without "discrete spectrum", it can be seen that the only forms consistent with our assumption are

$$(2.2a) \quad R_-(k) = \frac{P(k)}{\prod_{j=1}^{q} (\lambda_j - k)} \prod_{i=q+1}^{r} \frac{\varkappa_i - k}{\varkappa_i + k} \prod_{\ell=p+1}^{s} \frac{\lambda_\ell - k}{\lambda_\ell + k}$$

$$(2.2b) \quad T(k) = \frac{\prod_{i=1}^{q} (\varkappa_i + k)}{\prod_{j=1}^{q} (\lambda_j - k)}$$

$$(2.2c) \quad R_+(k) = \frac{P(-k)}{\prod_{j=1}^{q} (\lambda_j - k)} \prod_{i=2}^{r} \frac{\varkappa_i + k}{\varkappa_i - k} \prod_{\ell=p+1}^{s} \frac{\lambda_\ell + k}{\lambda_\ell - k}$$

where $\operatorname{Im} \lambda_i < 0$, $\operatorname{Im} \varkappa_i > 0$ except $\varkappa_1 = 0$. p may be smaller than q. The poles in the phase factors may be simple or not. Let $\mathcal{P}^+$ (resp. $\mathcal{P}^-$) be the set of poles $\varkappa_j$ (resp. λ_j) of R_+ (resp. R_-) in the upper half plane, with residues R_+^j (resp. R_-^j). Assume for the sake of simplicity that all the poles are simple. The equation (1.19) (in which the first integral has been dropped because there is no discrete spectrum) yields the two equations :

$$(2.3a)\quad F_+(k,x)-1 = \sum_{\varkappa_j \in \mathcal{P}^+} \frac{R_+^j\, F_+(\varkappa_j,x)\, \exp[2i\varkappa_j x]}{k + \varkappa_j} \qquad (x > 0)$$

$$(2.3b)\quad F_-(k,x)-1 = \sum_{-\lambda_j \in \mathcal{P}^-} \frac{R_-^j\, F_-(-\lambda_j,x)\, \exp[2i\lambda_j x]}{k - \lambda_j} \qquad (x < 0)$$

We can identify $K_\pm(x,y)$ for instance by comparing (2.3a,b) and (1.13)

$$(2.4a)\quad K_+(x,y) = -i \sum_{\varkappa_j \in \mathcal{P}^+} R_+^j\, F_+(\varkappa_j,x)\, \exp[i\varkappa_j(x+y)] \quad (y > x > 0)$$

$$(2.4b)\quad K_-(x,y) = -i \sum_{-\lambda_j \in \mathcal{P}^-} R_-^j\, F_-(-\lambda_j,x)\, \exp[i\lambda_j(x+y)] \quad (y < x < 0)$$

Now, let k run through $\mathcal{P}^+$ in (2.3a), through $\mathcal{P}^-$ in (2.3b). We obtain two linear systems whose solutions yield everything in our problem through (2.4a) and (2.4b). Writing down the solutions in the Cramer's form, it is possible to prove that

$$(2.5)\quad K_\pm(x,x) = \pm \frac{\mathcal{D}'_\pm(x)}{\mathcal{D}_\pm(x)}$$

where

$$(2.6a)\quad \mathcal{D}_+(x) = \det\{\delta_{ij} - (\varkappa_i + \varkappa_j)^{-1} R_+^j \exp[2i\varkappa_j x]\}$$

$$(2.6b)\quad \mathcal{D}_-(x) = \det\{\delta_{ij} + (\lambda_i + \lambda_j)^{-1} R_-^j \exp[2i\lambda_j x]\}$$

Hence it follows from (1.15) that $V(x)$ is given in a closed form. Notice that $x = 0$ is a special value related with the rational property of the coefficients. Indeed, a translation of the origin to $x = a$ induces into the reflection coefficients a phase factor $\exp[\pm 2ika]$ which is not a rational fraction.

If we introduce a discrete spectrum, there appears in (2.2b) an additional phase factor of the form

$$T_B(k) = \prod_{p=1}^{M} \frac{i\nu_p + k}{i\nu_p - k} \tag{2.7}$$

and two phase factors in $R_+(k)$ and $R_-(k)$, say, $R_B^+(k)$ and $R_B^-(k)$, such that

$$R_B^+(k)/R_B^-(-k) = T_B(k)/T_B(-k) = [T_B(k)]^2 \tag{2.8}$$

Let us now go back to the equation (1.19).
Assume that $\psi(i\nu_j,x)$ has been normalized in $L_2(\mathbb{R})$ and is equal to $c_j^+ f_+(i\nu_j,x)$ and $c_j^- f_-(i\nu_j,x)$. It is not difficult to show that

$$\operatorname*{Res}_{k = i\nu_j} T(k) = i\, c_j^+ c_j^- \tag{2.9}$$

The normalization coefficients c_j^+ and c_j^- otherwise can be arbitrarily chosen. Again, let $\mathcal{P}^+$ (resp. $\mathcal{P}^-$) be the set of poles of $R_+(k)$ (resp. $R_-(k)$) in the upperhalf plane, including those which may appear in the additional factors. The equation (1.19) reduces to

$$\begin{aligned} F_+(k,x)-1 = {} & \sum_{\varkappa_j \in \mathcal{P}^+} \frac{R_+^j F_+(\varkappa_j,x) \exp[2i\varkappa_j x]}{k + \varkappa_j} \\ & -(2\pi)^{-1} \sum_j (c_j^+)^2 F_+(i\nu_j,x) \exp[-2\nu_j x] \qquad (x > 0) \end{aligned} \tag{2.10a}$$

$$\begin{aligned} F_-(k,x)-1 = {} & \sum_{-\lambda_j \in \mathcal{P}^-} \frac{R_-^j F_-(-\lambda_j,x) \exp[2i\lambda_j x]}{k - \lambda_j} \\ & -(2\pi)^{-1} \sum_j (c_j^-)^2 F_-(i\nu_j,x) \exp[+2\nu_j x] \qquad (x < 0) \end{aligned} \tag{2.10b}$$

These equations are completely similar to the equations (2.3) and yield similar results. When there is no pole but those of the discrete spectrum, the two relations (2.10) can be continued into the whole x-axis. In all cases, the relations (2.10), as well as the relation (2.3), define a meromorphic continuation of $F_\pm(k,x)$ for fixed x throughout the k plane. When there are multiple poles, the results are more complicated, but not essentially different.

The litterature on rational coefficients in the one-dimensional scattering problem begins with three papers of Kay [17], [18], [19] and one by Kay and Moses [20] which give a fairly complete study of the problem. Needless to say, they had been inspired by the analogous results obtained by Bargmann [3] in the radial inverse problem. In [17], Kay introduces as a working assumption an expansion of $K_-(x,y)$ of the form (2.4) and shows on examples how it solves the problem. In [20], Kay and Moses study reflectionless potentials, in which only the discrete spectrum yields poles in (2.10). The system is solved in closed form and the formula (2.5) appears, apparently for the first time in the litterature. In the field of nonlinear partial differential equations, these reflectionless potentials met a great success, since they correspond to the N-solitons solutions of the Korteveg-de Vries equation. The 1959 and 1960 papers [18], [19], which contains essentially the same material, deal with the problem of rational coefficients without discrete spectrum, and with the restriction that $V(x)$ vanishes for negative x. Hence the input $R_-(k)$ has to be holomophic in the upper half plane. By the way, notice that Kay's assumptions on the numerator and denominator of $R_-(k)$ apparently allows $R_-(k)$ to grow at ∞ up to k^2. There is probably a misprint : in fact $R_-(k)$ should go to zero at least like k^{-2} if condition C5 is to be guarantied. Kay showed how $T(k)$ could be constructed from $R_-(k)$ by means of a dispersion relation for $\log T(k)$:

$$(2.11) \qquad \log T(k) = (2\pi i)^{-1} \int_{-\infty}^{+\infty} d\sigma(\sigma-k)^{-1} \log[1-R_-(\sigma)R_-(-\sigma)]$$

Again Kay introduced an expansion of the form (2.4) as a working assumption. Making then a repeated uses of the so-called reflection property (if $V(x) \to V(-x)$, then $R_-(k) \to R_+(k)$, $R_+(k) \to R_-(k)$, $T(k) \to T(k)$), he obtained by a rather complicated way a linear system of the form (2.3). Kay was able to solve it in the closed form (2.5). The results for the whole line, as well as those for multiple poles, could be derived by the machinary given by Kay as early as 1955. However, the first ones were written down explicitly, in the form (2.5), only very recently (Calogero and Degasperis, [5], Prosser [30]). The results for multiple poles are due to Pechenik and Cohen [29] . The very simple, although complete derivation given here seems new (Sabatier, [33]).

After the beautiful set of Kay's papers, the interest in rational reflection coefficients was confined for years to studies of the plasma physical problem, where the physical case implies no discrete spectrum, and $V(x) = 0$ on the half line. The closed formula (2.5) is of course not convenient for numerical calculations except for a very few poles (see e.g. Moses [23]). Determining the poles is also a difficult problem. There are numerically better ways to do it and to solve the linear system (2.3) (see e.g. Pechenik and Cohen [27]), but again the number of poles must be reasonably small. Other methods start by making a Laplace transform of the Marchenko's equation, thus deriving a functional equation which relates $F(x,s) = \int_{-x}^{x} K(x,\xi)e^{-s\xi}\,d\xi$, $G(x,s) = \int_{x}^{\infty} K(x,\xi)\,e^{-s\xi}\,d\xi$ and the Laplace transform $N(s)/D(\xi)$ of the reflection coefficient :

$$(2.12)\quad N(s)e^{sx}+N(s)F(x,-s)+D(x)F(x,s)+D(s)G(x,s) = 0$$

Oddly enough, this functional equation can be solved in terms of F and G (Szu et al. [34], Jordan and Ahn [16]). $K(x,x)$ is then obtained by the formula

$$(2.13)\quad K(x,x) = \lim_{s \to -\infty} |s|\, F(x,s)\, \exp[\,|s|\, x\,]$$

The method is convenient for a few poles only. The same limitation applies to a "differential method (Jordan and Ahn, [16], Reilly and Jordan [31]), where one constucts a linear differential operators $f(\frac{\partial}{\partial y})$ which cancels $M_{\pm}(x+y)$ (it is easily obtained from the poles and residues of $R_{\pm}(k)$), then one applies it to the Marchenko equation in order to derive a differential equation for $K(x,y)$. This differential equation may be eventually solved (see Reilly and Jordan [31] for a review and applications of these methods).

The possibility of deriving exact solutions to our problem has been used in several kinds of study. Some physicists did it to get a better understanding of the shadow, or valley, problems, appearing in semiclassical approximations (Pechenik and Cohen [28]). Others tried to exhibit singular results by violating the Deift and Trubowitz conditions. In particuler, Moses tried several unauthorized perturbations of a simple reflection coefficient (Moses [23], [24], Abraham, de Facio, and Moses [1], Moses [25]). A particularly illuminating result appears in the reference of Abraham and al. [1]), in which the authors exhibit two distinct potentials

$$(2.14)\quad \begin{aligned} V_1(x) &= -2\ \delta(x) + 8\ \theta(x)\ (2x+1)^{-2} \\ V_2(x) &= V_1(-x) \end{aligned}$$

corresponding to the same scattering data, without discrete spectrum :

$$(2.15)\quad R_+(k) = R_-(k) = \frac{i}{k+i}\ ;\quad T(k) = \frac{k}{k+i}$$

It is easy to see that conditions (C4) and (C5) are violated.

The numerous studies of the Korteweg-de Vries equation contain several ones dealing with the N-solitons equation, which is related with rational transmission coefficient, and zero reflection coefficients. We already noticed the Kay and Moses paper [20], which may be considered the first in this file. We shall point out only another paper, by Fokas and Ablowitz [10], because it introduces in the most general way the discrete measure associated in the k-space with rational coefficients, and because it paves the way for solving multidimensional inverse problems. Other references can be found for example in the book of Calogero and Degasperis ([5]).

3. How to undress a potential. The potentials corresponding to rational reflection coefficients belong to a special class, say, $\mathfrak{F}$. However, several techniques (e.g. Padé approximants) enable one to approach indefinitely by a rational fraction the reflection coefficient of any potential of L_2^1, known on the real axis. On the other hand, several authors (see e.g. Marchenko [22], Prosser [30]) have proved that if two reflection potentials (satisfying sufficient conditions) are close to each other, sc are the corresponding potentials. Besides, this is a strong stability property, showing a lipschitzian mapping for usual norms. From the physical point of view, the result is fairly obvious. Poles and residues in the lower half k-plane are nothing but resonances and their widths. Poles and residues in the upper half k-plane are nothing but bound states and their normalization constants. The cited results simply prove that by progressively fixing these physical quantities one progressively determines the potential.

Now suppose we know a step-by step and reversible way to strip the potential of these physical features and that in the spectral flow of potentials which is hereby explored, there is a peculiar one, which is in some sense "trivial", in some sense "undressed". We can then start from this peculiar potential and dress it back to construct the desired potential. While preparing this lecture, we have been able to fill this program (Sabatier [34]). We present here a more systematic exposure with some new results.

The basic remark is that in the set of reflection coefficients which differ from $R_-(k)$ only by phase factors there are ones which do not have any poles in the upper half plane. It follows from (2.10b) that the corresponding potentials vanish for any $x < 0$. By the same remark, in the set of reflection coefficients which differ from $R_+(k)$ only by phase factors there are ones which correspond to potentials vanishing for any $x > 0$. These potentials supported by one half line only will be our "undressed" potentials. Now we need ways to introduce phase factors.

Single step way. We shall use a transformation due to Darboux. Assume, say, $\mathrm{Im}\,\mu_2 > 0$, any k, and let $u^{(1)}$ and $f^{(1)}$ be solutions of the following equations :

$$(3.1) \qquad \frac{d^2u^{(1)}}{dx^2} + (\mu_1^2 - V^{(1)})\,u^{(1)} = 0$$

(3.2) $$\frac{d^2 f^{(1)}}{dx^2} + (k^2 - V^{(1)})\, f^{(1)} = 0$$

It is easy to check that if

(3.3) $$\psi^{(1)} = \frac{d}{dx} f^{(1)} - f^{(1)} (u^{(1)})^{-1} \frac{d}{dx} u^{(1)}$$

then

(3.4) $$\frac{d^2 \psi^{(1)}}{dx^2} + \left[k^2 - V^{(2)}\right] \psi^{(1)} = 0$$

(3.5) $$V^{(2)} = V^{(1)} - 2 \frac{d}{dx}\left[(u^{(1)})^{-1} \frac{d}{dx} u^{(1)}\right]$$

We can derive the reflection and transmission coefficients of $V^{(2)}$ by identifying Jost solutions and their relations. According to the value of α_1, β_1 (or α_1', β_1') in the following relation

(3.6) $$u^{(1)}(x) = \alpha_1 f_-^{(1)}(\mu_2,x)+\beta_1 f_-^{(1)}(-\mu_2,x) = \alpha_1' f_+^{(1)}(\mu_2,x)+\beta_1' f_+^{(1)}(-\mu_2,x)$$

we meet four possible cases :

(a) $\beta_1 \neq 0$, any α_1 except $\alpha_1 = \beta_1 R_-(\lambda_1)$ [i.e. $\beta_1' \neq 0$]

(3.7) $$T^{(2)}(k) = -\frac{\mu_2+k}{\mu_2-k} T^{(1)}(k) \qquad R_+^{(2)}(k) = \frac{\mu_2+k}{\mu_2-k} R_+^{(1)}(k)$$

(b) $\beta_1 \neq 0$, $\alpha_1 = \beta_1 R_-(\lambda_1)$ [i.e. $\beta_1' = 0$]

(3.8) $$T^{(2)}(k) = T^{(1)}(k) \qquad R_+^{(2)}(k) = \frac{\mu_2-k}{\mu_2+k} R_+^{(1)}(k)$$

(c) $\beta_1 = 0$, μ_2 not a bound state [$\beta_1' \neq 0$]

(3.9) $$T^{(2)}(k) = T^{(1)}(k) \qquad R_+^{(2)}(k) = \frac{\mu_2+k}{\mu_2-k} R_+^{(1)}(k)$$

(d) $\beta_1 = 0$, μ_2 is a bound state [$\beta_1' = 0$]

(3.10) $$T^{(2)}(k) = -\frac{\mu_2-k}{\mu_2+k} T^{(1)}(k) \qquad R_+^{(2)}(k) = \frac{\mu_2-k}{\mu_2+k} R_+^{(1)}(k)$$

The transformations of R_- are readily derived from those of T, R_+, and the formula (1.24). Clearly, any possible phase factor can be introduced by combining the formula (3.7) to (3.10). Hence, if we start from a consistent set $R_+(k)$, $R_-(k)$, $T(k)$, the inverse problem can be solved in the following way :

(1) Let us first be interested in the half line $x > 0$

(a) We split $R_+(k)$ into two factors $R_+^D(k)$ and $R_+^P(k)$, which is a <u>phase factor</u>, such that the only poles of $R_+^D(k)$ are in the lower half plane. It is easy to see that if $R_+^P(k)$ contains phase factors with poles in the lower half plane, the corresponding isospectral Darboux transform will leave $V(x)$ equal to zero on the half-line $x > 0$. Hence $R_+^O(k)$ is not uniquely defined. However, in practice, for minimizing the computation time, one must not put in $R_+^P(k)$ phase factors with poles in the lower half-plane. We denote by $(\mu_n - k)^{-1}(\mu_n + k)$ with $n = 1,2,\ldots,N$, the sequence of single phase factors composing $R_+^P(k)$ and we assume, for the sake of simplicity, that all the μ_n's are different (no multiple pole), with $\text{Im}\,\mu_n > 0$.

(b) The undressed potential $V_+^{(0)}(x)$ vanishes for any positive x, so that the Jost solution $f_+^{(1)}(k,x)$ flatly reduces to $\exp[ikx]$, and its derivative $f_+'^{(1)}(k,x)$ reduces to $ik\exp[ikx]$. From this point on, we ought to construct the algorithm in such a way that the nth step only uses results derived at the $(n-1)^{\text{th}}$ step <u>for positive x</u>. Besides, "differentiation" is not an allowed operation and must be replaced by elementary operations.This can be achieved by using (2.3).

(c) Suppose that for a fixed positive x, the $(n-1)^{\text{th}}$ step of our algorithm has furnished $V^{(n-1)}(x)$, and, for $i = 1,2,\ldots,(n-1)$, $f_+^{(n-1)}[\mu_i,x]$, $f_+'^{(n-1)}[\mu_i,x]$, the residues $R_+^{(n-1),i}$ and $\exp[i\mu_i x]$, then the same values for the order n are obtained after the following computation, where $d°[\bar{\ }]$ means that calculations of the preceding line are done for a new value of the parameter.

$$1°/\ f_+^{(n-1)}[\mu_n,x] = \exp[i\mu_n x] + \sum_{j=1}^{n-1} R_+^{(n-1),j}\ f_+^{(n-1)}[\mu_j,x]\ \frac{\exp[i(\mu_j+\mu_n)x]}{\mu_j+\mu_n}$$

$$2°/\ f_+^{(n-1)}[-\mu_n,x] = d°[-\mu_n]$$

$$3°/\ f_+'^{(n-1)}[\mu_n,x] = i\mu_n\exp[i\mu_n x]$$
$$+\ i\sum_{j=1}^{n-1} R_+^{(n-1),j}\ f_+^{(n-1)}[\mu_j,x]\exp[i(\mu_j+\mu_n)x]$$
$$+\sum_{j=1}^{n-1} R_+^{(n-1),j}\ f_+'^{(n-1)}[\mu_j,x]\,(\mu_j+\mu_n)^{-1}\exp[i(\mu_j+\mu_n)x]$$

4°/ $f_+^{'(n-1)}[-\mu_n,x] = d°[-\mu_n]$

5°/ $R_+^{(n-1)}(\mu_n) = \sum_{j=1}^{n-1} (\mu_n-\mu_j)^{-1} R_+^{(n-1),j}$

6°/ $u^{(n-1)}(x) = f_+^{(n-1)}(-\mu_n,x) + R_+^{(n-1)}(\mu_n) f_+^{(n-1)}(\mu_n,x)$

7°/ $u'^{(n-1)}(x) = f_+^{'(n-1)}(-\mu_n,x) + R_+^{(n-1)}(\mu_n)\, f_+^{'(n-1)}(\mu_n,x)$

8°/ $f_+^{(n)}(\mu_j,x) = -\frac{i}{2}(\mu_j)^{-1} \{f_+^{'(n-1)}(\mu_j,x) - f_+^{(n-1)}(\mu_j,x) u'^{(n-1)}(x)/$

$u^{(n-1)}(x)\}$ $\qquad j = 1,2,\ldots,n.$

9°/ $f_+^{'(n)}(\mu_j,x) = -\frac{i}{2}(\mu_j)^{-1} [u^{(n-1)}(x)]^{-1}$

$\{(\mu_n^2-\mu_j^2) f_+^{(n-1)}(\mu_j,x) f_+^{(n-1)}(\mu_n,x) - u'^{(n-1)}(x) f_+^{(n)}(\mu_j,x)\};$ $\quad j=1,2\ldots n$

10°/ $R_+^{(n),j} = (\mu_n-\mu_j)^{-1}(\mu_n+\mu_j)\, R_+^{(n-1),j}$ $\qquad j = 1,2,\ldots,n-1$

$R_+^{(n),n} = -2\mu_n \sum_{j=1}^{n-1} R_+^{(n-1),j} (\mu_n-\mu_j)^{-1}$

11°/ $V^{(n)}(x) = 2[u'^{(n-1)}(x)/u^{(n-1)}(x)]^2 + 2\mu_n^2 - V^{(n-1)}(x)$

The number of elementary operations in this n^{th} step is $O(n)$, so that the total number of elementary operations in the algorithm is $O(N^2)$. It is interesting to notice this figure, since the algorithm yields the exact value of $V(x)$ and of the N Jost solutions able to furnish any other solution (through (2.3) and (2.4)) by means of N additions only. This is to be compared with the closed formula (2.5), which needs $O(N^5)$ elementary operations to be calculated and only yields $V(x)$.

(2) Once $V(x)$ has been constructed from $R_+(k)$ on the $x > 0$ side, a similar algorithm starting from $R_-(k)$ makes the job for $x < 0$.

Condensed steps. It is necessary to condense two or several steps of the algorithm in case of multiple poles. It may be of interest also to do it for the coupled poles μ and $-\mu^*$ due to the resonances of a real potential. Anyway, it is possible to do it, and we explain below how two Darboux transforms can be condensed together. So as to make easier the recollection of results within the previous algorithm, the case we study in detail is that of two isospectral transforms of the third kind described above (under the title "$\beta_1 = 0$, μ_2 not a bound state"). It is easy to go through the other cases by using the same techniques. Thus, let us be given a potential $V_o(x)$, corresponding to the reflection coefficient $R_+^o(k)$, and let us choose solutions of the following equations

$$(3.11)\qquad u_1'' + (\mu_1^2 - V_o)u_1 = 0 \qquad (\mathrm{Im}\,\mu_1 > 0)$$

$$(3.12)\qquad u_2'' + (\mu_2^2 - V_o)u_2 = 0 \qquad (\mathrm{Im}\,\mu_2 > 0)$$

$$(3.13)\qquad f'' + (k^2 - V_o)f = 0$$

in such a way that they are used for Darboux transforms of the third kind. This yields the following potentials and reflection coefficients.

$$(3.14)\qquad V_1(x) = V_o(x) - 2\frac{d}{dx}(u_1'/u_1) \leftrightarrow R_+^1(k) = \frac{\mu_1+k}{\mu_1-k}R_+^o(k)$$

$$(3.15)\qquad V_2(x) = V_o(x) - 2\frac{d}{dx}(u_2'/u_2) \leftrightarrow R_+^2(k) = \frac{\mu_2+k}{\mu_2-k}R_+^o(k)$$

Applying now the Darboux transform to (3.11) by using the solution $\bar{u}_2 = u'_2 - u_2u'_1/u_1$ which is derived from u_2, we obtain

$$(3.16)\qquad V_{1,2}(x) = V_1(x) - 2\frac{d}{dx}(\bar{u}'_2/\bar{u}_2) \longleftrightarrow$$

$$R_+^{1,2}(k) = \frac{\mu_2+k}{\mu_2-k}\cdot\frac{\mu_1+k}{\mu_1-k}R_+^o(k)$$

and proceeding in the other sense

$$(3.17)\qquad V_{2,1}(x) = V_2(x) - 2\frac{d}{dx}(\bar{u}'_1/\bar{u}_1) \longleftrightarrow$$

$$R_+^{2,1}(k) = \frac{\mu_1+k}{\mu_1-k}\cdot\frac{\mu_2+k}{\mu_2-k}R_+^o(k)$$

It is convenient to introduce $W(x) = \int_x^\infty V(y)dy$. Then (3.16) can be written as

$$(3.18)\qquad W_{1,2}(x) = W_1(x) + 2i\mu_2 + 2(\bar{u}'_2/\bar{u}_2)$$

We can calculate the last term of (3.18) by using (3.11) and (3.13) and noticing that from (3.14) and (3.15) we can derive

(3.19) $$u'_2/u_2 - u'_1/u_1 = W_2 - W_1 - 2i(\mu_2 - \mu_1)$$

The result is

(3.20) $$W_{1,2} = W_{2,1} = W_0 + \frac{2i(\mu_1+\mu_2)(W_2-W_1)}{W_2-W_1-2i(\mu_2-\mu_1)}$$

It has already been obtained by Calogero and Degasperis [5]. A similar result can be obtained for the solutions. The Darboux transform of (3.13) shows that the following functions are solutions of the corresponding equations

(3.21) $$f_1 = f'-fu'_1/u_1 \leftrightarrow f''_1+(k^2-V_1)f_1 = 0$$

(3.22) $$f_2 = f'-fu'_2/u_2 \leftrightarrow f''_2+(k^2-V_2)f_2 = 0$$

(3.23) $$f_{1,2} = f'_1-f_1\bar{u}'_2/\bar{u}_2 \leftrightarrow f''_{1,2}+(k^2-V_{1,2})f_{1,2} = 0$$

(3.24) $$f_{2,1} = f'_2-f_2\bar{u}'_1/\bar{u}_1 \leftrightarrow f''_{2,1}+(k^2-V_{2,1})f_{2,1} = 0$$

Again, $u'_1/u_1-u'_2/u_2$ can be expressed in terms of f_1-f_2. Some elementary derivations yields

(3.24) $$f_{2,1} = f_{1,2} = f[\mu_1^2-k^2- \frac{\mu_1^2-\mu_2^2}{f_1-f_2} f_1]$$

(3.25) $$= f[\mu_2^2-k^2- \frac{\mu_2^2-\mu_1^2}{f_2-f_1} f_2]$$

Needless to say, if Jost solutions are to be considered, the normalization must be recasted. Suppose for instance that $f \equiv f_1(k,x)$, then

(3.26) $$f_{2,1}(k,x) = -(\mu_1+k)(\mu_2+k)f_{2,1+}(k,x)$$

<u>Applications</u>. As we already said, the most important application is to double poles $(\mu_2 \to \mu_1)$. It is easy to derive from 3.20) and (3.24-3.25) the limit results :

(3.27) $$W_{11} = W_0 + \frac{4i\mu_1\, \partial W_1/\partial\mu_1}{\partial W_1/\partial\mu_1 - 2i}$$

(3.28) $$f_{11} = f[\mu_1^2-k^2-2\mu_1 f_1(\partial f_1/\partial\mu_1)^{-1}]$$

These limit results can easily be inserted into the algorithm in case a double pole comes in because the only new calculation they imply is that of $\frac{\partial}{\partial\mu_1}(u'_1/u_1)$. This is because (3.14) implies

(3.29) $$\partial W_1/\partial\mu_1 = 2i + 2\,\frac{\partial}{\partial\mu_1}(u'_1/u_1)$$

and (3.22) implies

(3.30) $$\partial f_1/\partial\mu_1 = -f\,\frac{\partial}{\partial\mu_1}(u'_1/u_1)$$

Now $\frac{\partial}{\partial\mu_1}(u'_1/u_1)$ can be readily calculated if we known $\frac{\partial}{\partial\mu}[f_+(\mu,x)]$ at the desired step of the algorithm. But at any step of the algorithm, $f_+(\mu,x)$ is given by a formula of the form

(3.31) $$f_+(\mu,x) = \exp[i\mu x] + \sum_j R_+^j(\mu_j+\mu)^{-1} f_+(\mu_j,x)$$

whose μ derivative is quite obvious

(3.32) $$\frac{\partial}{\partial\mu} f_+(\mu,x) = ix\,\exp[i\mu x] - \sum_j R_+^j(\mu_j+\mu)^{-2} f_+(\mu_j,x)$$

We see that the order of the number of elementary operations in the algorithm remains unchanged. We leave to the interested reader the pleasure to go himself through further details and other cases.

4. Generalization. Two kinds of generalizations of the method described in section 3 are interesting for geophysical applications. The first one, which is concerned with electromagnetic sounding, acoustic soundings in presence of absorption, etc, deals with the Schrödinger equation whose potential depends linearly on k [32], [15] :

(4.1) $$y'' + [k^2 - V(x) - ik\,Q(x)]\,y = 0$$

Replacing $-ik$ by ik in (4.1) we obtain the so called "conjugate equation". It is well-known that the system of these two equations can be studied by means of generalizations of the machinery we described in section 1. We shall discuss later the results obtained for rational coefficients.

The second generalization deals with problems governed by equations of the form

(4.2) $$A^{-1}\frac{\partial}{\partial x} A \frac{\partial}{\partial x} p + (k^2 - B)p = 0$$

where p and $A\frac{\partial p}{\partial x}$ must be continuous, but A is not necessarily. This equation is equivalent to a system of two first order equations and it has been studied as so by Howard [13], who gave a complete description of the direct problem and showed that A (in his case, $B = 0$) can be reconstructed by means of a generalized Marchenko equation. It has also been studied in the particular case where $B = 0$, and A is constant between discontinuities (layered media of Goupillaud [11], Clearbout [7], Hron & Razavy [14], Kunetz & d'Erceville [21], Newton [26]

Ware and Aki [37], Berryman and Greene [4]). Here we shall sketch an approach of the problem which keeps us close to the remainder of our lecture. We assume throughout that A is twice differentiable everywhere but at a finite number of points (set S) where A and $\frac{\partial A}{\partial x}$ may exhibit simple jumps, and that A goes to a constant as $x \to \pm \infty$. We assume in addition that B, and $A^{-1/2} \frac{\partial^2}{\partial x^2} A^{1/2}$ outside of S,

are of class L^1_1. Clearly the conserved quantity along x is the "wronskian" of two solutions

$$(4.3) \qquad \tilde{W}(p_1,p_2) = p_1 A \frac{\partial}{\partial x} p_2 - p_2 A \frac{\partial}{\partial x} p_1$$

The Jost solutions $p_\pm(k,x)$ are respectively the solutions going to $[A(x)]^{-1/2} \exp[ikx]$ as $x \to +\infty$ and $[A(x)]^{-1/2} \exp[-ikx]$ as $x \to -\infty$. The reflection and transmission coefficients are defined by the relations :

$$(4.4) \qquad \tilde{T}(k)\, p_-(k,x) = p_+(-k,x) + \tilde{R}_+(k)\, p_+(k,x)$$

$$(4.5) \qquad p_-(-k,x) + \tilde{R}_-(k)\, p_-(k,x) = \tilde{T}(k)\, p_1(k,x)$$

It is easy to write down formulas giving $\tilde{R}_\pm$ and $\tilde{T}$ in terms of wronskians like those given in section 1. Similarly, the formulas (1.24), (1.25), and, when A and B are real, (1.26), hold for $\tilde{R}_\pm$ and $\tilde{T}$.

Let us now go back to the equation (4.2), and, at each point $x \notin S$, let us set $p = A^{-1/2} p$. Then, on each internal where A is twice differentiable, we see that (4.2) is equivalent to the Schrödinger equation :

$$(6.6) \qquad \frac{d^2 \Phi}{dx^2} + [k^2 - B - A^{-1/2} \frac{\partial^2}{\partial x^2} A^{-1/2}]\, \Phi = 0$$

We shall introduce the usual Jost solutions $f_+(k,x)$ and $f_-(k,x)$ of the Schrödinger equation (4.6). Let $h_0, h_1, h_2, \ldots, h_N$, be the increasing abscissas of the points forming the set S. Between any two neighbouring points, say h_{n-1} and h_n, we can write down the relation between $p_-(k,x)$ or $p_+(k,x)$ and the Jost solutions of (4.6) :

$$(4.7) \quad p_-(k,x) = u_n [A(x)]^{-1/2} f_+(-k,x) + v_n [A(x)]^{-1/2} f_+(k,x)$$

$$(4.8) \quad p_+(k,x) = x_n [A(x)]^{-1/2} f_-(-k,x) + y_n [A(x)]^{-1/2} f_-(k,x)$$

Beyond h_N, for $x > 0$, $[A(x)]^{-1/2} f_+(k,x)$ is nothing but $p_+(k,x)$, so that u_n and v_n becomes trivially related to $\tilde{T}(k)$ and $\tilde{R}(k)$ for $n = N$. Below h_0, for $x < 0$, $[A(x)]^{-1/2} f_-(k,x)$ is nothing but $p_-(k,x)$, yielding a similar remark. Now, it is a matter of lengthy but simple calculations to derive from the continuity of $\frac{\partial p}{\partial x}$ and $A \frac{\partial p}{\partial x}$ the relations

$$(4.9) \quad \begin{bmatrix} u_n \\ v_n \end{bmatrix} = \begin{bmatrix} \alpha_n(k) & \beta_n(k) \\ \beta_n(-k) & \alpha_n(-k) \end{bmatrix} \begin{bmatrix} u_{n-1} \\ v_{n-1} \end{bmatrix}$$

where

$$(4.10) \quad \alpha_n(k) = t_n^{-1}\{1 + r_n \frac{f_+'(k,h_n) f_+(-k,h_n) + f_+'(-k,h_n) f_+(k,h_n)}{2ik} + s_n \frac{f_+(k,h_n)\, f_+(-k,h_n)}{ik}\}$$

$$(4.11) \quad \beta_n(k) = (ikt_n)^{-1}\{s_n [f_+(k,h_n)]^2 + r_n f_+(k,h_n) f_+'(k,h_n)\}$$

and

$$(4.12) \quad t_n^{-1} = \frac{1}{2}\{[A(h_n^+)/A(h_n^-)]^{1/2} + [A(h_n^-)/A(h_n^+)]^{1/2}\}$$

$$(4.13) \quad t_n^{-1} r_n = \frac{1}{2}\{[A(h_n^+)/A(h_n^-)]^{1/2} - [A(h_n^-)/A(h_n^+)]^{1/2}\}$$

$$(4.14) \quad t_n^{-1} s_n = -\frac{1}{4}[A(h_n^+)]^{-1/2} [A(h_n^-)]^{-1/2} [A'(h_n^+) - A'(h_n^-)]$$

These relations enable us to construct

$$(4.15) \quad u_N = [\tilde{T}(k)]^{-1}, \quad v_N = \tilde{R}_+(k)/\tilde{T}(k)$$

from

$$(4.16) \quad u_{-1} = [T(k)]^{-1}, \quad v_{-1} = R_+(k)/R(k)$$

which are the scattering data of the Schrödinger equation (4.6), i.e. of the $(A \in C_2)$ problem. In the same way, we derive the relations

$$(4.17) \quad \begin{bmatrix} x_n \\ y_n \end{bmatrix} = \begin{bmatrix} \bar{\alpha}_n(k) & \bar{\beta}_n(k) \\ \bar{\beta}_n(-k) & \bar{\alpha}_n(-k) \end{bmatrix} \begin{bmatrix} x_{n-1} \\ y_{n-1} \end{bmatrix}$$

or the following one, which is more useful (notice that these matrices have their determinant equal to 1) :

$$(4.18)\quad \begin{bmatrix} x_{n-1} \\ y_{n-1} \end{bmatrix} = \begin{bmatrix} \bar{\alpha}_n(-k) & -\bar{\beta}_n(k) \\ -\bar{\beta}_n(-k) & \bar{\alpha}_n(k) \end{bmatrix} \begin{bmatrix} x_n \\ y_n \end{bmatrix}$$

where

$$(4.19)\quad \bar{\alpha}_n(k) = t_n^{-1}\{1-r_n \frac{f'_-(k,h_n)f_-(-k,h_n) + f'_-(-k,h_n)f_-(k,h_n)}{2ik} - s_n \frac{f_-(k,h_n)f_-(-k,h_n)}{ik}\}$$

$$(4.20)\quad \bar{\beta}_n(k) = -(ikt_n)^{-1}\{s_n[f_-(k,h_n)]^2 + r_n[f_-(k,h_n)f'_-(k,h_n)]\}$$

and t_n, r_n, s_n have been defined in (4.12), (4.13), (4.14). This relation enables us to construct

$$(4.21)\quad x_{-1} = [\tilde{T}(k)]^{-1} \quad , \quad y_{-1} = \tilde{R}_-(k)/\tilde{T}(k)$$

from

$$(4.22)\quad x_N = [T(k)]^{-1} \quad , \quad y_N = R_-(k)/T(k)$$

The formulas (4.9) to (4.22) yield a complete solution of the direct problem subject to our assumptions. In this solution there exists a contribution from the background, i.e., from the equation (4.6), and a contribution from the discontinuities at the layers h_i. There are two mathematical cases with easy calculations. The first one is that of a small number of layers. The second one is that of a background depending on few parameters. The extremum of the second case is reached in almost all geophysical studies, where $B = 0$ and A is constant between the layers. Clearly, it would be a very nice and not very "expansive" improvement introducing a background that corresponds to rational coefficients with a small number of poles. It is interesting to notice that there is only one case in which the coefficients $\tilde{R}_\pm(k)$ and $\tilde{T}(k)$ would also be rational : the case where the discontinuity is at the point "zero" of the background problem (remember that "zero" is a special point). Indeed, in any other case, the behavior of the Jost solutions at large $|k|$ is such that factors $\exp[\pm 2i\,k\,\mathbf{h}_n]$ are involved in the off-diagonal elements of the matrices in (4.9) and (4.18). Hence the asymptotic behavior of $\tilde{R}_\pm(k)$ will show in the complex plane singularities which are not consistent with the rational property. Needless to say, there is no surprise : these properties are related with the almost periodical structure of $\tilde{R}_{\pm}(k)$ that precisely enables geophysicists to reconstruct their layered media.

We study now the case when there may be jumps of A and its derivatives at $x = 0$, and only at this point. In addition, we assume that A is constant for negative x. We easily derive from (4.15), (4.16), (4.9), (4.22) and (4.18) the values of $\tilde{T}(k)$ and $\tilde{R}_{\pm}(k)$:

(4.23) $\tilde{T}(k) = t_o T(k) \left[1 + s_o/ik + R_-(k)(s_o/ik - r_o)\right]^{-1}$

(4.24) $\tilde{R}_+(k)/\tilde{T}(k) = t_o^{-1}\left[T(k)\right]^{-1}\left[r_o - s_o/ik - R_-(-k)(1+s_o/ik)\right]$

(4.25) $\tilde{R}_-(k)/\tilde{T}(k) = t_o^{-1}\left[T(k)\right]^{-1}\left[-r_o - s_o/ik + R_-(k)(1-s_o/ik)\right]$

One readily sees that if the "background" coefficients $T(k)$ and $R_-(k)$ are rational, so are $\tilde{R}_{\pm}(k)$ and $\tilde{T}(k)$. But they do not show the same asymptotic behavior : $\tilde{T}(k)$ goes to t_o, $\tilde{R}_{\pm}(k)$ goes to $\pm r_o - s_o/ik + O(k^{-2})$. In turn, these quantities (which must satisfy the condition $r_o^2 + t_o^2 = 1$) can be reconstructed from the asymptotic behavior of $\tilde{T}(k)$ and $\tilde{R}_-(k)$; then $T(k)$ and $R_-(k)$ are determined and the algorithms of section 3 (for instance) yield A for $x \neq 0$.

If we do not assume that V vanishes for negative x, the problem becomes more complicated, and ambiguities may appear like in the example reviewed in section 2 (see (2.15)), in which the $O(k^{-1})$ asymptotic behavior of $R_{\pm}(k)$ is due to a jump of the derivative $A'(x)$. Disentangling the part of the layers and the background in the inverse problem is certainly difficult, and here we shall not go further on this way because our aim is only to survey the problems in which rational coefficients can be useful. We shall not survey either the approaches to inverse problems resembling the ones studied here and where a continued fraction was saught for the solution (see e.g. [12], [36]) although they are more or less related with our problem. And finally we shall not survey the applications of rational coefficients to approximate solutions of the non linear partial differential equations which can be solved by the inverse method [34]. Let us only hope that we have been successful at giving the reader some desire to do it himself. For parallell reading on inverse problems, let us be allowed to recommend reference [6].

Acknowledgements. This paper would never have been written without the very kind invitation of Prof. J. Bee Bednar. I am glad to acknowledge also the friendly hospitality and the fruitful remarks of Prof. F. Calogero. Financial support has also been furnished by the CNRS (RCP 264 : Etudes interdisciplinaires des problèmes inverses).

REFERENCES

[1] P.B. ABRAHAM, B. DE FACIO, H.E. MOSES, Two distinct local potentials with no bound states can have the same scattering operator : a non uniqueness in inverse spectral transformations, Phys. Rev. Lett. 46, 1981, pp. 1657-59.

[2] D. ATKINSON, Marchenko in one dimension, Rept Inst. for Theoretical Physics Groningen, 1979.

[3] V. BARGMANN, On the connection between phase shifts and scattering potential, Rev. Mod. Phys. 21, 1949, pp. 488-493.

[4] J.C. BERRYMAN and R.R. GREENE, Discrete inverse methods for elastic waves in layered media, Geophysics 45, 1980, pp. 213-233.

[5] F. CALOGERO and A. DEGASPERIS, Spectral transforms and solitons, North-Holland, 1982.

[6] K. CHADAN and P.C. SABATIER, Inverse Problems in Quantum Scattering Theory, Springer-Verlag, New York, Heidelberg, Berlin, 1977.

[7] J.P. CLAERBOUT, Synthesis of a layered medium from its acoustic transmission response, Geophysicis 33, 1968, pp. 264-269. see also Fundamentals of geophysical data processing, Mac-Graw Hill. New York, 1976.

[8] P. DEIFT and E. TRUBOWITZ, Inverse scattering on the line, Comm. Pure Appl. Math. 32, 1979, pp. 121-251.

[9] L.D. FADDEEV, Properties of the S-matrix of the one-dimensional equation, Am. Math. Soc. Transl. 2, 65, pp. 139-166.

[10] A.S. FOKAS and M.J. ABLOWITZ, Linearization of the Korteweg-de Vries and Painlevé II Equations, Phys. Rev. Lett. 47, 1981, pp. 1096-1100.

[11] P.L. GOUPILLAUD, An approach to inverse filtering of near-surface layer effects from seismic records, Geophysics 26, 1961, pp. 754-760.

[12] M.A. HOOSHYAR and M. RAZAVY, A continued fraction approach to the inverse problem of electrical conductivity, Geophys. J.R. astr. Soc. 71, 1982, pp. 127-138.

[13] M.S. HOWARD, Inverse scattering for a layered acoustic medium using the first-order equations of motion, Geophysics 48, 1983, pp. 163-170. See also Inversion of the first-order equations governing sound propagation in a layered medium, Ph D Thesis Indiana University, 1981.

[14] M. HRON and M. RAZAVY, Two discrete forms of the inverse scattering problem, Can. J. of Phys. 55, 1977, pp. 1434-1441.

[15] M. JAULENT and C. JEAN, The inverse problem for the one-dimensional Schrödinger equation with an energy-dependent potential, Ann. Inst. Henri Poincaré 25, 1976, pp. 105-118 et 119-137.

[16] A.K. JORDAN and S. AHN, Inverse Scattering Theory and Profile reconstruction, Proc. I.E.E. 126, 1979, pp. 945-950.

[17] I. KAY, The Inverse Scattering Problem, Rept. New York University EM-74, 1955.

[18] I. KAY, On the determination of the free electron of an ionized gas, Rept New York University EM-141, 1959.

[19] I. KAY, The Inverse Scattering Problem when the reflection coefficient is a rational function, Comm. Pure Appl. Math. 13, 1960, pp. 371-393.

[20] I. KAY and H.E. MOSES, Reflectionless transmission through dielectrics and scattering potentials, J. Appl. Phys. 27, 1956, pp. 1503-1508. See also The determination of the Scattering Potential from the spectral measure function III, Nuovo Cimento 3, 1956, pp. 276-304. Idem IV, Suppl. Nuovo Cimento 5, 1957, pp. 230-242.

[21] G. KUNETZ et d'ERCEVILLE, Sur certaines propriétés d'une onde acoustique plane de compression dans un milieu stratifié, Ann. Geophys. 18, 1962, pp. 351-359.

[22] V.A. MARCHENKO, (Russian), Stability of the inverse problem of scattering theory, Math. Sb. (N.S.) 77, (119), 1968, pp. 139-162.

[23] H.E. MOSES, Calculation of the scattering potential from reflection coefficients, Phys. Rev. 102, 1956, pp. 559-567.

[24] H.E. MOSES, An example of the effect of rescaling of the reflection coefficient on the scattering potential for the one-dimensional Schrödinger equation, Stud. Appl. Math., 1979, pp. 177-181.

[25] H.E. MOSES, Gelfand-Levitan equations with comparison measures and potentials, J. Math. Phys. 20, 1979, pp. 2047-2053. See also unpublished report, 1983.

[26] R.G. NEWTON, Inversion of Reflection Data for Layered Media : A review of exact methods, Geophys. J.R. Astr. Soc. 65, 1981, pp. 191-215.

[27] K.R. PECHENIK and J.M. COHEN, Inverse scattering - exact solution of the Gelfand-Levitan equation, J. Math. Phys. 22, 1981, pp. 1513-1516.

[28] K.R. PECHENIK and J.M. COHEN, Exact solutions to the valley problem in inverse scattering, J. Math. Phys. 24, 1983, pp. 406-409.

[29] K.R. PECHENIK and J.M. COHEN, Inverse scattering with coinciding pole reflection coefficients, J. Math. Phys. 24, 1983, pp.115-119.

[30] R. PROSSER, On the solutions of the Gelfand-Levitan equation, (to be published in J. M. P.), 1983.

[31] M.H. REILLY and A.K. JORDAN, The applicability of an inverse method for reconstruction of electron-density profiles, IEEE Trans. Ant. Prop. AP-29, 1982, pp. 245-252.

[32] D.O. RISKA, On the electrodynamic inversion problem for vertically layered earth, Commentationes Physico-Mathematicae 53, 1982, pp. 1-24.

[33] P.C. SABATIER, Application de la théorie de l'inversion, to be published in Revue du Cethedec Paris. See also, Conférence d'Introduction. Proceedings of the meeting on inverse problems "RCP 264", 1982, to be published in Cahier de Mathématiques, Montpellier.

[34] P.C. SABATIER, Rational reflection coefficients and inverse scattering on the line, to be published in Il Nuovo Cimento.

[35] H.H. SZU, C.E. CARROLL, C.C. YANG and S. AHN, A new fonctional equation in the plasma inverse problem and its analytic properties, J. Math. Phys. 17, 1976, pp. 1236-1247.

[36] G. TURCHETTI and C. SAGRETTI, Stieltjes functions and approximate solutions of an inverse problem, in "Applied Inverse Problems", P.C. Sabatier Ed. Springer-Verlag Berlin Heidelberg New York, 1978.

[37] Y.A. WARE et K. AKI, Continuous and discrete inverse scattering problems in a stratified elastic medium, J. Ac. Soc. Amer. 45, 1969, pp. 911-921.

Approximation Methods and Error Estimates for Inverse Scattering Problems

Reese T. Prosser*

Abstract. Various approximation methods for inverse scattering problems are presented, and quantitative estimates for the resulting errors are derived.

Introduction. I want to present here some useful approximation methods for inverse scattering problems, along with some quantitative estimates for the errors introduced by these approximations. We know that in most practical applications of inverse scattering theory, the scattering data are obtained from a finite number of measurements, and the desired potential, impedance, or other outcome is obtained from a finite computational scheme. But in theory, both the data and outcome are functions of one or more continuous variables, so that approximations are necessary, and error estimates are essential.

Background. To fix ideas, let's start with the prototype problem of inverse potential scattering on the line without bound states. Roger Newton has described this problem in his lectures in detail, so it's enough to summarize. We assume that a potential $V(x)$, $-\infty < x < +\infty$, gives rise to a reflection coefficient $r(k)$, $-\infty < k < +\infty$, satisfying $r(-k) = r(k)$ and $|r(k)| \leq 1$. To recover $V(x)$ from $r(k)$, we set

$$R(x,y) = \hat{r}(x+y) = \frac{1}{2\pi} \int_{-\infty}^{+\infty} e^{-ikx} r(k) e^{-iky}\, dk. \tag{1}$$

Then we solve for $K(x,y)$ the Gelfand-Levitan equation

$$K(x,y) + R(x,y) + \int_{-\infty}^{x} K(x,z)R(z,y)\,dz = 0, \tag{2}$$

and find that

$$V(x) = 2 \frac{d}{dx} K(x,x). \tag{3}$$

This procedure is a little easier to analyze if we regard equation (2) as a member of a one-parameter family of equations, with parameter w, $-\infty < w < +\infty$:

*Department of Mathematics, Dartmouth College, Hanover, NH 03755

(4) $$K(x,y,w) + R(x,y) + \int_{-\infty}^{w} K(x,z,w)R(z,y)dz = 0.$$

Note that when w = x, (4) reduces to (2) and K(x,y,w) = K(x,y). In operator notation, (4) becomes

(5) $$K(w) + R(w) + K(w)R(w) = 0,$$

where K(w) and R(w) are integral operators acting on $L^2(R)$ with kernels K(x,y,w) and

(6) $$R(x,y,w) = \begin{cases} R(x,y) & \text{if } x,y \leq w \\ 0 & \text{else.} \end{cases}$$

Since [for suitable r(k)] R(w) is a bounded real symmetric operator, the same is true of K(w). Moreover, (5) yields

(7) $$[I+K(w)][I+R(w)] = I,$$

so that these operators are inverses.

If we iterate (5) N times, we obtain

(8) $$K(w) = - R(w) + R(w)^2 - R(w)^3 + \cdots \pm R(w)^N \mp R(w)^N K(w).$$

If we drop the last term on the right, the remaining terms give an Nth order approximation for K(w), often called the Nth Born approximation in this context. This is a good approximation whenever the remainder term is small.

Norms. Now we need a way to estimate the "size" of an integral operator. This is usually done by introducing a norm ‖ ‖ subject to the usual requirements, and also

(9) $$\|AB\| \leq \|A\| \, \|B\|$$

If we can find such a norm for the integral operators of our problem, then from (5) we get

(10) $$\|K\| \leq \|R\| + \|R\| \, \|K\|,$$

and from (8)

(11) $$\left\| K - \sum_{n=1}^{N} (-R)^n \right\| \leq \|R\|^N \, \|K\|.$$

In particular, if

(12) $$\|R\| < 1,$$

then

(13) $$\|K\| \leqslant \frac{\|R\|}{1-\|R\|}$$

and

(14) $$\|K - \sum_{n=1}^{N} (-R)^n \| \leqslant \|R\|^N \|K\| \leqslant \frac{\|R\|^{N+1}}{1 - \|R\|}$$

In this case, we see that the Born approximations converge geometrically. In these estimates, we have suppressed the dependence on w; they hold for all w for which (12) holds, and they hold uniformly for all w if (12) does.

What can we use as a norm? There are several choices.

The Operator Norm. One choice is the operator norm, obtained by regarding the integral operator A as acting on $L^2(R)$, and setting

(15) $$\|A\|_0 = \sup \{\|Af\|: f\varepsilon L^2 (R), \|f\|_2 = 1\}.$$

With this choice of norm, we find:

Lemma 1. $\|R(w)\|_0 \leqslant \sup_k |r(k)| = \|r\|_\infty$.

In particular, if $\|r\|_\infty = a < 1$, then the Born approximations always converge in the operator norm. To see this, we first set $w = +\infty$, $R = R(+\infty)$, and calculate

(16) $$\begin{aligned} R^2(x,y) &= \int_{-\infty}^{+\infty} R(x,z)R(z,y)dz \\ &= \int_{-\infty}^{+\infty} R(x,-z)R(-z,y)dz \\ &= \int_{-\infty}^{+\infty} \hat{r}(x-z)\hat{r}^*(z-y)dz \\ &= (\hat{r}*\hat{r}^*)(x-y) = r\cdot\overline{r}(x-y). \end{aligned}$$

Thus R^2 is given by convolution by the Fourier transformation of $|r(k)|^2$. Hence $\|R^2\|_0 = \|r\|_\infty^2$. Since R is bounded real symmetric, we have $\|R\|_0 = \|r\|_\infty$. For $-\infty < w < +\infty$, we note that $R(w) = P(w)RP(w)$ where P(w) is the projection on $(-\infty,w]$, and hence $\|R(w)\|_0 \leqslant \|R\|_0 = \|r\|_\infty$. A somewhat more refined analysis shows that the eigenvalues λ of R(w) all safisfy $|\lambda| < 1$, so that $\|R(w)\|_0 < 1$ for all w. Roger Newton has already referred to this result in his lectures.

This result is not the last word, however, because it's not easy to relate the operator norm to the structure of the integral kernel.

The Hilbert-Schmidt Norm. Another choice of norm in common use is the so-called Hilbert-Schmidt norm:

(17) $$\|A\|_{HS}^2 = \iint_{-\infty}^{+\infty} |A(x,y)|^2 dxdy.$$

Here the norm is given directly in terms of the integral kernel, and contains direct information on its size in the mean-square sense. It is well known that for any A, $\|A\|_{HS} \geq \|A\|_0$.

Lemma 2. $\|R(w)\|^2_{HS} = \int_{-\infty}^{2w} (2w-z)\,|\hat{r}(z)|^2 dz.$

In particular, if $(1 + z)|\hat{r}(z)|^2$ is integrable, then $\|R(w)\|_{HS} \to 0$ or $+\infty$ as $w \to -\infty$ or $+\infty$, and hence $\|R(w)\|_{HS} < 1$ for $-\infty < w < w_0$ for some critical value w_0 of w. Thus our results all hold at least for w in this range.

To see this, we calculate from (17):

$$\|R(w)\|^2_{HS} = \int_{-\infty}^{w} \int_{-\infty}^{w} |\hat{r}(x+y)|^2 dxdy \tag{18}$$

$$= -\frac{1}{2} \int_{-\infty}^{0} \int_{-u}^{u} |\hat{r}(u+2w)|^2 dvdu$$

$$= \int_{-\infty}^{2w} (2w-z)\,|\hat{r}(z)|^2 dz.$$

To get uniform estimates on the integral kernels in our problem, we need another choice of norm.

The Holmgren Norm. This choice is defined as follows:

$$\|A\|_H = \max\left\{\sup_x \int |A(x,y)|\,dy,\ \sup_y \int |A(x,y)|\,dx\right\} \tag{19}$$

It is easy to check that this norm, along with the preceeding ones, satisfies (9) and that $\|A\|_H \geq \|A\|_0$.

Lemma 3. $\|R(w)\|_H \leq \int_{-\infty}^{2w} |\hat{r}(z)|\,dz$

In particular, if $\hat{r}(z)$ is integable, then $\|R(w)\|_H \to 0$ or $\|\hat{r}\|_1$ as $w \to -\infty$ or $+\infty$, so that $\|R(w)\|_H < 1$ for $-\infty < w < w_0$; and if $\|\hat{r}\|_1 < 1$, then $\|R(w)\|_H < 1$ uniformly in w.

To see this, we observe that

$$\sup_y \int_{-\infty}^{w} |\hat{r}(x+y)|\,dx \leq \int_{-\infty}^{w} |\hat{r}(x+w)|\,dx \tag{20}$$

$$= \int_{-\infty}^{2w} |\hat{r}(z)|\,dz.$$

The same result holds if x and y are interchanged, and our conclusion follows by combining (19) and (20).

The Holmgren norm is not very informative by itself. But by combining it with another choice of norm, we obtain uniform estimates for our integral kernels.

The Uniform Norm. In this choice, we set

$$\|A\|_\infty = \sup_{x,y} \left| A(x,y) \right| . \tag{21}$$

This norm is defined directly in terms of A(x,y) and does give uniform estimates of its size. Unfortunately, it doesn't satisfy (9), so that we can't use it alone in our estimates. However, it does satisfy

$$\begin{aligned} \|AB\|_\infty &\leq \|A\|_H \|B\|_\infty \\ \|AB\|_\infty &\leq \|A\|_\infty \|B\|_H, \end{aligned} \tag{22}$$

so that we may use it in conjunction with the Holmgren norm. Instead of (10), for instance, we may use

$$\|K\|_\infty \leq \|R\|_\infty + \|K\|_\infty \|R\|_H, \tag{23}$$

so that, if $\|R\|_H < 1$,

$$\|K\|_\infty \leq \frac{\|R\|_\infty}{1-\|R\|_H} . \tag{24}$$

Similarly, instead of (11),

$$\begin{aligned} \|K - \sum_{n=1}^{N} (-R)^n\|_\infty &\leq \|R\|_H^N \|K\|_\infty \\ &\leq \frac{\|R\|_H^N \|R\|_\infty}{1 - \|R\|_H} . \end{aligned} \tag{25}$$

Lemma 4. $\|R(w)\|_\infty \leq \|r\|_1$.

Proof. $\|R(w)\|_\infty \leq \sup_{x,y} \left| \hat{r}(x+y) \right| = \|\hat{r}\|_\infty \leq \|r\|_1$.

It follows that the Born approximations converge uniformly to K(x,y,w) if r(k) and $\hat{r}(x)$ are both integrable, and $\|\hat{r}\|_1 < 1$.

This result is still not the last word, since we are really interested in uniform estimates for the potential V(x) as given by (3). This involves the derivatives of K(x,y,w).

The Derivative Norm. To take account of these derivatives, we introduce another choice:

$$\|A\|_D = \|A\|_\infty + \|\partial_x A\|_\infty + \|\partial_y A\|_\infty \tag{26}$$

where $\partial_x A(x,y) = \frac{\partial}{\partial x} A(x,y)$ etc. Then instead of (23) we have, in similar fashion,

(27) $$\|K\|_D \leq \|R\|_D + \|K\|_D \, \|R\|_H,$$

so that, if $\|R\|_H < 1$,

(28) $$\|K\|_D \leq \frac{\|R\|_D}{1-\|R\|_H}$$

and instead of (25)

(29) $$\|K - \sum_{n=1}^{N} (-R)^n\|_D \leq \frac{\|R\|_H^N \, \|R\|_D}{1 - \|R\|_H}$$

Lemma 5. $\|R\|_D \leq \|(1+2|k|)\, r\|_1$.

Proof: $\|R\|_D \leq \|\hat{r}\|_\infty + \|\hat{r}'\|_\infty + \|\hat{r}'\|_\infty \leq \|r\|_1 + 2\|kr\|_1$.

Finally, we need an estimate for $\|\partial_w K\|_\infty$. By differentiating (4) with respect to w and taking the uniform norm of the result, we obtain [3].

(30) $$\|\partial_w K\|_\infty \leq \frac{\|R\|_\infty^2}{1 - \|R\|_H^2}$$

(31) $$\|\partial_w (K - \sum_{n=1}^{N} (-R)^n)\|_\infty \leq \frac{N\|R\|_H^{N-1} \, \|R\|_\infty^2}{(1 - \|R\|_H)^2}$$

Now, since $\frac{1}{2}V(x) = \frac{d}{dx}K(x,x) = (\partial_x + \partial_y + \partial_w)K(x,y,w)\Big|_{x=y=w}$, we arrive at

Theorem 1. If $\|(1+2|k|)r\|_1 = b < \infty$ and if $\|\hat{r}\|_1 = a < 1$, then the potential $V_N(x)$ obtained from the Nth Born approximation converges uniformly to $V(x)$, and

(32) $$\|V-V_N\|_\infty \leq \frac{(N+1)a^N b^2}{(1-a)^2}$$

* * *

So far, we have focussed on the familiar Born approximation, since it is easy to describe and easy to analyze. It presupposes that we know the reflection coefficient exactly,and that we know a suitable numerical scheme for calculating the Fourier transform of its powers. In many applications, however, we know the reflection coefficient only approximately and in a form awkward for the calculation of Fourier transforms. This raises a problem of the following type: Suppose we know the reflection coefficient only to within a prescribed error. Then how well do we know the resulting potential?

Perturbations. Accordingly, we suppose now we are given two reflection coefficients $r_i(k)$, $i = 0, 1$, which are close together in some sense. Let $R_i(x,y)$, $K_i(x,y)$ and $V_i(x)$ be the integral kernels and potential associated with $r_i(k)$, as in (1)-(3).

Then from (7) we derive the basic relation

(33) $$K_0 - K_1 = (1+K_1)(R_1-R_0)(1+K_0)$$

(Again we have suppressed here the dependence on w). By applying our previous methods and results to this equation, we obtain in similar fashion the estimates [3]

(34) $$\|K_1-K_0\|_\infty \leq \frac{\|R_1 - R_0\|_\infty}{(1-\|R_1\|_H)(1-\|R_0\|_H)}$$

(35) $$\|K_1-K_0\|_D \leq \frac{\|R_1-R_0\|_D\ (1+\|R_1\|_D + \|R_0\|_D)}{(1-\|R_1\|_H)(1-\|R_0\|_H)}$$

(36) $$\|\partial_w(K_1-K_0)\| \leq \frac{\|R_1-R_0\|_\infty\left(\|R_1\|_\infty(1+\|R_1\|_H)+\|R_0\|_\infty(1+\|R_0\|_H)\right)}{(1-\|R_1\|_H)^2(1-\|R_0\|_H)^2}$$

These estimates lead to

Theorem 2. *If* $\|\hat{r}_i\|_1 = a_i < 1$, $\|(1+2|k|)r_i\|_1 = b_i < \infty$ *and* $\|(1+2|k|)(r_1-r_0)\|_1 < \varepsilon$, *then* $\|V_1-V_0\|_\infty < C\varepsilon$ *where the constant* C *depends only on* a_i *and* b_i, $i = 0, 1$.

Roughly speaking, this result says that under the conditions of the theorem the inversion procedure is stable: small changes in r(k) result in small changes in V(x). This suggests the following practical approximation procedure. Given $r_1(k)$ from field data, construct a *rational* approximation $r_0(k)$. Now Pierre Sabatier has shown in his lecture that the inversion procedure for a rational reflection coefficient may be carried out *exactly* by inverting a finite linear system. Our result then shows that the resulting error in the potential is bounded by a constant times the error in the reflection coefficient. See also [3].

One flaw remains. Our results are obtained only under the condition $\|\hat{r}_i\|_1 < 1$. It seems likely that this restriction is a fault of our methods, and that a better analysis may show that it can be dropped. In any case, our results hold at least for $-\infty < w < w_0$, where w_0 is chosen so that $\int_{-\infty}^{2w_0} |\hat{r}_i(z)|\, dz \leq 1$.

* * *

Now we turn briefly to the same problem in higher dimensions. Here the analogue of the inversion procedure in one dimension, upon which all our results are based, is not yet available, and we have to rely on a cruder substitute. (I don't know yet how to use Roger Newton's very recent results in two and three dimensions for this purpose.) Our substitute is based on an old method of Jost and Kohn, which was all but forgotten in the triumphant appearance of the Gelfand-Levitan procedure.

More Background. In the 3-dimensional problem, again without bound states, a potential $V(x)$, $\underline{x} \in R^3$, gives rise to a T-matrix $T(\underline{k}', \underline{k})$, $\underline{k}', \underline{k} \in R^3$, which contains the scattering data. The role of the reflection coefficient is played by the backscattering coefficient $B(2\underline{k}) = T(-\underline{k}, \underline{k})$. I have shown in [1] that $T(\underline{k}', \underline{k})$ may be recovered from $B(2\underline{k})$ by solving the non-linear equation

(37) $$T(\underline{k}',\underline{k}) = B(\underline{k}'-\underline{k}) - (I-P)\int \frac{T(\underline{k}',\underline{k}'')T^*(\underline{k}'',\underline{k})d\underline{k}''}{\underline{k}''^2 - \underline{k}^2 + i0}$$

or, in operator form

(38) $$T = B + (I-P)T\Gamma T^*.$$

Here Γ and P denote the operations

(39) $$\Gamma A(\underline{k}',\underline{k}) = \frac{A(\underline{k}',\underline{k})}{\underline{k}'^2 - \underline{k}^2 + i0}$$

(40) $$PA(\underline{k}',\underline{k}) = A\left(\frac{\underline{k}'-\underline{k}}{2}, \frac{\underline{k}-\underline{k}'}{2}\right).$$

I was able to solve (37) for T in terms of B by a contraction mapping procedure if B is small enough in a suitable norm. Once T is known, then V may be obtained from T via

(41) $$V = T + T\Gamma T^*.$$

The crux of this procedure is equation (38), which here plays the role of the Gelfand-Levitan equation (2). Note that it is quadratically non-linear. (So is the Gelfand-Levitan equation, for that matter, but the triangularity of the kernel $K(x,y)$ causes the non-linear term to vanish for $y \leqslant x$!). Equation (38) shows that the T-matrix is fully determined by a certain 3-parameter subset of its data, namely, $B(k) = T(-\underline{k},\underline{k})$. I want to emphasize that this equation holds in general, whether or not B is small, as long as there are no bounded states.

The Friedrichs Norm. Because of the singularity introduced into the integral kernels by the operation Γ, none of our previous norms will serve to give estimates from (37). For this purpose, we need a somewhat more sophisticated norm. We define

$$\|A\|_F = \max\left\{\|MM'A\|_\infty, \|NM'A\|_\infty, \|MN'A\|_\infty, \|NN'A\|_\infty\right\}, \tag{42}$$

where, for any fixed β, γ, $1/2 < \beta$, $\gamma < 1$,

$$MA(\underline{k},\underline{m}) = (1 + |\underline{k}|)^\gamma A(\underline{k},\underline{m}) \tag{43}$$

$$M'A(\underline{k},\underline{m}) = (1 = |\underline{m}|)^\gamma A(\underline{k},\underline{m})$$

$$NA(\underline{k},\underline{m}) = \sup_{|\underline{h}| \leq 1} (2|\underline{h}|)^{-\beta} \left|A(\underline{k}+\underline{h},\underline{m}) - A(\underline{k}-\underline{h},\underline{m})\right|$$

$$N'A(\underline{k},\underline{m}) = \sup_{|\underline{h}'| \leq 1} (2|\underline{h}'|)^{-\beta} \left|A(\underline{k},\underline{m}+\underline{h}') - A(\underline{k},\underline{m}-\underline{h}')\right| .$$

Thus for $\|A\|_F$ to be finite, $A(\underline{k},\underline{m})$ must decay faster than $(1+|k|)^{-\gamma}$ as $\underline{k} \to \infty$, and satisfy a uniform Holder condition of order β in $\underline{k}$ for all finite $\underline{k}$, and similarly for $\underline{m}$. I have recently shown [2] that for a slight variant of (42) we have

$$10\|A\|_\infty \leq \|A\|_F \leq 1000\, \|A\|_D \tag{44}$$

for all convolution kernels $A(\underline{k}'-\underline{k})$.

The Friedrichs norm does not satisfy (9), but satisfies instead

$$\|A\Gamma B\|_F \leq C\|A\|_F\|B\|_F, \tag{45}$$

for some constant C; in the variant mentioned above, we can take $C = 1$.

Now if we define, for any A,

$$F(A) = B - (I-P)A\Gamma A^*, \tag{46}$$

then we find

$$\|F(A)\|_F \leq \|B\|_F + 2\|A\|_F^2. \tag{47}$$

Hence if

$$\|B\|_F = b, \tag{48}$$

and

$$\|A\|_F \leq 2b, \tag{49}$$

then

(50) $$\|F(A)\|_F \leq b + 8b^2.$$

It follows that if $b < 1/8$, $\|F(A)\|_F \leq 2b$, so that F maps the ball of radius 2b into itself. Moreover, if A_i and B_i, $i = 0, 1$, are two pairs of operators

(51) $$F(A_1) - F(A_0) = B_1 - B_0 + (I-P)\big((A_1-A_0)\Gamma A_1^* + A_0\Gamma(A_1-A_0)^*\big),$$

so that

(52) $$\|F(A_1)-F(A_0)\|_F \leq \|B_1-B_0\|_F + 2\|A_1-A_0\|\big(\|A_1\| + \|A_0\|\big).$$

In particular, if $B_1 = B_0$ and $\|B_0\|_F = b < 1/8$,

(53) $$\|F(A_1)-F(A_0)\|_F \leq 8b\|A_1-A_0\|_F.$$

This means that $\underline{F}$ is a contraction mapping, and so must have a unique fixed point $\bar{A}=T$ satisfying (38). Moreover, if we set

(54) $$T_0 = 0$$

$$T_N = F(T_{N-1}) \quad N \geq 1,$$

then the sequence T_N converges in norm to the solution T, and

(55) $$\|T-T_N\|_F \leq \frac{1}{2}\frac{(8b)^N}{1-8b}.$$

It follows that if V_N is obtained from T_N via (41),

$$\|V-V_N\|_F \leq \frac{(8b)^N}{1-8b}.$$

Finally, if B_i, $i = 0, 1$, are two different backscattering coefficients, with $\|B_i\|_F \leq b < 1/8$, then from (52)

(56) $$\|T_1-T_0\|_F \leq \|B_1-B_0\|_F + 8b\|T_1-T_0\|_F,$$

so that

(57) $$\|T_1-T_0\|_F \leq \frac{\|B_1-B_0\|_F}{1-8b},$$

and, from (41),

(58) $$\|V_1-V_0\|_F \leq \frac{1+4b}{1-8b}\|B_1-B_0\|_F.$$

Now we can state

Theorem 3: If $\|B\|_F \leq b < 1/8$, then the potential $V_N(x)$ obtained from the Nth iterate of (46) converges to $V(x)$ in the Friedrichs norm, and

(59) $$\|V-V_N\|_F \leq \frac{(8b)^N}{1-8b}.$$

Theorem 3. If $\|B_i\|_F \leq b < 1/8$, $i = 0, 1$, and V_i is the potential obtained from B_i, then

(60) $$\|V_1-V_0\|_F \leq \frac{1+4b}{1-8b} \|B_1-B_0\|_F.$$

Note again the restriction that the scattering data be small: $b < 1/8$. Again this is probably a fault of our method and can probably be dropped, although I have no idea how to establish a better result. Unfortunately this restriction is so severe in the 3-dimensional problem as to preclude any practical interest. It does show, however, that under this restriction the inverse problem in 3-dimensions is remarkably stable.

Acoustic Scattering. The scattering of an acoustic wave function from a variable index of refraction in 3-dimensions can be treated by the same method. Here the variable index of refraction $N(\underline{x}) = 1-W(\underline{x})$ gives rise to a T-matrix $T(\underline{k}',\underline{k})$ and backscatter coefficient $B(2\underline{k})$ as before. Now, however, the $\underline{k}$-dependence is different. We set

(61) $$R(\underline{k}',\underline{k}) = \underline{k}^{-2}T(\underline{k}',\underline{k}),$$

and

(62) $$B(2\underline{k}) = R(-\underline{k},\underline{k}).$$

Then $R(\underline{k}',\underline{k})$ may be recovered from $B(2\underline{k})$, and $W(\underline{k})$ from $R(\underline{k}',\underline{k})$ by solving simultaneously the system

(63) $$\begin{aligned} R &= B - (I-P)W\Delta R \\ W &= B + PW\Delta R, \end{aligned}$$

where Δ denotes the operation

(64) $$\Delta A(\underline{k}',\underline{k}) = \underline{k}^2\Gamma K(\underline{k}',\underline{k}).$$

Again we find that if $\|B\|_F = b < 1/8$, then the system (63) has a unique solution obtained by a contraction mapping argument, and if W_N and R_N denote the Nth order approximations to the solution, we have

(65) $$\|R-R_N\|_F \leq \frac{1}{2}\frac{(8b)^N}{1-8b}$$

(66) $$\|W-W_N\|_F \leq \frac{(8b)^N}{1-8b}$$

(See [1], paragraph three, for details).

This result depends again on the restriction $\|B\|_F < 1/8$, again precluding any practical interest, but again suggesting a remarkable stability.

REFERENCES

[1] REESE T. PROSSER, Formal solutions of inverse scattering problems III, J. Math. Phys. 21 (1980), pp. 2648-2653.

[2] REESE T. PROSSER, Formal solutions of inverse scattering problems IV, J. Math. Phys. 23 (1982), pp. 2127-2130.

[3] REESE T. PROSSER, On the general solution of the Gelfand-Levitan equation, J. Math. Phys. (submitted).

Iterated Spherical Means in Linearized Inverse Problems

Gregory Beylkin*

Abstract. We consider a representation of the function

$$F(x) = \frac{1}{(2\pi)^n} \int_{|p|<2k} \hat{F}(p) e^{ip\cdot x} dp,$$

in terms of the iterated spherical mean of $\hat{F}(p)$. Here, n is the dimension of the space. We also review applications of such a representation to linearized inverse problems and present as examples problems of diffraction tomography and inverse scattering in Born (and Rytov) approximations.

1. Introduction. Experiments in scattering usually yield the measured scattered field as a function of two unit vectors which represent the direction of propagation of the incident wave and the direction at which the field is recorded. In many cases (we provide two examples in this article) if we fix the direction of the incident wave then what we obtain in a single experiment is the Fourier transform of the quantity we would like to recover restricted to some sphere (or circle in the two-dimensional case). Recently algorithms which make use of such data were suggested by A. J. Devaney (see Refs. [1-3]). These algorithms which solve linearized inverse problems are based on the representation of a function in terms of the iterated spherical mean of its Fourier transform. A uniform derivation of such a representation independent of the dimension of the space is presented in Ref. [4].

In this article we briefly describe the derivation of the representation of a function in terms of the iterated spherical mean of its Fourier transform and consider applications of this representation to linearized inverse problems. We treat problems of inverse scattering and diffraction tomography. In the case of diffraction tomography our consideration differs from one presented in Ref. [1].

2. Spherical Means, Iterated Spherical Means and the Fundamental Identity. Let f be a continuous function in R^n. The spherical mean of the function f is defined as

$$I(x,r) = \frac{1}{\omega_n} \int_{|\nu|=1} f(x + r\nu) d\omega_\nu, \tag{2.1}$$

* Courant Institute of Mathematical Sciences, 251 Mercer St., New York, NY 10012, present adress: Schlumberger-Doll Research, P.O. Box 307, Ridgefield, CT 06877

where $\omega_n = \dfrac{2\pi^{n/2}}{\Gamma(\frac{n}{2})}$ is the surface area of the unit sphere in R^n, x is a point in R^n, ν is a unit vector in R^n and $d\omega_\nu$ is the standard measure on the unit sphere (the solid angle differential form), such that $\int_{|\nu|=1} d\omega_\nu = \omega_n$. The function I(x,r) is the normalized average of the function f on a sphere of radius |r| about the point x. We note that the function I(x,r) is even with respect to r.

The iterated spherical mean $M(x,\alpha,\beta)$ is defined as follows

$$M(x,\alpha,\beta) = \frac{1}{\omega_n^2} \int_{|\mu|=1} \int_{|\nu|=1} f(x + \alpha\mu + \beta\nu) d\omega_\nu d\omega_\mu, \tag{2.2}$$

where α,β are real numbers and ν,μ are unit vectors in R^n. F. John [5] obtained the fundamental identity

$$M(x,\alpha,\beta) = \frac{2\omega_{n-1}}{(2\alpha\beta)^{n-2}\omega_n} \int_{\beta-\alpha}^{\beta+\alpha} [(r+\beta-\alpha)(r+\beta+\alpha)(\alpha+r-\beta)(\alpha-r+\beta)]^{(n-3)/2} r I(x,r) dr, \tag{2.3}$$

which relates the iterated spherical mean of a function to the spherical mean of that function.

3. The Representation of a Function in Terms of the Iterated Spherical Mean of its Fourier Transform. The fundamental identity in (2.3) can be used (see [4]) to obtain the representation of a function in terms of the iterated spherical mean of its Fourier transform. Let us briefly describe the derivation.

We consider the function

$$f_y(p) = \frac{|p|}{(4k^2-|p|^2)^{(n-3)/2}} \hat{F}(p) e^{ip\cdot y}, \tag{3.1}$$

where p and y belong to R^n and the function $\hat{F}(p)$ has support inside the n-dimensional ball

$$B_{2k} = \{p: |p| < 2k\}. \tag{3.2}$$

Let vector y in (3.1) be a parameter. First, we compute the spherical mean $I_y(0,r)$ of the function $f_y(p)$. Then we compute the iterated spherical mean of the function $f_y(p)$, the function M(0,k,k), using the fundamental identity in (2.3) and the definition in (2.2). Comparing the results we obtain the following representation

$$F(x) = \frac{k^n}{8\pi^n \omega_{n-1}} \int_{|\mu|=1} \int_{|\nu|=1} \frac{|\nu-\mu|}{(4-|\nu-\mu|^2)^{(n-3)/2}} \hat{F}(k\nu - k\mu) e^{i(k\nu-k\mu)\cdot x} d\omega_\nu d\omega_\mu, \tag{3.3}$$

where

$$F(x) = \frac{1}{(2\pi)^n} \int_{|p|<2k} \hat{F}(p) e^{ip\cdot x} dp. \tag{3.4}$$

If (as we assumed initially) the support of the function $\hat{F}$ is contained in the ball B_{2k} described in (3.2) then the function F(y) defined in (3.4) coincides with the inverse Fourier transform of $\hat{F}(p)$. The identity in (3.3) in this case is the representation of a function in terms of the iterated spherical mean of its Fourier transform.

If the support of $\hat{F}(p)$ is not restricted to the ball B_{2k} in (3.2), then (3.4) defines the low-pass-filtered version of the function whose Fourier transform is $\hat{F}(p)$. In this case (3.3) is the representation of the low-pass-filtered version of the function in terms of the iterated spherical mean of its Fourier transform.

The representation in (3.3) was derived in [4]. For n = 2 and n = 3 it reduces to formulae obtained by A. J. Devaney [1,3].

4. Inverse Scattering in Born Approximations. The most simple example of an application of the representation in (3.3) is the inversion formula for inverse scattering within Born approximation [3]. Let us consider the three-dimensional case for simplicity and let $e^{ik\nu\cdot x}$ (a plane wave) be the incident field. Consider the wave function $\Psi(x,k,\nu)$ which satisfies the Lippmann-Schwinger integral equation

$$\Psi(x,k,\nu) = e^{ik\nu\cdot x} - \frac{1}{4\pi}\int \frac{e^{ik|x-y|}}{|x-y|} V(y)\, \Psi(y,k,\nu)\,dy, \tag{4.1}$$

where the potential V is such that for large $|x|$ the solution of (4.1) has the asymptotics

$$\Psi(x,k,\nu) = e^{ik\nu\cdot x} + \frac{e^{ik|x|}}{|x|} f(k,\nu,\mu) + o\left(\frac{1}{|x|}\right),$$

where $\mu = \dfrac{x}{|x|}$.

If the solution $\Psi(x,k,\nu)$ of the integral equation in (4.1) is known then the scattering amplitude $f(k,\nu,\mu)$ can be written as follows

$$f(k,\nu,\mu) = -\frac{1}{4\pi}\int e^{-ik\mu\cdot x} V(x)\, \Psi(x,k,\nu)\, dx. \tag{4.2}$$

Using Born approximation by setting $\Psi(x,k,\nu) = e^{ik\nu\cdot x}$ in (4.2) we linearize the relation between the potential and the scattering amplitude and obtain

$$f(k,\nu,\mu) = -\frac{1}{4\pi}\int e^{-ik\mu\cdot x} V(x) e^{ik\nu\cdot x} dx = -\frac{1}{4\pi}\hat{V}(k\mu - k\nu). \tag{4.3}$$

Similarly, we derive that within Born approximation

$$|f(k,\nu,\mu)|^2 = \frac{1}{(4\pi)^2}\hat{Q}(k\mu - k\nu), \tag{4.4}$$

where $\hat{Q}$ is the Fourier transform of the function

$$Q(x) = \int V(x+y)\, V^*(y)\, dy.$$

(The function Q(x) is the so-called interatomic distance function).

Making use of the representation in (3.3), where we set the dimension n = 3, we obtain

$$V_{LP}(x) = -\frac{k^3}{4\pi^3}\int_{|\mu|=1}\int_{|\nu|=1} |\nu-\mu|\, f(k,\nu,\mu) e^{i(k\nu - k\mu)\cdot x} d\omega_\nu\, d\omega_\mu, \tag{4.5}$$

and

$$Q_{LP}(x) = \frac{k^3}{\pi^2} \int_{|\mu|=1} \int_{|\nu|=1} |\nu-\mu| |f(k,\nu,\mu)|^2 e^{i(k\nu-k\mu)\cdot x} d\omega_\nu d\omega_\mu . \tag{4.6}$$

We note, that the sphere of radius 2k which contains the ball B_{2k} in (3.2) is the so-called Ewald limiting sphere.

Thus, we obtain that if we can measure the phase of the scattering amplitude we have the explicit inversion formula in (4.5) for the reconstruction of the low-pass-filtered version of the potential. In the case when the phase of the scattering amplitude cannot be directly measured we can explicitly reconstruct the interatomic distance function using (4.6). Formulae (4.5) and (4.6) were first obtained in Refr. [3].

Remark 1: In the case of inverse scattering in the n-dimensional space one obtains the analogous result as soon as the scattering amplitude is properly defined.

Remark 2: We can always write

$$V(x) = \lim_{k\to\infty} -\frac{k^3}{4\pi^3} \int_{|\mu|=1} \int_{|\eta|=1} |\nu - \mu| f(k,\nu,\mu) e^{i(k\nu-k\mu)\cdot x} d\omega_\nu d\omega_\mu$$

This statement is equivalent to the uniqueness theorem (if we know the scattering amplitude for large k).

5. Diffraction Tomography in Born (and Rytov) Approximations. We use the inhomogeneous Helmholtz equation to describe the wave propagation; namely, we consider

$$(\Delta + k^2)U(x,k) = k^2 O(x) U(x,k), \tag{5.1}$$

where

$$O(x) = 1 - n^2(x).$$

The Helmholtz equation in (5.1) describes the acoustic field in a fluid medium. The parameter $k = 2\pi/\lambda$ is the wavenumber (here λ is a wavelength). We call the function $O(x)$ an object profile. We assume that the index of refraction

$$n(x) = 1,$$

if $|x| > R$ for some $R > 0$. It means that the support of the object profile $O(x)$ is contained within the ball $B_R = \{x: |x| < R\}$.

The inverse problem of diffraction tomography consists of determining the object profile $O(x)$ from the scattered acoustic field measured outside the ball B_R. This problem is nonlinear. We will use the first Born approximation to obtain a linear relation between the scattered field and the object profile. We consider the two-dimensional case for simplicity.

We start with the integral equation for the Fourier transform of the function $U(x,k)$ in (5.1),

$$\Psi(p,k,\nu) = \delta(p-k\nu) + \frac{k^2}{k^2-|p|^2-i0} \int \hat{O}(p-p')\Psi(p',k,\nu)dp', \tag{5.2}$$

where

$$\Psi(p,k,\nu) = \int U(x,k)e^{-ip\cdot x}dx,$$

$\delta(p-k\nu)$ represents the incident plane wave, p is a vector in R^2, ν is a unit vector in R^2 and

$$\hat{O}(p) = \int O(x)e^{-ip\cdot x}dx.$$

We introduce a system of coordinates which is related to the direction of propagation of the initial plane wave. We set

$$p = \eta\nu + \xi\nu^{\perp}, \tag{5.3}$$

where $\nu^{\perp}$ is the unit vector orthogonal to the vector ν: $\nu = (\nu_1,\nu_2)$ and $\nu^{\perp} = (-\nu_2,\nu_1)$.

Let us consider the scattered field $\Psi_{sc}(p,k,\nu) = \Psi(p,k,\nu) - \delta(p-k\nu)$. We find

$$\Psi_{sc}(p,k,\nu) = \frac{k^2}{k^2 - |p|^2 - i0} \int \hat{O}(p-p')\,\Psi(p',k,\nu)dp', \tag{5.4}$$

and in the system of coordinates (5.3) we have

$$\Psi_{sc}(\eta\nu+\xi\nu^{\perp},k,\nu) = \frac{k^2}{k^2-\xi^2-\eta^2-i0} \int \hat{O}(\eta\nu+\xi\nu^{\perp}-p')\,\Psi(p',k,\nu)dp'. \tag{5.5}$$

We take the inverse Fourier transform of the function Ψ_{sc} in η-coordinate

$$\Psi_{sc}(y,\xi,k,\nu) = \frac{1}{2\pi} \int_{-\infty}^{\infty} \Psi_{sc}(\eta\nu+\xi\nu^{\perp},k,\nu)e^{i\eta y}d\eta,$$

and obtain

$$\Psi_{sc}(y,\xi,k,\nu) = -\frac{i}{2}\,\frac{k^2 e^{i\sqrt{k^2-\xi^2}\,|y|}}{\sqrt{k^2-\xi^2}} \int \hat{O}(\sqrt{k^2-\xi^2}\,\nu+\xi\nu^{\perp}-p')\Psi(p',k,\nu)dp', \tag{5.6}$$

for $|\xi| < k$. We denote

$$\mu = \frac{1}{k}(\sqrt{k^2-\xi^2}\,\nu+\xi\nu^{\perp}) \quad \text{if } y>0,$$

and

$$\mu = \frac{1}{k}(-\sqrt{k^2-\xi^2}\,\nu+\xi\nu^{\perp}) \quad \text{if } y<0.$$

Here μ is a unit vector. We also have $k|\mu\cdot\nu| = \sqrt{k^2-\xi^2}$ and $\text{sign}(y) = \text{sign}(\mu\cdot\nu)$. Thus,

$$\Psi_{sc}(y,\mu,k,\nu) = -\frac{i}{2}\,\frac{k\, e^{ik\mu\cdot\nu y}}{|\mu\cdot\nu|} \int \hat{O}(k\mu-p')\,\Psi(p',k,\nu)dp'. \tag{5.7}$$

Using Born approximation by setting $\Psi(p',k,\nu) = \delta(p'-k\nu)$ in (5.7) we obtain

$$\hat{O}(k\mu-k\nu) = \frac{2i\,|\mu\cdot\nu|}{k}\,e^{-ik\mu\cdot\nu y}\Psi^{b}_{sc}(y,\mu,k,\nu), \tag{5.8}$$

where Ψ^{b}_{sc} denotes the scattered field in Born approximation.

We can measure the scattered acoustic field outside the ball B_R. Let us fix $|y|>R$ and note that $\text{sign}(y) = \text{sign}(\mu\cdot\nu)$. We make use of the representation in (3.3) (where we set $n=2$) to obtain

$$O_{LP}(x) = \frac{ik}{4\pi^3} \int_{|\nu|=1} \int_{|\mu|=1} (1-(\mu\cdot\nu)^2)^{1/2} |\mu\cdot\nu| e^{-ik|\mu\cdot\nu|y} \Psi^{b}_{sc}(y,\mu,k,\nu) e^{i(k\nu-k\mu)\cdot x} d\omega_\nu d\omega_\mu . \quad (5.9)$$

The formula (5.9) is a backpropagation inversion formula which was first obtained by A. J. Devaney [1] and is presented here in a slightly different form.

The case of Rytov approximation is analogous to Born approximation and can be found in Ref. [1]. We note that in the case of a plane incident wave there is a simple relation between the scattered field in Born and Rytov approximations (see [1], for example), and we can obtain the expression for $\hat{O}(k\mu-k\nu)$ in Rytov approximation using relation in (5.8).

In conclusion let us emphasize that the use of the representation in (3.3) in combination with formulae (4.3), (4.9) and (5.8) allows us to compute contributions of each separate experiment independently. (A separate experiment is a measurement made with a fixed direction of the incident field). Then we integrate over all experiments. Such an integration is a computation of a spherical mean and, thereby, is a stable numerical procedure.

REFERENCES

[1] A. J. DEVANEY, A filtered backpropagation algorithm for diffraction tomography, Ultrasonic Imaging, 4, 336-350, (1982).

[2] A. J. DEVANEY, A computer simulation study of diffraction tomography, IEEE Trans. Biomedical Eng., to appear.

[3] A. J. DEVANEY, Inversion formula for inverse scattering within Born approximation, Optics Letters, 1, 111-112, (1982).

[4] G. BEYLKIN, The fundamental identity for iterated spherical means and the inversion formula for diffraction tomography and inverse scattering, Jour. Math. Physics, 24(6), June, 1983.

[5] F. JOHN, *Plane Waves and Spherical Means*, Interscience Publishers, New York, 1955.

Stable Triangular Decomposition of Symmetric Kernels

Kenneth Driessel* and William W. Symes**

Table of Contents

1. Introduction. In this report we show that the triangular (Cholesky) decomposition of positive definite symmetric matrices can be used to obtain a similar decomposition of symmetric kernels. In particular, let $s: (0,X) \times (0,X) \to R$ be a kernel (that is, $s(x,y)$ is a real valued function of two real arguments defined on the square subset $(0,X) \times (0,X)$ of $R \times R$). We say that s is "symmetric" if $s(x,y) = s(y,x)$. We say that a kernel $\ell(x,y)$ is "lower triangular" if $y > x$ implies $\ell(x,y) = 0$. We study the following problem: Given symmetric kernel $s(x,y)$, find lower triangular kernel $\ell(x,y)$ such that

$$s(x,y) = \ell(x,y) + \ell(y,x) + \int_0^X dz\, \ell(x,z)\ell(y,z) \quad .$$

This equation arises in the study of inverse problems(see Gelfand-Levitan (1951), Burridge (1980), Symes (1979, 1981)). We shall present an algorithm which solves this nonlinear problem and we shall prove the stability of this algorithm. (For more precise statements of the problem and the results, see the section below on triangular decomposition.) Note that the given equation between kernels is analogous to the following equation between matrices.

---

*Research Center, Amoco Production Co., Tulsa, OK 74102
**Michigan State University, East Lansing, MI 48824

$$s_{ij} = \ell_{ij} + \ell_{ji} + \sum_k \ell_{ik} \ell_{jk}$$

which may be rewritten as

$$s = \ell + \ell^{tr} + \ell \, \ell^{tr}$$

("tr" for "transpose") or as

$$\delta + s = (\delta + \ell)(\delta + \ell)^{tr}$$

where δ is the identity matrix. We recognize this last equation as the triangular (Cholesky) decomposition. Our algorithm exploits this analogy.

In the following section on stability and convergence, we present a (functional analytic) framework which we believe is the appropriate abstract setting for the solution of the given problem. We prove several stability and convergence results in this abstract setting. In the section on triangular decomposition we present our algorithm and we verify the hypotheses of the abstract stability and convergence theorems.

2. Stability and Convergence. Let W be a Banach space and let F: $U \to V$ be a (generally nonlinear) mapping between subsets of W. We will consider the following problem: Given $v \in V$ find $u \in U$ such that $Fu = v$. We use approximation methods to study this problem. In particular, with every positive integer n, we associate a finite dimensional space W(n) and linear operators p(n) : $W(n) \to W$ ("p" for "prolongation"), and r(n) : $W \to W(n)$ ("r" for "restriction").

Remark. The use of approximation methods to study operator equations has a long history. See, for example, Courant-Friedrichs-Lewy (1928). The "abstract" framework that we present in this section is a modification of the one appearing in Linz (1979) §4.3 "Stability and Convergence".//

We assume that these operators satisfy the following conditions:

$$\text{there exists } r < \infty \text{ , } \forall n \text{ , norm } (r_n) \le r \text{ ,}$$

$$\text{there exists } p < \infty \text{ , } \forall n \text{ , norm } (p_n) \le p \text{ ,}$$

$$\forall n \text{ , } r_n p_n = I_n \text{ ,}$$

$$\lim_{n\to\infty} p_n r_n w = w \text{ ,}$$

$$\lim_{n\to\infty} \text{norm } (r_n w) = \text{norm } (w) \quad .$$

where w is in W and I(n) is the identity map on W(n). (In order to avoid clashes between adjacent lines of single-spaced type, we try to minimize occurrences of subscripts and superscripts in paragraphs of text. We freely use them in displays. Consequently, for example, we write W(n) or W_n depending on the context.)

With every n, we also associate (generally nonlinear) mappings F(n): U(n) → V(n) where U(n) and V(n) are subsets of W(n). We assume that r(n)U, r(n)V, p(n)U(n), p(n)V(n) are subsets of U(n), V(n), U, and V, respectively. We say that the approximation (F(n), r(n), p(n)) is "consistent with F" if ∀u in U

$$\lim_{n\to\infty} \text{norm}\,(r_n Fu - F_n r_n u) = 0 .$$

We shall write r(n)Fu ~ F(n)r(n)u in place of this limit.

We say that a sequence of mappings F(n) is "stable" if each F(n) is injective and surjective and the sequence Inverse (F(n)) is uniformly Lipschitz continuous; that is, there exists K, such that

$$\forall n,\ \forall v_1, v_2 \in V_n,\ \text{norm}\,(F_n^{-1}(v_1) - F_n^{-1}(v_2)) \le K\ \text{norm}\,(v_1 - v_2) .$$

Theorem (convergence). Let (F(n), r(n), p(n)) be a consistent stable approximation of the mapping F: U → V. If Fu = v and for all n, F(n)u(n) = r(n)v then p(n)u(n) → u as n → ∞.

Proof. By consistency, F(n)r(n)u ~ r(n)Fu = r(n)v = F(n)u(n). Hence (using stability) r(n)u ~ u(n). Finally, we have u ~ p(n)r(n)u ~ p(n)u(n).//

Remark. The proofs which appear in nonstandard analysis have inspired us to adopt the "streamlined" style of proof like the last one. The streamlined proofs that we present here may easily be translated into (longer, messier) standard proofs.//

Theorem (uniqueness). Let (F(n), r(n), p(n)) be a consistent stable approximation of the mapping F: U → V. Then F is injective.

Proof. Suppose Fu(1) = Fu(2). Then F(n)r(n)u(1) ~ r(n)Fu(1) = r(n)Fu(2) ~ F(n)r(n)u(2). Hence r(n)u(1) ~ r(n)u(2) and u(1) ~ p(n)r(n)u(1) ~ p(n)r(n)u(2) ~ u(2).//

In the convergence theorem, we assumed the existence of a solution of the equation Fu = v as part of the hypothesis. We need a stronger theorem that guarantees the existence of such a solution.

Theorem (existence and stability). Let $F: U \to V$ be a continuous mapping and let $(F(n), r(n), p(n))$ be a consistent, stable approximation of F. If U is closed and $V = \{v \in W: \forall n,\ r(n)v \in V(n)\}$ then F is injective and surjective. Furthermore, Inverse $(F): V \to U$ is Lipschitz continuous.

Remark. Note that the condition $V = \{v \in W: \forall n,\ r(n)v \in V(n)\}$ is a natural one: If $v = Fu$ for some $u \in U$ then, by consistency, $r(n)v = r(n)Fu \sim F(n)r(n)u \in V(n)$.//

We find that diagrams clarify the proof of this theorem. We say, for example, that the following diagram "commutes" ("approximately")

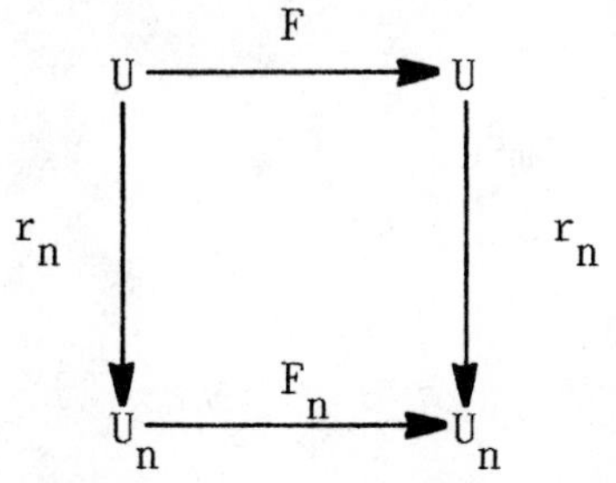

if $\forall u \in U$, $\forall\ \delta > 0$ there exists N, $\forall n \geq N$, norm $(r(n)Fu - F(n)r(n)u) < \delta$. Note that the commutativity of this diagram follows from the consistency of the approximation $(F(n), p(n), r(n))$. As another example, note that the assumptions $r(n)p(n) = I(n)$ and $p(n)r(n)u \to u$ imply that the following diagram commutes:

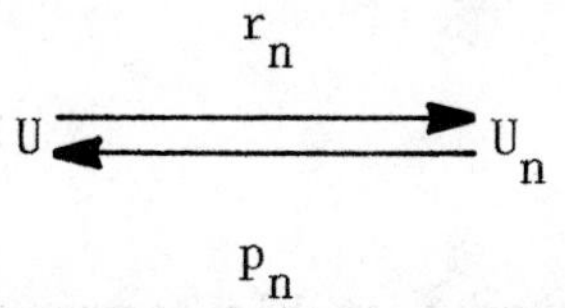

Lemma. Let $(F(n), r(n), p(n))$ be a consistent approximation of F. Then the following diagram commutes:

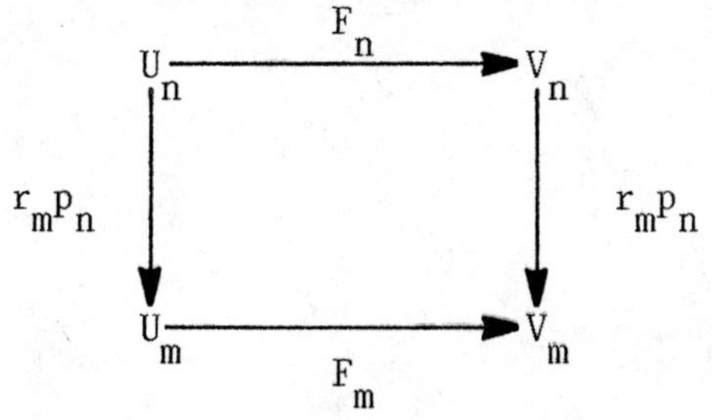

(i.e., $F_m r_m p_n u_n \sim r_m p_n F_n u_n$ or

$\forall u_n \varepsilon U_n$, $\forall \delta > 0$ there exists N, $\forall m,n \geq N$,

$$\text{norm}\,(F_m r_m p_n u_n - r_m p_n F_n u_n) < \delta\ ) .$$

Proof. We simply use the commutativity of the building blocks of the following diagram:

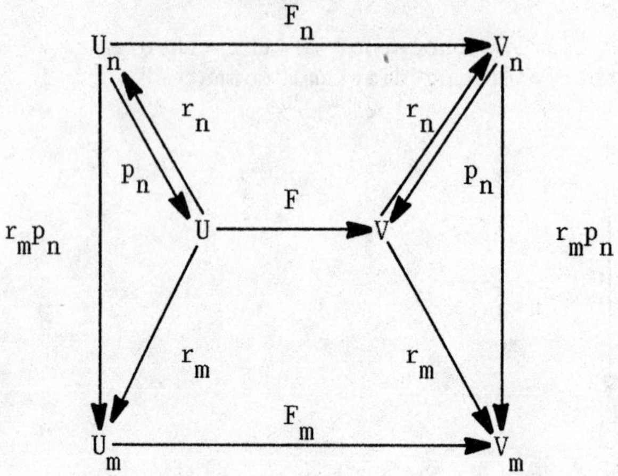

More specifically, we have

$$\begin{aligned} F_m r_m p_n u_n &\sim r_m F p_n u_n \\ &\sim r_m p_n r_n F p_n u_n \\ &\sim r_m p_n F_n r_n p_n u_n \\ &= r_m p_n F_n u_n \quad . \quad // \end{aligned}$$

Lemma. Let (F(n), r(n), p(n)) be a consistent, stable approximation of F. Then the following diagram commutes:

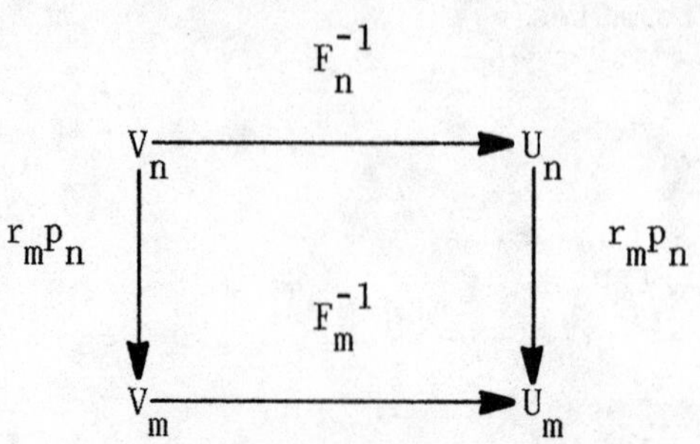

(i.e., $F_m^{-1} r_m p_n v_n \sim r_m p_n F_n^{-1} v_n$, or

$\forall v_n \in V_n$, $\forall \delta > 0$ there exists N, $\forall m,n \geq N$,

$$\text{norm}\ (F_m^{-1} r_m p_n v_n - r_m p_n F_n^{-1} v_n\ ) < \delta\ ) \quad .$$

Proof. From the previous lemma, we have

$$r_m p_n v_n = r_m p_n F_n F_n^{-1} v_n \sim F_m r_m p_n F_n^{-1} v_n \quad .$$

Hence (using stability)

$$F_m^{-1} r_m p_n v_n \sim r_m p_n F_n^{-1} v_n \quad . //$$

We now turn to the proof of the theorem. We already know that F is injective (by the uniqueness theorem). We now show that F is surjective. Given v $\in$ V we must find u $\in$ U such that Fu = v. To begin, we set u(n):= Inverse (F(n))r(n)v. We prove that p(n)u(n) is a Cauchy sequence (i.e., p(n)u(n) ~ p(m)u(m)). To see this, we consider the following commutative diagram:

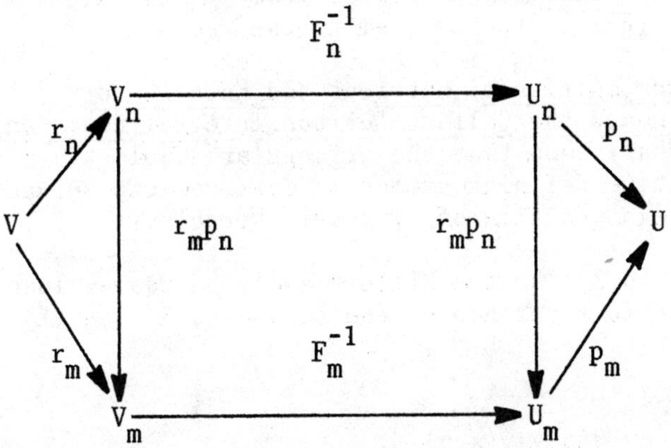

We have

$$\begin{aligned} p_n u_n &= p_n F_n^{-1} r_n v \\ &\sim p_m r_m p_n F_n^{-1} r_n v \\ &\sim p_m F_m^{-1} r_m p_n r_n v \\ &\sim p_m F_n^{-1} r_m v \\ &= p_m u_m \quad . \end{aligned}$$

We now set $u := \lim p(n)u(n)$. Then $u \in U$ (since U is closed). We next prove that $Fu = v$. We consider the following commutative diagram:

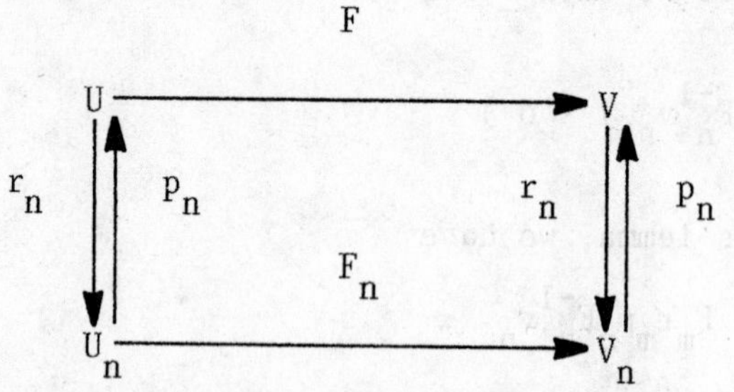

We have $u \sim p(n)u(n)$ and hence (using the continuity of F) $Fu \sim Fp(n)u(n)$. Consequently (using consistency),

$$r_n Fu \sim r_n F p_n u_n \sim F_n r_n p_n u_n = F_n u_n = r_n v$$

and

$$Fu \sim p_n r_n Fu \sim p_n r_n v \sim v \; .$$

We leave the proof of the last statement (namely, the Lipschitz continuity of Inverse (F)) of the theorem to the reader.//

<u>3. Triangular Decomposition of Matrices and Kernels (or Cholesky Decomposition and the Gelfand-Levitan Integral Equation).</u> In this section, we shall show that the triangular (Cholesky) decomposition of positive definite symmetric matrices can be used to obtain a similar decomposition of symmetric kernels.

Let $W := L_2((0,X) \times (0,X))$ be the Hilbert space of real valued, square integrable functions defined on the square $(0,X) \times (0,X)$ with inner product

$$(u,v) := \int_0^X dx \int_0^X dy \; u(x,y)v(x,y) \quad .$$

We call an element of W a "kernel". If a is a real number and u and v are kernels, then we can define kernels au ("multiplication by a scalar"), u^{tr} ("transpose"), u+v ("sum"), uv ("convolution product") as follows:

$$(au)(x,y) := au(x,y)$$

$$(u+v)(x,y) := u(x,y) + v(x,y)$$

$$u^{tr}(x,y) := u(y,x)$$

$$(uv)(x,y) := \int_0^X dz\, u(x,z)v(z,y) \quad .$$

<u>Remark</u>. Elements of W are often called "Hilbert-Schmidt kernels" or "square integrable kernels". Note that with the algebraic operations defined above, W is a Banach algebra with involution. For basic facts on kernels, see Hochstadt (1973), Halmos-Sunder (1978) and/or Courant-Hilbert (1953).//

Let $L_2(0,X)$ be the Hilbert space of real valued, square integrable functions defined on the interval $(0,X)$ and let $B(L_2(0,X))$ be the set of bounded linear mappings on this space. We shall call an element of $B(L_2(0,X))$ an "operator". If a is a real number and u and v are operators then we can define operators au ("multiplication by a scalar"), u^{tr} ("adjoint"), u+v ("sum"), uv ("product") as follows:

$$(au)f := a(uf)$$

$$(u+v)f := uf + vf$$

$$(u^{tr}f,g) := (f,ug)$$

$$(uv)f := u(vf) \quad .$$

We shall use e to denote the identity map on $L_2(0,X)$. The natural norm on $B(L_2(0,X))$ is the "spectral norm"; i.e., the operator norm induced by the usual Hilbert space norm on $L_2(0,X)$: norm(u) := sup {norm(uf): norm(f) = 1} . An operator u in $B(L_2(0,X))$ is "positive definite" if there exists $\gamma > 0$ such that for all $f \in L_2(0,X)$, $(uf,f) \geq \gamma(f,f)$.

<u>Remark</u>. Note $B(L_2(0,X))$ is an associative Banach algebra with involution and identity.//

With any kernel w(x,y) we may associated a mapping Int w ("Int" for "integral operator") Int w: $L_2(0,X) \to L_2(0,X)$ defined by

$$(\text{Int } w)\, f(x) := \int_0^X dy\, w(x,y)f(y) \quad .$$

By the Cauchy-Schwarz inequality, we have

$$\left(\int_0^X dy\, w(x,y)f(y)\right)^2 \leq \int_0^X dy\, w^2(x,y) \int_0^X dy\, f^2(y) \quad .$$

It follows that (Int w)f is in $B(L_2(0,X))$. Note that the mapping

$$\text{Int}: L_2((0,X) \times (0,X)) \to B(L_2(0,X))$$

preserves the algebraic operations given above. It also follows that norm(Int w) $\leq$ norm(w) and hence that the mapping Int is continuous.

Remark. In summary the map Int is a morphism from the Banach algebra $L_2((0,X) \times (0,X))$ into the Banach algebra $B(L_2(0,X))$.//

We say that a kernel $\ell(x,y)$ is "lower triangular" (see figure) if $x < y$ implies $\ell(x,y) = 0$. We say that a kernel $s(x,y)$ is "symmetric" if $s^{tr} = s$

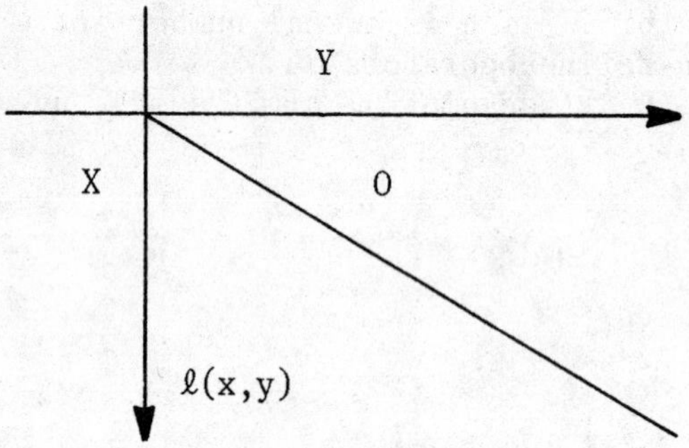

(i.e., $s(x,y) = s(y,x)$). In this section, we shall show that if $s(x,y)$ is a symmetric kernel and e + Int s is a positive definite operator, then there exists a lower triangular kernel $\ell(x,y)$ such that

$$s = \ell + \ell^{tr} + \ell\,\ell^{tr}$$

$$\text{(i.e., } s(x,y) = \ell(x,y) + \ell(y,x) + \int_0^X dz\, \ell(x,z)\ell(y,z)) \quad .$$

Remark. This equation between kernels is called a "Gelfand-Levitan equation". A similar equation appears in Gelfand-Levitan (1951). Note that this last equation implies

$$e + \text{Int } s = (e + \text{Int } \ell)(e + \text{Int } \ell)^{tr} \quad .$$

We see immediately an analogy with (Cholesky) triangular decomposition of matrices.//

We shall study this equation by the approximation methods introduced above. We turn to the task of defining the appropriate finite dimensional spaces and the restriction and prolongation maps. Let $h := X/n$; for $i = 0, 1, \ldots, n$, let $x_i := ih$; for $i = 1, 2, \ldots, n$, we define the "boxcar" function $b_i(n)(x)$ by

$$b_i^{(n)}(x) := 1 \text{ if } x_i \leq x \leq x_{i+1}\ , \quad := 0 \quad \text{otherwise} \quad .$$

With a kernel $w(x,y)$, we associate an "n x n kernel" (see figure), Avg(n) w, by "averaging":

$$(\mathrm{Avg}_n\ w)(x,y) := \sum_{i,j=1}^{n} (a_n\ w)_{ij}\ b_i^{(n)}(x) b_j^{(n)}(y)$$

where a(n)w is the n x n matrix defined by

$$(a_n w)_{ij} := \frac{1}{h^2} \int_{x_{i-1}}^{x_i} dx \int_{x_{j-1}}^{x_j} dy\ w(x,y) \quad .$$

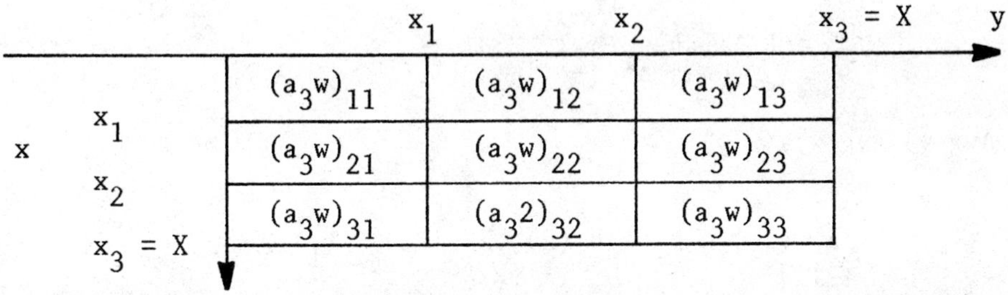

We shall use the following formulas later:

<u>Proposition</u>.

i) $\mathrm{norm}^2(\mathrm{Avg}_n w) = h^2 \sum_{i,j} (a_n w)_{ij}^2$

ii) $\mathrm{Avg}_n((\mathrm{Avg}_n v)w) = (\mathrm{Avg}_n v)(\mathrm{Avg}_n w)$

iii) $((\mathrm{Avg}_n v)(\mathrm{Avg}_n w))(x,y)$

$$= \sum_{i,k} h \left(\sum_j (a_n v)_{ij} (a_n w)_{jk}\right) b_i^{(n)}(x)\ b_k^{(n)}(y)$$

Proof. We simply calculate (dropping some of the superscript and subscript n's):

$$\text{norm}^2(\text{Avg } w) = \int_0^X dx \int_0^X dy \sum_{i,j,k,\ell} (aw)_{ij}\, b_i(x) b_j(y) (aw)_{k\ell}\, b_k(x)\, b_\ell(y)$$

$$= \sum_{i,j,k,\ell} (aw)_{ij} (aw)_{k\ell} (h\delta_{ik})(h\delta_{j\ell})$$

$$((\text{Avg } v)w)(x,y) = \int_0^X dz \sum_{i,j} (av)_{ij} b_i(x) b_j(z) w(z,y)$$

$$= \sum_{i,j} (av)_{ij}\, b_i(x) \int_{x_{j-1}}^{x_j} dz\; w(z,y)$$

$$a((\text{Avg } v)w)_{ij} = \frac{1}{h^2} \int_{x_{i-1}}^{x_i} dx \int_{x_{j-1}}^{x_j} dy \;\Big(\sum_{k,\ell} (av)_{k\ell} b_k(x) \int_{x_{\ell-1}}^{x_\ell} dz\; w(z,y)\Big)$$

$$= \frac{1}{h^2} \sum_{k,\ell} (av)_{k\ell} (h\delta_{ik}) h^2 (aw)_{\ell j}$$

$$= h \sum_{\ell} (av)_{i\ell} (aw)_{\ell j}$$

$$((\text{Avg } v)(\text{Avg } w))(x,y)$$

$$= \int_0^X dz \sum_{i,j} (av)_{ij}\; b_i(x) b_j(z) \sum_{k,\ell} (aw)_{k\ell}\; b_k(z) b_\ell(y)$$

$$= \sum_{i,j,k,\ell} (av)_{ij} (aw)_{k\ell} b_i(x) b_\ell(y)\; h\delta_{jk} \quad . \; //$$

Let $w(x,y) = \sum_{i,j=1}^{n} w_{ij} b_i(x) b_j(y)$ be an n x n kernel. With each such kernel we associate a matrix Mat(n) w defined by (Mat(n) w)(i,j):= hw(i,j). We regard Mat(n) as a mapping from n x n kernels to n x n matrices. For the norm on n x n matrices we take the "Euclidean" (or "Frobenius") norm

$$\text{F-norm}^2(a_{ij}) := \sum_{i,j} a_{ij}^2 \; .$$

Note that Mat(n) is injective and surjective. We collect several other properties of this function in the following proposition.

Proposition. Let

$$w(x,y) = \sum_{i,j} w_{ij} b_i(x) b_j(y) , \quad v(x,y) = \sum_{i,j} v_{ij} b_i(x) b_j(y)$$

be n x n kernels and let $L_2(n)$ be the span of $b_1(n)(x), \ldots, b_n(n)(x)$ in $L_2(0,X)$. Then

(i) The matrix of the operator Int w (restricted to $L_2(n)$) with respect to the basis $b_1(n)(x), \ldots, b_n(n)(x)$ of $L_2(n)$ is Mat(n) w; that is,

$$(\text{Int } w) \sum_k a_k b_k(x) = \sum_{i,j} h w_{ij} a_j b_i(x) \quad ;$$

(ii) $\text{Mat}_n(vw) = (\text{Mat}_n v)(\text{Mat}_n w)$;

(iii) $\text{F-norm}(\text{Mat}_n w) = \text{norm}(w)$;

Proof.

$$(\text{Int } w) \sum_k a_k b_k(x) = \int_0^X dy \sum_{i,j} w_{ij} b_i(x) b_j(y) \sum_k a_k b_k(y)$$

$$= \sum_{i,j,k} w_{ij} a_k b_i(x) h \delta_{jk} .$$

Using the previous proposition, we have

$$\text{Mat}(vw)_{ik} = \text{Mat}\Big(\sum_{i,k} h \big(\sum_j v_{ij} w_{jk}\big) b_i(x) b_k(y)\Big)_{ik}$$

$$= h^2 \sum_j v_{ij} w_{jk}$$

$$= \sum_j (\text{Mat } v)_{ij} (\text{Mat } w)_{jk} .$$

Again using the previous proposition we have

$$\text{norm}^2(w) = \sum_{i,j} h^2 w_{ij}^2$$

$$= \text{F-norm}^2(\text{Mat } w) \quad . \; //$$

Remark. It is clear that Mat(n) preserves the other algebraic operations (namely multiplication by scalars and transpose). Thus Mat(n) is an (iso)morphism from the Banach algebra of n x n kernels to the Banach algebra of n x n matrices.//

We are finally ready to define the restriction maps r(n) and the prolongation maps p(n). For W we take $L_2((0,X) \times (0,X))$; for W(n) we take the space of n x n matrices with the Frobenius norm. We define the restriction map

$$r_n : W \to W_n \quad \text{by} \quad r_n := \text{Mat}_n \, \text{Avg}_n \quad ,$$

that is, $(r_n w)_{ij} := h(a_n w)_{ij}$.

We define the prolongation map $p_n : W_n \to W$ by $p_n := \text{Mat}_n^{-1}$,

$$\text{that is, } p_n(w_{ij}) = \sum_{i,j=1}^{n} \frac{1}{h} w_{ij} \, b_i(x) b_j(y) \quad .$$

Proposition.

(i) $\forall n$, $\text{norm}(r_n) \le r < \infty$, where $r = 1$;

(ii) $\forall n$, $\text{norm}(p_n) \le p < \infty$, where $p = 1$;

(iii) $\forall n$, $r_n p_n = I_n$;

(iv) $\forall w \in W$, $\lim_{n\to\infty} p_n r_n w = w$;

(v) $\forall w \in W$, $\lim_{n\to\infty} \text{F-norm}(r_n w) = \text{norm}(w)$.

Proof. The second and third parts are easy to check. The fourth and fifth parts are well-known facts in the theory of integration. (See, for example, Lang (1969), especially Chapter X "The General Integral" and Chapter XI "Duality and Representation Theorems".) We prove the first part. We need to show F-norm(r(n)w) $\le$ norm(w). By the Cauchy-Schwarz inequality, we have

$$(a_n w)_{ij}^2 = \left(\frac{1}{h^2}\int_{x_{i-1}}^{x_i} dx \int_{x_{j-1}}^{x_j} dy\; w(x,y)\right)^2$$

$$\leq \frac{1}{h^4}\left(\int_{x_{i-1}}^{x_i} dx \int_{x_{j-1}}^{x_j} dy\; 1\cdot 1\right)\left(\int_{x_{i-1}}^{x_i} dx \int_{x_{j-1}}^{x_j} dy\; w^2(x,y)\right)$$

$$= \frac{1}{h^2}\int_{x_{i-1}}^{x_i} dx \int_{x_{j-1}}^{x_j} dy\; w^2(x,y) \quad .$$

Hence

$$\text{F-norm}^2(r_n w) = \sum_{i,j} h^2 (aw)_{ij}^2$$

$$\leq \sum_{i,j} \int_{x_{i-1}}^{x_i} dx \int_{x_{j-1}}^{x_j} dy\; w^2(x,y)$$

$$= \text{norm}^2(w) \quad . //$$

Remark. Let $w(x,y)$ be a differentiable kernel with bounded derivatives; i.e., $\text{abs}(\partial w/\partial x)$, $\text{abs}(\partial w/\partial y) < M$. Then

$$\text{norm}(w - p_n r_n w) \leq \sqrt{2}\, M\, h\, X \quad .$$

Proof. Consider one of the h x h squares Ω. Let avg(w), max(w), min(w) be respectively the average, maximum, and minimum value of w on this square Ω. Then, by the mean value theorem, we have

$$\max(w) - \text{avg}(w) \leq M\sqrt{2}\, h \quad ,$$

$$\text{avg}(w) - \min(w) \leq M\sqrt{2}\, h \quad .$$

Hence

$$\int\int_\Omega dx\, dy\, [w(x,y) - p_n r_n w(x,y)]^2$$

$$\leq (M\sqrt{2}\, h)^2 h^2 = 2\, M^2\, h^4$$

and

$$\mathrm{norm}^2(w - p_n r_n w) = \sum_{i,j} \int_{x_{i-1}}^{x_i} dx \int_{x_{j-1}}^{x_j} dy\ [w(x,y) - p_n r_n w(x,y)]^2$$

$$\leq n^2\ 2M^2\ h^4 = 2M^2\ h^2\ X^2 \quad . \ //$$

We define the map $F: W \to W$ by

$$Fw := w + w^{tr} + w\, w^{tr}$$

and we define $F_n : W_n \to W_n$ by (the same formula)

$$F_n w := w + w^{tr} + w\, w^{tr} \quad .$$

Proposition. (i) The map F is (Frechet) differentiable; in particular,

$$F'w = (u \to u + u^{tr} + uw^{tr} + wu^{tr}) \quad ,$$

that is, $F'w$ is the (linear) map that sends u to $u + u^{tr} + uw^{tr} + wu^{tr}$.

(ii) The map $F'w$ is bounded; in particular,

$$\mathrm{norm}(F'w) \leq 2(1 + \mathrm{norm}(w)) \quad .$$

Proof.

(i) $F(w + u) = w + u + (w + u)^{tr} + (w + u)(w + u)^{tr}$

$$= F(w) + u + u^{tr} + uw^{tr} + wu^{tr} + uu^{tr}$$

(ii) $\mathrm{norm}(F'wu)$

$$\leq \mathrm{norm}(u) + \mathrm{norm}(u^{tr}) + \mathrm{norm}(uw^{tr}) + \mathrm{norm}(wu^{tr})$$

$$\leq 2\ \mathrm{norm}(u) + 2\ \mathrm{norm}(u)\ \mathrm{norm}(w) \quad . \ //$$

Remark. The map $w \to F'w$ is Lipschitz continuous.

Proof.

$$\mathrm{norm}((F'w_1 - F'w_2)u) = \mathrm{norm}((uw_1^{tr} + w_1 u^{tr}) - (uw_2^{tr} + w_2 u^{tr}))$$

$$\leq 2\ \mathrm{norm}(w_1 - w_2)\ \mathrm{norm}(u) \quad .$$

Hence

$$\text{norm}(F'w_1 - F'w_2) \le 2\ \text{norm}(w_1 - w_2) \quad . //$$

Proposition. (F_n, r_n, p_n) is a consistent approximation of F.

Proof. From above, we have $\text{Avg}_n((\text{Avg}_n w)w^{tr}) = (\text{Avg}_n w)(\text{Avg}_n w^{tr})$.

Hence

$$\begin{aligned} r_n((p_n r_n w)w^{tr}) &= \text{Mat}_n \text{Avg}_n((\text{Mat}_n^{-1} \text{Mat}_n \text{Avg}_n w)w^{tr}) \\ &= \text{Mat}_n((\text{Avg}_n w)(\text{Avg}_n w^{tr})) \\ &= (\text{Mat}_n \text{Avg}_n w)(\text{Mat}_n \text{Avg}_n w)^{tr} \\ &= (r_n w)(r_n w)^{tr} \end{aligned}$$

and

$$\begin{aligned} \text{F-norm}(r_n Fw - F_n r_n w) &= \text{F-norm}(r_n(w + w^{tr} + ww^{tr}) \\ &\quad - (r_n w + r_n w^{tr} + (r_n w)(r_n w)^{tr})) \\ &= \text{F-norm}(r_n(ww^{tr}) - r_n((p_n r_n w)w^{tr})) \\ &\le \text{norm}(r_n)\ \text{norm}(ww^{tr} - (p_n r_n w)w^{tr}) \\ &\le \text{norm}(w - p_n r_n w)\ \text{norm}(w) \quad . // \end{aligned}$$

Remark. If we limit our attention to C^1 kernels then there exists a constant K such that for all n and all $w \in W$

$$\text{F-norm}(F_n r_n w - r_n F_n w) \le Kh \quad . //$$

We now limit our attention to certain subsets of W. By considering diagonal matrices (and recalling that the square root function is not Lipshitz continuous at 0) we expect that we must in some way bound the kernels to be decomposed away from 0. That these kernels need to be bounded above is somewhat surprising, but the matrix examples that we present at the end of this section show that we must do so. Let $0 < m < M$ be fixed positive real numbers. We define the subset V of W by $V(m,M) := V :=$

$$\{v \in W : v \text{ is symmetric and Rayleigh } (e + \text{Int } v) \text{ is a subset of } [m,M]\}$$

where Rayleigh (e + Int v) is the numerical range of values of the Rayleigh quotient of the operator e + Int v:

$$\text{Rayleigh } (e + \text{Int } v) := \{((e + \text{Int } v)f, f) : f \in L_2(0,X) \text{ and } (f,f) = 1\}.$$

We define the subset V_n of W_n by

$$V_n := \{r_n v : v \varepsilon V\} .$$

Remark. In Tikhonov-Arsenin (1977) we find the following statement (p. 27): "The possibility of determining approximate solutions of ill-posed problems that are stable under small changes in the initial data is based on the use of supplementary information regarding the solution. Various kinds of supplementary information are possible. In the first category of cases, the supplementary information which is of a quantitative nature, enables us to narrow the class of possible solutions, for example, to a compact set, and the problem becomes stable under small changes in the initial data." We wish to emphasize the fact that we have not narrowed the class of possible solutions to a compact set; in general the set V is not compact (and consequently, since F is continuous, U is not compact). For example, suppose $0 < m < 1$ and $2 < M$. Let $c_1(x)$, $c_2(x)$, ..., be an orthonormal basis of $L_2(0,X)$ and, for $n = 1, 2, \ldots$, let

$$v_n(x,y) := c_n(x)c_n(y) .$$

We show that $v_n \varepsilon V = V(m,M)$ and that v_n cannot have a convergent subsequence. For

$$f(x) = \sum_i f_i c_i(x) \text{ we have}$$

$$(e + \text{Int } v_n)f(x) = f(x) + \int_0^X dy\, v_n(x,y)f(y)$$

$$= f(x) + c_n(x) \int_0^X dy\, c_n(y)f(y)$$

$$= f(x) + f_n c_n(x)$$

and

$$\frac{((e + \text{Int } v_n)f,f)}{(f,f)} = \frac{(f + f_n c_n, f)}{(f,f)}$$

$$= 1 + f_n^2/(f,f) \leq 2 .$$

Also

$$\int_0^X dx \int_0^X dy\ v_m(x,y)v_n(x,y) = \int_0^X dx\ c_m(x)c_n(x) \int_0^X dy\ c_m(y)c_n(y)$$

$$= \delta_{mn} \quad . \; //$$

Proposition. (Invariance of the Rayleigh quotient)

Let $f(x) = \sum_{i=1}^{n} f_i b_i(x)$. Then, for all $w \in W$,

$$\frac{((\text{Int } w)f,f)}{(f,f)} = \frac{((\text{Int Avg}_n\ w)f,f)}{(f,f)} = \frac{((r_n w)f,f)}{(f,f)} \quad ,$$

where $\dfrac{((r_n w)f,f)}{(f,f)} = \sum_{i,j} (r_n w)_{ij} f_j f_i / \sum_i f_i^2$.

Proof.

$$((\text{Int } w)f,f) = \int_0^X dx \int_0^X dy\ w(x,y)f(y)f(x)$$

$$= \sum_{i,j} f_i f_j \int_0^X dx \int_0^X dy\ w(w,y)b_i(y)b_j(x)$$

$$= \sum_{i,j} f_i f_j \int_{x_{i-1}}^{x_i} dx \int_{x_{j-1}}^{x_j} dy\ w(x,y)$$

$$= \sum_{i,j} f_i f_j\ h^2(a_n w)_{ij}$$

$$= \sum_{i,j} f_i f_j\ h(r_n w)_{ij}$$

$$((\mathrm{Int}\ \mathrm{Avg}_n w)f,f) = \int_0^X dx \int_0^X dy\ \mathrm{Avg}_n\ w(x,y)f(y)f(x)$$

$$= \int_0^X dx \int_0^X dy\ (\sum_{k,\ell} (a_n w)_{k\ell} b_k(x) b_\ell(y)) \sum_i f_i b_i(y) \sum_j f_j b_j(k)$$

$$= \sum_{i,j,k,\ell} (a_n w)_{k\ell}(h\delta_{ik})(h\delta_{j\ell}) f_i f_j$$

$$(f,f) = \int_0^X dx \sum_i f_i b_i(x) \sum_j f_j b_j(x)$$

$$= \sum_{i,j} f_i f_j h\ \delta_{ij}\quad . //$$

Proposition. For all $w \in W$,

Rayleigh $(\delta(n) + r(n)w)$ is a subset of Rayleigh $(e + \mathrm{Int}\ w)$

where $\delta(n)$ is the n x n identity matrix.

Proof. Consider any Rayleigh quotient

$$R(f) := ((\delta(n) + r_n w)f,f)/(f,f)$$

where $f := (f_1, f_2, \ldots, f_n)$ is a nonzero vector. Let $f(x) := \sum_{i=1}^{n} f_i b_i(x)$.

Then $R(f) = ((\delta(n) + r(n)w)f,f)/(f,f) = ((e + \mathrm{Int}\ w)f,f)/(f,f)$

and $R(f) \in$ Rayleigh $(e + \mathrm{Int}\ w)$.//

Proposition. $V(n) = \{v \in W(n)$: v is an n x n symmetric matrix and Rayleigh $(\delta(n) + v)$ is a subset of $[m,M]\}$.

We recall the following theorem which is well-known (see, for example, Strang (1980)):

Theorem (triangular or Cholesky factorization). If v is a positive definite symmetric matrix, then there exists a unique lower triangular matrix ℓ with positive diagonal elements such that

$$v = \ell\ \ell^{tr}.$$

We define the subset U_n of W_n by

$U_n := \{\ell \in W_n : \delta(n) + \ell$ is a lower triangular matrix with positive diagonal elements and $F_n \ell \in V_n\}$.

Proposition. $F_n : U_n \to V_n$ is injective and surjective.

Proof. Use the triangular factorization theorem and the equivalence of the following two equations:

$$\ell + \ell^{tr} + \ell\, \ell^{tr} = v$$

$$(\delta + \ell)(\delta + \ell)^{tr} = \delta + v \quad . //$$

We shall show that the sequence of maps F_n^{-1} is uniformly Lipschitz continuous.

Theorem. For all n and all $v_1, v_2 \in V_n$

$$\text{F-norm}(F_n^{-1} v_1 - F_n^{-1} v_2) \leq (M/m^2)\ \text{F-norm}(v_1 - v_2) .$$

Proof. Since V(n) is convex, by the mean value theorem, we need only show that for all n and all $v \in V(n)$

$$\text{norm}((F_n^{-1})' v) \leq M/m^2 .$$

We turn to the proof of this inequality. Recall that

$$F_n' w = (z \to z(\delta(n) + w)^{tr} + (\delta(n) + w) z^{tr}) .$$

In the next proposition we exhibit the inverse of this map.

Proposition. Let $\delta(n) + w$ be an invertible lower triangular matrix and let v be a symmetric matrix. Then

$$z(\delta(n) + w)^{tr} + (\delta(n) + w) z^{tr} = v$$

has a unique lower triangular solution z given by

$$z = (\delta(n) + w)\ \text{Lower}\ ((\delta(n) + w)^{-1} v (\delta(n) + w)^{tr-1})$$

where $(\text{Lower } u)_{ij} := u_{ij}$ if $i>j$; $:= u_{ii}/2$ if $i=j$; $:= 0$ otherwise.

Proof. Note that the following two equations are equivalent:

$$z(\delta + w)^{tr} + (\delta + w) z^{tr} = v \quad ,$$

$$(\delta + w)^{-1} z + ((\delta + w)^{-1} z)^{tr} = (\delta + w)^{-1} v (\delta + w)^{tr-1} \quad .$$

Also note that $(\delta + w)^{-1} v (\delta + w)^{tr-1}$ is symmetric and $(\delta + w)^{-1} z$ is lower triangular if z is lower triangular. Finally note that if u is symmetric then Lower u is the unique lower triangular matrix satisfying

$$\text{Lower } u + (\text{Lower } u)^{tr} = u \quad . //$$

In the estimates given below, we shall be using both the Frobenius norm and the spectral (operator) norm on matrices. In order to clearly distinguish between these norms we shall write F-norm(w) and 2-norm(w), respectively; thus

$$\text{F-norm}^2(w) := \sum_{i,j} w_{ij}^2$$

and

$$\text{2-norm}^2(w) := \sup_{f\neq 0} (wf,wf)/(f,f) \quad .$$

We recall the following facts about these norms:

Proposition. For an n x n matrix w

i) $\text{F-norm}^2(w) = \text{trace } (w^{tr}w)$

ii) $\text{2-norm}^2(w) = \lambda_{max} \ (w^{tr}w)$

where $\lambda_{max} \ (w^{tr}w)$ is the largest eigenvalue of $w^{tr}w$.

Proof.

i) $\text{Trace } (w^{tr}w) = \sum_i (w^{tr}w)_{ii} = \sum_i \sum_j w_{ij}^2$.

ii) Note $(wf,wf) = (w^{tr}wf,f)$ and consider an orthonormal basis of eigenvectors of $w^{tr}w$.//

Theorem.

$$\text{F-norm}(uv) \leq \text{2-norm}(u) \text{ F-norm}(v)$$

$$\text{F-norm}(uv) \leq \text{F-norm}(u) \text{ 2-norm}(v) \quad .$$

Proof. Recall (or calculate) that trace (uv) = trace (vu). Consequently, we have

$$\begin{aligned} \text{F-norm}^2(uv) &= \text{trace } ((uv)^{tr}uv) \\ &= \text{trace } (v^{tr}u^{tr}uv) \\ &= \text{trace } (u^{tr}uvv^{tr}) \quad . \end{aligned}$$

If u is a diagonal matrix then $\text{2-norm}^2(u) = \max_i u_{ii}^2$ and we have

$$\begin{aligned}\text{trace } (u^{tr}uvv^{tr}) &= \sum_i u_{ii}^2 \; (\sum_j v_{ij}^2) \\ &\le \sum_i \text{2-norm}^2(u) \; (\sum_j v_{ij}^2) \\ &= \text{2-norm}^2(u) \text{ F-norm}^2(v) \quad .\end{aligned}$$

We now reduce the general case to this special one. There exists an orthonormal matrix z such that

$$z^{tr}u^{tr}uz = d$$

where d is a diagonal matrix of (nonnegative) eigenvalues of $u^{tr}u$. We have

$$\begin{aligned}\text{trace } (u^{tr}uvv^{tr}) &= \text{trace } (zz^{tr}u^{tr}uzz^{tr}vv^{tr}) \\ &= \text{trace } (z^{tr}u^{tr}uzz^{tr}vv^{tr}z) \\ &= \text{trace } (d(v^{tr}z)^{tr}v^{tr}z) \\ &\le \text{2-norm}^2(u) \text{ trace } (z^{tr}vv^{tr}z) \\ &= \text{2-norm}^2(u) \text{ F-norm}^2(v) \quad .\end{aligned}$$

The second part follows from the first

$$\begin{aligned}\text{F-norm}(uv) &= \text{F-norm}((uv)^{tr}) \\ &= \text{F-norm}(v^{tr}u^{tr}) \\ &\le \text{2-norm}(v^{tr})\text{F-norm}(u^{tr}) \\ &= \text{2-norm}(v)\text{F-norm}(u) \quad . \quad //\end{aligned}$$

<u>Lemma</u>. F-norm(Lower v) $\le$ F-norm(v)

<u>Proof</u>.

$$\begin{aligned}\text{F-norm (Lower(v))} &= \sum_{i>j} v_{ij}^2 + \sum_i (v_{ii}/2)^2 \\ &\le \sum_{i,j} v_{ij}^2 \quad . \; //\end{aligned}$$

<u>Lemma</u>. For all n and all $v \in V_n$ and all $w \in U_n$,

$$\text{F-norm}((F'w)^{-1}v) \leq (M/m^2)\ \text{F-norm}(v)$$

Proof. From above, $(F'w)^{-1}v = (\delta + w)\text{Lower}((\delta + w)^{-1}v(\delta + w)^{tr-1})$.

Hence

$$\text{F-norm}((F'w)^{-1}v) \leq$$
$$\text{2-norm}(\delta + w)\ \text{F-norm}(\text{Lower}((\delta + w)^{-1}v\ (\delta+w)^{tr-1})$$
$$\leq \text{2-norm}(\delta + w)\ \text{2-norm}(\delta + w)^{-1}\ \text{F-norm}(v)\ \text{2-norm}(\delta + w)^{tr-1}$$

Furthermore, we have

$$\begin{aligned}\text{2-norm}(\delta + w) &= \lambda_{max}((\delta + w)^{tr}(\delta + w))\\ &= \lambda_{max}((\delta + w)(\delta + w)^{tr}(\delta + w)(\delta + w)^{-1})\\ &= \lambda_{max}((\delta + w)(\delta + w)^{tr})\\ &\leq M\end{aligned}$$

and

$$\begin{aligned}\text{2-norm}((\delta + w)^{-1}) &= \text{2-norm}(\delta + w)^{tr-1}\\ &= \lambda_{max}((\delta + w)^{tr-1}(\delta + w)^{-1})\\ &= \lambda_{max}((\delta + w)(\delta + w)^{tr})^{-1}\\ &\leq 1/\lambda_{min}((\delta + w)(\delta + w)^{tr})\\ &\leq 1/m\ .\ //\end{aligned}$$

Remark. We conjectured (on the basis of the square root analogy) that the constant M/m^2 could be replaced by $1/m$. We offered a prize for the settling of this conjecture. Wayne Barrett (Brigham Young University) won the prize. He provided the following counter-example:

$$\delta + w := \begin{bmatrix} 1 & 0 \\ a & 1 \end{bmatrix}, \qquad v := \begin{bmatrix} b & c \\ c & d \end{bmatrix}$$

Helaman Ferguson (Brigham Young University) noted that taking $v := \delta$ simplifies Barrett's example. After seeing these examples, we were able to find the following example which shows that the constant M/m^2 cannot be substantially improved. We assume $0 < m \ll M$ and take $\varepsilon := m/M$, $v := \delta$ and w to be a lower triangular matrix satisfying the following matrix equation:

$$(\delta + w)^{tr}(\delta + w) = \frac{1}{2}\begin{bmatrix} 1 & 1 \\ -1 & 1 \end{bmatrix}\begin{bmatrix} m^2 & 0 \\ 0 & M^2 \end{bmatrix}\begin{bmatrix} 1 & -1 \\ 1 & 1 \end{bmatrix}$$

$$= \frac{1}{2}\begin{bmatrix} M^2+m^2 & M^2-m^2 \\ M^2-m^2 & M^2+m^2 \end{bmatrix}$$

$$= \frac{M^2}{2}\begin{bmatrix} 1+\varepsilon^2 & 1-\varepsilon^2 \\ 1-\varepsilon^2 & 1+\varepsilon^2 \end{bmatrix}$$

Note that

$$((\delta + w)^{tr}(\delta + w))^{-1} = \frac{1}{2}\begin{bmatrix} M^{-2}+m^{-2} & M^{-2}-m^{-2} \\ M^{-2}-m^{-2} & M^{-2}+m^{-2} \end{bmatrix}$$

$$= \frac{1}{2m^2}\begin{bmatrix} \varepsilon^2+1 & \varepsilon^2-1 \\ \varepsilon^2-1 & \varepsilon^2+1 \end{bmatrix}$$

Also note that

$$\text{2-norm}(\delta+w) = M , \quad \text{and}$$

$$\text{2-norm}(\delta+w)^{-1} = m \ .$$

Now

$$\text{F-norm}^2((\delta+w)\text{Lower}((\delta+w)^{-1}v(\delta+w)^{tr-1}))$$

$$= \text{trace}((\text{Lower}((\delta+w)^{tr}(\delta+w))^{-1})^{tr}(\delta+w)^{tr}(\delta+w)\text{Lower}((\delta+w)^{tr}(\delta+w))^{-1})$$

$$= \text{trace}\ \frac{1}{4m^2}\begin{bmatrix} \varepsilon^2+1 & 0 \\ 2(\varepsilon^2-1) & \varepsilon^2+1 \end{bmatrix}^{tr}\frac{M^2}{2}\begin{bmatrix} 1+\varepsilon^2 & 1-\varepsilon^2 \\ 1-\varepsilon^2 & 1+\varepsilon^2 \end{bmatrix}\frac{1}{4m^2}\begin{bmatrix} \varepsilon^2+1 & 0 \\ 2(\varepsilon^2-1) & \varepsilon^2+1 \end{bmatrix}$$

Ignoring the small term ε^2, we have (approximately)

$$\text{trace}\ \frac{M^2}{32m^4}\begin{bmatrix}1 & -2\\ 0 & 1\end{bmatrix}\begin{bmatrix}1 & 1\\ 1 & 1\end{bmatrix}\begin{bmatrix}1 & 0\\ -2 & 1\end{bmatrix}$$

$$= \frac{M^2}{32m^4}\ \text{trace}\begin{bmatrix}1 & -2\\ 0 & 1\end{bmatrix}\begin{bmatrix}-1 & 1\\ -1 & 1\end{bmatrix}$$

$$= \frac{M^2}{32m^4}\ \text{trace}\begin{bmatrix}1 & -1\\ -1 & 1\end{bmatrix}$$

$$= \frac{M^2}{16m^4}\ . \quad //$$

Remark. Dan Vasicek (Amoco Production Company, Research, Tulsa) has suggested that many of the results of this report can probably be generalized from the triangular (Cholesky) decomposition ($\ell\ \ell^{tr}$) to the lower-diagonal-upper (ℓdu) decomposition.//

REFERENCES

[1] R. BURRIDGE (1980) "The Gelfand-Levitan, the Marchenko, and the Gopinath-Sondhi integral equations of inverse scattering theory regarded in the context of inverse impulse-response problems," Wave Motion 2, pp. 305-323.

[2] R. COURANT, K. O. FRIEDRICHS, H. LEWY (1928) "Uber die partiellen Differenzengleichungen der mathematischen Physik" Math. Ann. 100 pp. 32-74 (English translation: "On the partial difference equations of mathematical physics," IBM J. 11 (1967) pp. 215-234).

[3] R. COURANT & D. HILBERT (1953) Methods of Mathematical Physics, Volume I, Wiley.

[4] I. M. GELFAND & B. M. LEVITAN (1951) "On the determination of a differential equation from its spectral function" (Russian) Izv. Akad. Nauk SSSR Ser. Mat. 15 pp. 309-360; (English translation Amer. Math. Soc. Transl. 1 (1955) pp. 253-304).

[5] P. R. HALMOS & V. S. SUNDER (1978) Bounded Integral Operators on L^2 Spaces, Springer.

[6] H. HOCHSTADT (1973) Integral Equations, Wiley.

[7] S. LANG (1969) Real Analysis, Addison Wesley.

[8] P. LINZ (1979) Theoretical Numerical Analysis, Wiley.

[9] G. STRANG (1980) Linear Algebra and its Applications, second edition, Academic.

[10] W. W. SYMES (1979) "Inverse boundary value problems and a theorem of Gelfand and Levitan," J. Math. Anal. & Appl. 71, pp. 318-402.

[11] W. W. SYMES (1981) "Stable solution of the inverse reflection problem for a smoothly stratified elastic medium," SIAM J. Math. Anal. 12, pp. 421-453.

[12] A. N. TIKHONOV, V. Y. ARSENIN (1977) Solutions of Ill-Posed Problems, Wiley.

Acknowledgments (by Driessel). I thank the following people for listening to me talk about these problems and offering encouragement: Rod Deyo (University of Utah), Helaman R. P. Ferguson (Brigham Young University), Aubrey Poore (Colorado State University), Bill Firey (Oregon State University - I still think that proofs of some of these results by means of convexity arguments should be possible and enlightening), Jan Mycielski (University of Colorado - He said that I should report: "He only yawned three times."), Alan Pierce (Amoco Production Company, Research, Tulsa), Phil Bording (Amoco Production Company, Research, Tulsa), and Sam Gray (Amoco Production Company, Research, Tulsa). I also wish to thank Amoco Production Company for supporting this research and allowing me to publish this report.

Acoustic Inverse Scattering Solutions by Moment Methods and Backpropagation

Steven A. Johnson*, Yong Zhou,**
Michael J. Berggren* and Michael L. Tracy**

Abstract. A new method is presented for solving the inverse scattering problem for the scalar, inhomogeneous, exact, Lippmann-Schwinger integral wave equation for a spatially band limited scattering potential. No perturbation approximations are used and the method is applicable even for many cases where weak to moderate attenuation and moderate to strong refraction of incident fields occur. The ill-posed nature of the inverse scattering problem for a single monochromatic source is known. However, the use of multiple sources, the collection of redundant (i.e., overdetermined) data, and the constraining of the fields and complex refractive index to be spatially band limited constitutes a new problem. The cases we have tested by computer simulation indicate that the new problem is well posed, has a unique solution, and is stable with noisy data. The method is an application of the well-known method of moments with sinc basis and delta or sinc testing functions to discretize the problem. The inverse scattering solution may be obtained by solving the resulting pair of sets of simultaneous, quadratic, multivariate equations. Fast methods for solving these equations using the fast Fourier transform are suggested.

1. Introduction. The use of scattered electromagnetic and acoustic waves to determine the internal material properties of objects (called the inverse scattering problem) is a much studied problem in the fields of geophysics, nondestructive testing, sonar, and medical imaging. The problem is generally considered to be so difficult that it has been common to employ approximate solutions to obtain some indication of internal structure. This paper will describe new inverse scattering approaches which provide an image of the actual material properties of the object (and not just the internal fields) without use of perturbation or other drastic approximations. For a summary of many of the approximate methods and of the present state of

*Department of Bioengineering, University of Utah, Salt Lake City, UT 84112
**Department of Electrical Engineering, University of Utah, Salt Lake City, UT 84112.

development of acoustic imaging, we suggest our recent papers on the solutions of the inverse scattering problem [1, 2].

We now present methods for obtaining an inverse scattering solution to the wave equation which do not use perturbation theory. The methods presented here are an extension and refinement of our earlier work [3-5].

The wave equation for ultrasonic pressure wave propagation $p(\underline{x})$ may be written [6]:

$$\nabla^2 p(\underline{x}) + k^2(\underline{x})\, p(\underline{x}) - \nabla \ln \rho(\underline{x}) \cdot \nabla p(\underline{x}) = 0 \tag{1}$$

The substitution $p = f/\sqrt{\rho}$, where ρ is density, transforms the above equation into the more familiar Helmholtz equation for field f:

$$\nabla^2 f(\underline{x}) + K(\underline{x}) f(\underline{x}) = 0 \tag{2}$$

where

$$K(\underline{x}) \triangleq k^2(\underline{x}) - \sqrt{\rho(\underline{x})}\, \nabla^2 \sqrt{1/\rho(\underline{x})} \tag{3}$$

where

$$k^2 = [\omega/c(\underline{x})]^2 + i\omega\alpha_{loss} \tag{4}$$

and where $c(\underline{x})$ is speed of sound, ω is angular frequency, and $\omega\alpha_{loss}$ is the imaginary part of k^2 representing power absorption. We define the complex refractive index to be k/k_o, where $k_o = \omega/c_o$ and c_o is the speed of sound of the background fluid.

The Lippmann-Schwinger equation [7], obtained from (2), is

$$f_\phi^{(sc)}(\underline{x}) \triangleq f_\phi(\underline{x}) - f_\phi^{(inc)}(\underline{x}) = \int \gamma(\underline{x}')\, f_\phi(\underline{x}')\, g(|\underline{x} - \underline{x}'|)\, d^3\underline{x}' \tag{5}$$

where $f_\phi(\underline{x})$ is the actual field at $\mathbf{x}$ for a source at ϕ, where $f_\phi^{(sc)}(\underline{x})$ is the scattered field, where $f_\phi^{(inc)}(\underline{x})$ is the incident field with no object present, and where $g(\cdot)$ is a free space Green's function and

(6)
$$\gamma(\underline{x}) = K(\underline{x}) - k_o^2$$

We note that solving (5) for $\gamma(\underline{x})$ at two frequencies allows $K(\underline{x})$ and $k(\underline{x})$ to be obtained. Given $K(\underline{x})$ and $k(\underline{x})$, we obtain $\rho(\underline{x})$ from (3). See [1] for additional discussion.

We now derive a solution for $\gamma(\underline{x})$ from equation (5) based on the method of moments. We start by expanding the product γf_ϕ. Assume the product $\gamma(\underline{x}') f_\phi(\underline{x}')$ is band limited and can be expanded in terms of a set of basis functions $\{\psi_j\}$ which are shifted versions of each other, i.e. $\psi_j(\underline{x}) = \psi(\underline{x} - \underline{x}_j)$. Here $\underline{x}_j$ is the coordinate of the jth grid point and the basis set $\{\psi_j\}$ is also chosen, such that the jth coefficients in the expansion of function G is the value of the function at $\underline{x}_j$, i.e.

(7)
$$G(\underline{x}) = \sum_j G(\underline{x}_j)\ \psi(\underline{x} - \underline{x}_j)$$

If $G(\underline{x})$ is taken to be $\gamma(\underline{x})\ f_\phi(x)$ then we may write

(8)
$$\gamma(\underline{x})\ f_\phi(x) = \sum_j \gamma(\underline{x}_j)\ f_\phi(\underline{x}_j)\ \psi(\underline{x} - \underline{x}_j)$$

The sinc functions, the pulse functions, the triangle functions, and their extensions to higher dimensions form a basis set consistent with equations (7, 8).

Following the example of Stenger [8], we adopt a Q-dimensional sinc function basis set $\{\psi_j(\underline{x})\}$ defined by

(9)
$$\psi_j(\underline{x}) = \prod_{q=1}^{Q} \frac{\sin[(\pi/h)(x_q - n_{qj}h)]}{(\pi/h)(x_q - n_{qj}h)}$$

where $\underline{x}$ has components given by $\underline{x} = (x_1, \ldots, x_q, \ldots, x_Q)$, where h is the constant step size between grid points in each coordinate x_q, where j is an index which specifies each grid point $(n_{1j}h, \ldots, n_{qj}h, \ldots, n_{Qj}h)$, and where n_{qj} are integers. Appropriate band limited functions $G(\underline{x})$ may be expanded using (7) and (9). The sinc basis functions have the advantage of providing a full 100 percent spatial frequency response up to the maximum spatial frequency allowed by the sampling grid interval h; furthermore, the expansion coefficients are obtained by inspection via (7). Upon substituting (8) into (5) and adding the subscript ω to denote the frequency of the incident wave (if the subscript ω is omitted, measurements at only one frequency will be assumed), we obtain

$$f^{(sc)}_{\phi\omega}(\underline{x}) \stackrel{\Delta}{=} f_{\phi\omega}(\underline{x}) - f^{(inc)}_{\phi\omega}(\underline{x})$$

$$= \int \sum_j \gamma(\underline{x}'_j) f_{\phi\omega}(\underline{x}'_j)\psi(\underline{x}' - \underline{x}'_j) g_\omega(|\underline{x}' - \underline{x}|) d^3\underline{x}' \tag{10}$$

Let

$$C_{\ell j\omega} \stackrel{\Delta}{=} \int \psi(\underline{x}' - \underline{x}_j)\; g_\omega(|\underline{x}' - \underline{x}_\ell|)\; d^3\underline{x}' \tag{11}$$

Then upon interchanging integration and summation and evaluating $f(\underline{x})$ at discrete points $\underline{x}_\ell$, we obtain for an object space with N grid points, Φ source positions, and measurements at Ω distinct frequencies.

$$f_{\phi\omega}(\underline{x}_\ell) - f^{(inc)}_{\phi\omega}(\underline{x}_\ell) = \sum_j^N \gamma(\underline{x}'_j)\; f_{\phi\omega}(\underline{x}'_j)\; C_{\ell j\omega}, \qquad \begin{array}{l}\ell = 1, \ldots, N\\ \phi = 1, \ldots, \Phi\\ \omega = 1, \ldots, \Omega\end{array} \tag{12}$$

Similarly, we may write an expression for measured $f^{(sc)}_{\phi\omega}(\underline{x})$ where $\underline{x}$ is sampled at all M detector positions $\underline{x}_m$

$$f^{(sc)}_{\phi\omega}(\underline{x}_m) = \sum_{j=1}^N \gamma(\underline{x}_j)\; f_{\phi\omega}(\underline{x}_j)\; D_{mj\omega}, \qquad \begin{array}{l}m = 1, \ldots, M\\ \phi = 1, \ldots, \Phi\\ \omega = 1, \ldots, \Omega\end{array} \tag{13}$$

Here, although $D_{mj\omega} = C_{mj\omega}$, a distinct symbol $D_{mj\omega}$ is used to remind us the system of equations (13) involves measurements on a detector while system of equations (12) contains no measurement information. A derivation of formulae to numerically evaluate $C_{\ell j\omega}$ and $D_{mj\omega}$ for the case of two-dimensional sinc basis functions has been given [2].

Formulae to numerically evaluate $C_{\ell j\omega}$ and $D_{mj\omega}$ for pulse basis functions are given by Richmond in his treatment of the direct scattering problem [9]. The advantage of pulse basis functions is the simple formulae for computing $C_{\ell j\omega}$ and $D_{mj\omega}$. The disadvantage of their use is the fineness of the grid which must be used to insure accuracy of Richmond's formulae; a grid separation of 0.1 wavelength is recommended.

Care must be exercised in expanding the product γf_ϕ in sinc functions. If γ and f_ϕ are both band limited to have spatial frequencies below $\Omega^{(sp)}_{max} = 1/\lambda_{min}$, then their product has spatial frequencies up to $2\,\Omega^{(sp)}_{max}$. Thus, sampling on a grid with a spacing of less than 1/4 wavelength is necessary to preserve a 1/2 wavelength resolution in γ. If $\gamma = \exp(i\Omega^{(sp)}_\gamma x)$ and $f_\phi = \exp(i\Omega^{(sp)}_f x)$ then $\gamma f_\phi = \exp\left[i(\Omega^{(sp)}_\gamma + \Omega^{(sp)}_f)x\right]$. If $\Omega^{(sp)}_p = \frac{1}{h}$ is the sampling frequency where h is the sample separation, then $\Omega^{(sp)}_\gamma$ is given by $\Omega^{(sp)}_\gamma = \frac{1}{h} - \Omega^{(sp)}_f$. If the refractive index is greater than unity, then the wavelength inside the object is smaller than the incident wavelength λ_o and $\Omega^{(sp)}_p \geq \frac{2}{\lambda_o}$.

2. Algorithms for Numerical Solution. We next list four slow but working algorithms for solving equations (12, 13) for γ from simulated scattering data. One of the algorithms will be described in detail. Possible ways to obtain fast solutions are discussed in the next section.

Simulated scattering data for inversion algorithm testing was produced by assuming a given, spatially band limited $\gamma(x)$. Equations (12) were then solved for the internal fields by application of the Kaczmarz [10], i.e., ART [11], iterative linear equation solving scheme. The scattered field was then calculated using equations (13).

Given the scattered field, the set of equations (12, 13) was solved for γ. Four iterative methods for solving equations (12, 13) for γ were investigated:

1. Alternating variable fixed point.
2. Alternating variable linear Kaczmarz.
3. Kaczmarz modified for nonlinear equations.
4. Steepest descent with line search on an objective function.

All of these methods provided a sequence of trial solutions which converged to the original test object γ. We only describe the first of these methods. The reader is referred to [1, 2] for a description of the other three methods.

The alternating variable fixed point method combines a fixed point and linear equation solving step. The algorithm may be described as follows:

1. Pick a trial value for $\gamma(\underline{x})$ and for $f_\phi(\underline{x})$. Pick accuracy δ.
2. Solve for $(k+1)$'th value of $f_\phi(x)$, i.e., $f_\phi^{(k+1)}(\underline{x})$ by

(14) $$f_{\phi}^{(k+1)}(\underline{x}_{\ell}) = f_{\phi}^{(inc)}(\underline{x}_{\ell}) + \sum_{j} \gamma^{(k)}(\underline{x}_{j})\, f_{\phi}^{(k)}(\underline{x}_{j})\, C_{\ell j}$$

for all ϕ.

Step 2 may be repeated several times if necessary before going to Step 3.

3. Find the $(k+1)$'th value of $\gamma(x)$ by solving the linear system of equations for $\gamma(\underline{x})^{(k+1)}$ using $f_{\phi}^{(k+1)}$ from Step 2

$$f_{\phi}^{(sc)}(\underline{x}_{m}) = \sum_{j} \gamma^{(k+1)}(\underline{x}_{j})\, f_{\phi}^{(k+1)}(\underline{x}_{j})\, D_{mj}$$

(15) $\phi = 1, \ldots, \Phi$ and $m = 1, \ldots, M$

4. Test for convergence of solution by examination of the residuals by forming the objective function F

(16) $$F \overset{\Delta}{=} \sum_{\phi}\sum_{\ell} |r_{1\ell\phi}| + \sum_{\phi}\sum_{m} |r_{2m\phi}|$$

(17) $$r_{1\ell\phi} \overset{\Delta}{=} f_{\phi}^{(k+1)}(\underline{x}_{\ell}) - f_{\phi}^{(inc)}(\underline{x}_{\ell}) - \sum_{j} \gamma(\underline{x}_{j})\, f_{\phi}^{(k)}(\underline{x}_{j})\, C_{\ell j}$$

(18) $$r_{2m\phi} \overset{\Delta}{=} f_{\phi}^{(sc)}(\underline{x}_{m}) - \sum_{j} \gamma^{(k+1)}(\underline{x}_{j})\, f_{\phi}^{(k+1)}(\underline{x}_{j})\, D_{mj}$$

If $F \leqslant \delta$, go to Step 5 or else go to Step 2.

5. Stop. Print results or display image.

The methods described in this section have been implemented in FORTRAN on a DEC PDP-11/34A computer [1, 2]. Images as large as 11 by 11 pixels have been obtained with simulated scattering data [1, 2]. The method is robust and has produced images with a signal-to-noise ratio (SNR) of about 20 to 1 from simulated data with an SNR of 10 to 1 [1, 2]. The 11 by 11 inverse scattering solution required about five hours of computing time. Clearly faster methods are called for.

3. <u>Suggested Fast Methods for Solution of Inverse Scattering Problem.</u> The methods described in the previous section must compute the scattering between all pairs of points in an n by n image for about n source positions. Thus the scattering between about n^5 scattering pairs were computed. If the scattering between each pair is computed individually then about n^5 calculations per iteration is required. The use of the fast-Fourier-transform (FFT) algorithm to compute the

convolutions in equations (12) and (13) permits the scattering from n^5 pairs to be computed in a time proportional to (n^3 log n). We now examine in more detail how these fast operations might be implemented to alternately solve equation (12) for $f_\phi(\underline{x}_j)$ and equation (13) for $\gamma(\underline{x}_j)$. The extension to multiple frequencies follows naturally.

We note that the summation over j in equation (12) is a convolution of the product $(\gamma f_\phi)(\underline{x}_j)$ with $C_{\ell j}$. Thus the convolution may be implemented using the FFT. For 2-D objects where $N = n^2$, the iterations in (14) are thus performed in time proportional to (n^3 log n). An alternate method for solving (12) for f_ϕ with γ given (i.e., solving the direct or forward scattering problem) in (n^3 log n) time using the conjugate gradient technique has been given by Borup [12].

We now seek a way to solve equation (13) for 2-D objects in time proportional to (n^3 log n). We report progress on the development of a fast backward wave propagation method for solving (13) which is also analogous to the back projection method of x-ray C.T. [11].

We define the forward scattered wave propagation operator P by writing (13) as

$$f_{\phi\omega}^{(sc)} = P[\gamma] = \sum_{j=1}^{N} \left[D_{mj} f_{\phi\omega}(\underline{x}_j)\right] \gamma(\underline{x}_j) \tag{19}$$

By taking the complex conjugate D_{mj}^* of D_{mj} we can propagate the influence of the wave backward in time from detector m to point j. Summing over all m effectively propagates the product $f_{\phi\omega}\gamma$ from all m to $\underline{x}_j$. However, since we want an estimate of $\gamma(\underline{x}_j)$ we must also sum over all source positions weighted by $(1/f_{\phi\omega})$. A further sum over all frequencies, if present in the scattered data, is also called for. In the following discussion only one frequency is assumed and the above concepts may be incorporated into the following formula for an approximate value $\bar{\gamma}$ for γ. This formula is thus denoted by the operator B for back propagation

$$\bar{\gamma}(\underline{x}_\ell) = B\left[f_\phi^{(sc)}(\underline{x}_m)\right] = \frac{2\pi}{\Phi} \sum_{\phi=1}^{\Phi} \left(1/f_\phi(\underline{x}_\ell)\right) \sum_{m=1}^{M} D_{m\ell}^* f_\phi^{(sc)}(\underline{x}_m) \tag{20}$$

For the detectors located in the far scattered field and for weak scattering, i.e., Born approximation, we have shown that $\bar{\gamma}$ equals γ convolved with $J_o^2(k_o\underline{x})$ for two-dimensional problems and $\bar{\gamma}$ equals γ convolved with sinc $(k_o\underline{x})$ for three-dimensional problems. Thus a deblurring operation must be applied to $\bar{\gamma}$. Consider the intuitively pleasing concept of adding to γ the correction obtained by the operation of B on the difference of $f_\phi^{(sc)}$ and the predicted scattered field $P\bar{\gamma}$. This may be written for the first iteration as

$$\gamma \approx B[f_\phi^{(sc)} - P\bar{\gamma}] + \bar{\gamma} \tag{21}$$

The operation may be repeated to give the general iteration formula

$$\bar{\gamma}^{(k+1)} = \bar{\gamma}^{(k)} + B[f_\phi^{(sc)} - P\bar{\gamma}^{(k)}] \tag{22}$$

This may be rewritten in a more instructive form

$$\bar{\gamma}^{(k+1)} = Bf_\phi^{(sc)} + [I - BP]\bar{\gamma}^{(k)} \tag{23}$$

It can be shown that this process converges only if (I - BP) has eigenvalues which lie within the unit circle (see [15, p. 188]). Since this has not been observed to occur in our experiments, we seek to modify (23) to meet these conditions. One candidate is the iteration formula which uses an operator with positive eigenvalues.

$$\bar{\gamma}^{(k+1)} = \alpha(BP)^\dagger\, Bf_\phi^{(sc)} + [I - \alpha(BP)^\dagger\,(BP)]\bar{\gamma}^{(k)} \tag{24}$$

The formula (24) can be motivated by multiplying both sides of (19) by $[(BP)^\dagger B]$ to obtain

$$(BP)^\dagger\, Bf_\phi^{(sc)} = (BP)^\dagger\, BP[\gamma] \approx \gamma \tag{25}$$

Since $(BP)^\dagger$ is itself a blurring operation, i.e., $(BP)^\dagger$ is close to the identity matrix I, then $[(BP)^\dagger B]$ is also a "backprojection-like" operation. Using $[\alpha(BP)^\dagger B]$ as the replacement for B in (21) and (22) leads to (24), where α is an appropriate positive real number and $(BP)^\dagger$ is the complex conjugate transpose of (BP). Convergence of (24) has been observed in all of the limited number of experiments performed, using for f_ϕ the correct internal fields.

An iteration formula which also has shown convergence to γ in our experiments is given by

$$\bar{\gamma}^{(k+1)} = \alpha\left(P^{\dagger}\right)f_{\phi}^{(sc)} + \left[I - \alpha\left(P^{\dagger}P\right)\right]\bar{\gamma}^{(k)} \tag{26}$$

The formula (26) can be motivated in a manner similar to (25) by multiplying both sides of (19) by $P^{\dagger}$ to obtain

$$P^{\dagger}f_{\phi}^{(sc)} = P^{\dagger}P[\gamma] \tag{27}$$

Since $P^{\dagger}$ has some of the features of backprojection, we associate $P^{\dagger}$ as the replacement for B in (21) and (22) to obtain (26).

Still faster convergence may be possible by replacing B in (24) by (SB). Here S is the sharpening operator which deconvolves the effect of BP acting on a single unit scattering point in a homogeneous medium for the detectors in the far field, i.e., SBP = I. The search for an appropriate S may be started by noting that, for the conditions above, $BP\delta(\underline{x} - \underline{x}_o) = J_o^2(k_o|\underline{x} - \underline{x}_o|)$, e.g., try for S the inverse Fourier transform of the reciprocal of the Fourier transform of $J_o^2(k_o|\underline{x}|)$. Here J_o is the zero order Bessel function.

All of the operations in the above iterative formulas (23, 24, 26) may be computed in order (n^3 log n) time per iteration. The performance of the formulas (24, 26) in giving solutions γ for larger n and the dependence of the rate of iterative convergence of solutions to the coupled set (12) and (13) must be determined before an overall evaluation of the potentially fast methods of this section can be made.

4. Conclusions. We have presented methods for solving the inverse scattering problem for an inhomogeneous body in a homogeneous surrounding media by the use of data collected from multiple detectors and multiple sources. Our methods assume that the fields and material properties, e.g., the complex refractive index, are functions of position which are spatially band limited.

Some properties of our solution method are similar to those of the method of x-ray computed tomography [11]:

1. Both use multiple source and detector positions located on a curve circumscribing the object (although some positions are not used for x-ray CT)

2. In both modes, the number of detectors times the number of sources should be greater than the number of pixels, i.e., $M\Phi$ >

N, for a unique solution (for the acoustic problem we have assumed a single frequency). For multiple frequencies, the condition becomes $M\Phi\Omega > N$. This condition provides for more equations than unknowns.

Of course, in x-ray CT, the detector mainly measures transmission along the line joining the source and detector while equation (13) indicates that each detector measures scattering from all points within a body.

The numerical implementation of our method has demonstrated many of the features common to the x-ray CT problem. In particular, for the cases tested, for $|\gamma/k_o^2| \leq .1$ our method converges to a unique solution γ/k_o^2 for noise-free data $f_\phi^{(sc)}(\underline{x}_m)$ when $M\Phi \geqslant \zeta N$ where $\zeta \gtrsim 1.3$ [2]. For data $f_\phi^{(sc)}(\underline{x}_m)$ with added noise, the noise in the image γ/k_o^2 decreases rapidly as ζ is increased in the range $1 < \zeta < 3$, but increasing ζ greater than 3 produces diminishing improvements [2].

Increased computational speed may be possible by use of fast algorithms. For low contrast objects where method one works well, the evaluation of the sum in equation (12) can be done by fast Fourier transform techniques since (12) is a convolution, see [12]. We also suggest a general method that is fast for solving equation (13) for $\gamma(\underline{x}_j)$.

5. Acknowledgements. We appreciate the suggestions of D. T. Borup concerning formulation of fast algorithms in terms of convolution operations using the fast Fourier transform [12]. Discussions with T. H. Yoon, S. Y. Shin, J. W. Ra, Z. H. Cho, S. B. Park and G. H. Kim of the Department of Electrical Engineering, Korea Advanced Institute of Science and Technology, Seoul, Korea, are appreciated. Exchanges of information with M. J. Hagmann, now at the National Institutes of Health, Bethesda, Maryland, are also appreciated. We appreciate discussions on sinc functions with F. Stenger and discussions on iterative methods for solving nonlinear equations, e.g., equations (12, 13), with C. Wilcox, both residing in the Department of Mathematics, University of Utah. The support of our colleague D. A. Christensen is appreciated. The editing and typing help of the Department of Electrical Engineering is also appreciated. Support in part from grants PDP-110B from the American Cancer Society and R01-CA1-29728 from the National Cancer Institute are appreciated.

REFERENCES

[1] S. A. JOHNSON and M. L. TRACY, Inverse scattering solutions by a sinc basis moment method -- part I: theory, submitted to Acoustical Imaging, Plenum Press.

[2] M. L. TRACY and S. A. JOHNSON, Inverse scattering solutions by a sinc basis, moment method -- part II: numerical evaluation, submitted to Acoustical Imaging, Plenum Press.

[3] S. A. JOHNSON, J. W. RA, S. Y. SHIN, and T. H. YOON, Potential of the inverse scattering problem with multiple sources for 3-D image reconstruction, Chapter 6, pp. 198-233, from "Development of Multidimensional Image Processing Algorithms and Imaging Systems," I.S.S. Lab Report No. 3 (May 20, 1982), Imaging System Science Laboratory, Department of Electrical Sciences, Korea Advanced Institute of Science and Technology, Seoul, Korea.

[4] S. A. JOHNSON, Recent advances in ultrasonic imaging by solution of inverse scattering, proceedings of "Workshop on Computerized Tomography and Multi-Dimensional Digital Image Processing," Korea Advanced Institute of Science and Technology, Seoul, Korea, May 6-7, 1982.

[5] S. A. JOHNSON, T. H. YOON, and J. W. RA, Inverse scattering solutions of the scalar Helmholtz wave equation by a multiple source, moment method, Electronics Letters, February 17, 1983.

[6] S. A. JOHNSON, F. STENGER, C. WILCOX, J. BALL, and M. BERGGREN, Wave equations and inverse solutions for soft tissue, Acoustical Imaging 11(1982), pp. 409-424, Plenum Press.

[7] P. M. MORSE AND K. V. INGARD, Theoretical Acoustics, McGraw-Hill Book Company, New York, 1968.

[8] F. STENGER, Numerical methods based on Whittaker cardinal, or sinc functions, SIAM Review 23-2(1981).

[9] J. RICHMOND, Scattering by a dielectric cylinder of arbitrary cross-sectional shape, IEEE Transactions on Antennas and Propagation 69(1981), pp. 1517-1519.

[10] S. KACZMARZ, ANGENAHERTE AUFLOSUNG VON SYSTEM LINEARER GLEICHUNGEN, Bull. Akad. Polon. Science Lett. 35(1935), pp. 355-357.

[11] G. T. HERMAN, Image Reconstruction from Projections, The Fundamentals of Computerized Tomography, Academic Press, New York, 1980.

[12] D. T. BORUP and O. P. GANDHI, Fast-Fourier-transform method for calculation of SAR distributions in finely discretized inhomogeneous models of biological bodies, IEEE Transactions on Microwave Theory and Techniques (revised version accepted for publication, March 1983).

[13] R. W. SCHAFER, ET. AL., Constrained iterative restoration algorithms, Proceedings of the IEEE 69-4(1981), pp. 432-450.

[14] D. C. YOULA, Generalized image restoration by the method of alternating orthogonal projections, IEEE Transactions on Circuits and Systems 25-9(1978).

[15] D. K. FADDEEV and V. N. FADDEEVA, Computational Methods of Linear Algebra, W. H. Freeman and Co., San Francisco, 1963.

The Inverse Problem of Torsional Vibration at Two Frequencies

M. A. Hooshyar* and M. Razavy*

Abstract. A procedure is developed for constructing the shear modulus and the density profiles of a laterally inhomogeneous medium from the known values of the logarithmic derivative of the torsional displacement on the surface when these values are given at two different frequencies. This method exploits a particular difference equation which approximates the differentional equation governing the lateral displacement in the inhomogeneous medium. The logarithmic derivative of the torsional displacement at the surface is then given by a continued fraction. From Thiele's theorem it follows that the coefficients of this continued fraction expansion are related to the values of the density and the shear modulus at different depths, and hence the expansion enables one to evaluate these elastic parameters from the known torsional data.

1. Introduction. Among a number of inverse problems concerned with the determination of the elastic properties of a laterally inhomogeneous medium, the inversion of the torsional vibration data seems to be one of the most promising methods, since the measurement of the input data is practically feasible and the mathematical problem has a simple formulation, i.e. the wave has a single component. Here one considers the three-dimensional wave propagation in a medium where the elastic properties depend on the coordinate z alone. If one uses cylindrical coordinates, then the symmetry of the problem about the z-axis reduces the number of variables to two (r and z coordinates). The inhomogeneous medium according to this model, is bounded on one side by a free surface $z = 0$ and extends to a depth $z = d$ where it joins smoothly to a homogeneous medium of infinite extent. The wave is generated by a circular vibrator placed at the free surface, the vibrator produces torsional vibrations with a well-defined frequency. By measuring the torsional displacement at the surface as a function of r and by knowing the applied stress, one can determine the torsional impedance at the boundary. Using this torsional impedance as a function of the wave number q, one can deduce the shear modulus and the density provided that the empirical data are available at two different frequencies of

* Theoretical Physics Institute, Department of Physics, University of Alberta, Edmonton, Alberta T6G 2J1, Canada

the vibrator. This problem has been discussed by Markushevich and Reznikov [1] and by Coen [2], using the Gel'fand-Levitan formulation of the inverse scattering theory to obtain the profiles. Recent numerical results obtained by Daley, Markushevich and Reznikov [3] indicate that in this approach the input characteristic values must be known very accurately in order to get reasonable results for rapidly changing profiles, a condition on the input information which is hard to meet. The present work is based on the T-fraction expansion [4] of a special difference equation which approximates the differential equation governing the propagation of the disturbance in the z-direction. In Section 2 the mathematical formulation of the problem is presented, and in Section 3 the results of inversion are given and the accuracy and the stability of the method is discussed. In the Appendix it is shown that the difference equation which forms the basis of this inversion can be derived from a Lagrangian for a system of massive particles and connecting springs.

2. <u>A Continued Fraction Expansion for the Torsional Impedance.</u> If a circular rigid torsional vibrator of radius b is placed on the free surface of a medium, then the torsional displacement of the medium at the depth z satisfies the partial differential equation

$$\left(\frac{\partial^2}{\partial r^2} + \frac{1}{r}\frac{\partial}{\partial r} - \frac{1}{r^2} + \frac{\partial^2}{\partial z^2} + L(z)\frac{\partial}{\partial z} + \frac{\omega^2}{c^2(z)}\right)u = 0 \tag{2.1}$$

where ω is the angular frequency of the vibration, $c^2 = \mu(z)/\rho(z)$ is the shear velocity, $\mu(z)$ is the shear modulus, $\rho(z)$ is the density and $L(z)$ is the logarithmic derivative of the shear modulus. When both $u(r,0)$ and the torsional stress τ which is defined by

$$\tau(r,\omega) = \mu(z)\frac{\partial}{\partial z}u(r,z,\omega)\bigg|_{z=0} \qquad 0 \le r \le b$$

$$\tau(r,\omega) = 0 \qquad\qquad r > b \tag{2.2}$$

are known, then the boundary value of the torsional impedance $(d/dz \log u)_{z=0}$ will also be known for a given frequency of the vibrator. But both the amplitude u and the stress τ can be measured for different r values, and therefore at $z = 0$, the Hankel transforms of u and τ are determinable, i.e., if we define $\tilde{u}$ and $\tilde{\tau}$ by

$$\tilde{u}(z,q,\omega) = \int_0^\infty u(r,z,\omega)rJ_1(qr)dr \tag{2.3}$$

and

$$\tilde{\tau}(q,\omega) = \int_0^b \tau(r,\omega)rJ_1(qr)dr \tag{2.4}$$

then

$$\frac{d}{dz}\log \tilde{u}(z,q,\omega)\bigg|_{z=0} = \tilde{\tau}(q,\omega)/\mu(0)\tilde{u}(0,q,\omega) \tag{2.5}$$

is empirically obtainable information which can be used to construct the velocity and the density profiles of the inhomogeneous medium. By taking the Hankel transform of eq. (2.1) we find an ordinary differential equation for $\tilde{u}(z,q,\omega)$;

$$\left(\frac{d^2}{dz^2} - q^2 + \frac{\omega^2}{c^2(z)} + L(z)\frac{\partial}{\partial z}\right)\tilde{u}(z,q,\omega) = 0 . \tag{2.6}$$

The function $\tilde{u}$ depends on the two parameters q and ω, but its defining equation contains the unknown functions c(z) and L(z). In the present study we assume that the boundary value of the torsional impedance, i.e. $(d/dz \log \tilde{u})_{z=0}$ is given for one or two frequencies and for different values of q. Now depending on the availability of information we can have one of the following types of inversion:

(a) Empirical information is known at a given frequency of the vibrator and this is supplemented by the knowledge of L(z) and the object is to determine c(z).

(b) The torsional impedance at z=0, is given at one frequency in addition to the known velocity profile, and the problem is to find L(z).

(c) The data are known at two frequencies, and we want to obtain both c(z) and L(z).

In all three forms, we need to know the asymptotic shear velocity in the medium. In order to use this information in our formulation we assume that the inhomogeneous medium has an effective depth d beyond which $\tilde{u}(z)$ will not contain any reflection term and that both $\mu(z)$ and $\rho(z)$ become constants for $z > d$, hence in the latter range $L(z) = 0$ and $c(z) = c(d)$. This asymptotic wave velocity, c(d), and the frequency ω yield the asymptotic wave number which appears naturally in eq. (2.5). We assume that the data are given for q values equal or greater than $\omega/c(d)$. Now let us write (2.5) in a form where only quantities with the dimension of length appear in the equation of $\tilde{u}$. To this end we introduce an arbitrary constant c_o with the dimension of velocity and write (2.6) as

$$\left(\frac{d^2}{dz^2} - \eta^2 + k^2 W(z) + L(z)\frac{d}{dz}\right)\tilde{u} = 0 \tag{2.7}$$

where

$$\eta^2 = q^2 - \omega^2/c^2(d) \tag{2.8}$$

and

$$V(z) = c(z)/c_o , \quad W(z) = \frac{1}{V^2(z)} - \frac{1}{V^2(d)} \quad \text{and} \quad k = \omega/c_o \tag{2.9}$$

For the depths greater than d, we observe that in (2.7) $W(z) = 0$ and $L(z) = 0$, and therefore $\tilde{u}$ is simply given by

$$\tilde{u} = T\, e^{-\eta z} \tag{2.10}$$

where T is a constant. We choose this solution, which is correct for all points if the medium is homogeneous, as the comparison solution, i.e. we choose $W(z) = 0$ and $L(z) = 0$ as the base functions. Then the departure of the actual solution from (2.10) which is caused by the inhomogeneity of the medium can be expressed in terms of a function $\psi(z)$, where

$$\psi = e^{\eta z}\,\tilde{u}/T \tag{2.11}$$

and satisfies the differential equation

$$\left\{\frac{d^2}{dz^2} + [L(z) - 2\eta]\frac{d}{dz} + [k^2 W(z) - \eta L(z)]\right\}\psi = 0 \quad . \tag{2.12}$$

The boundary conditions for $\psi(z)$ at $z = d$ are given by

$$\psi(d) = 1, \qquad \psi'(d) = 0 \tag{2.13}$$

and thus $\psi(z) = 1$, is the solution of (2.12) for a homogeneous medium. At the surface we denote the logarithmic derivative of ψ by $D(q,\omega)$;

$$D(q,\omega) = \frac{d}{dz}\log\psi(z)\Big|_{z=0} = \eta + \tilde{\tau}(q,\omega)/\mu(0)\tilde{u}(0,q,\omega) \ . \tag{2.14}$$

Now for the direct solution of the problem we can integrate (2.12) with the boundary conditions (2.13) from z=d to z=0 and find the torsional impedance, $d/dz \log \tilde{u}|_{z=0}$ or the related quantity $D(q,\omega)$. Similar results can be obtained if we replace (2.12) by its finite difference analogue:

$$(1-\eta\Delta)(1+\tfrac{1}{2}L_n\Delta)\psi_{n+1} + (1+\eta\Delta)(1-\tfrac{1}{2}L_n\Delta)\psi_{n-1} - (2-k^2\Delta^2 W_n)\psi_n = 0 \tag{2.15}$$

where $\Delta = d/N$ and $\psi_n = \psi(z=n\Delta)$. This difference equation satisfies the boundary conditions

$$\psi_N = \psi_{N+1} = 1 \tag{2.16}$$

and the solution of (2.15) subject to (2.16) approximates $\psi(z)$ to the order Δ^4. The reason for our choice of (2.15) over other possible forms of difference equations approximating (2.12) is that (2.15) can be transformed to a form for which the torsional impedance is expressible as a T-fraction [4]. This property enables one to obtain the solution of the inverse problem from the coefficients of the the T-fraction expansion. A special T-fraction results from solving a difference equation of the type [4]

$$F_{n-1} = \Omega_n F_n + yF_{n+1} \tag{2.17}$$

for F_0/F_1;

$$F_0/F_1 = \Omega_1 + \frac{y}{\Omega_2 +}\,\frac{y}{\Omega_3 +}\cdots\frac{y}{\Omega_{N-2} +}\,\frac{y}{\Omega_{N-1} + yF_N/F_{N-1}} \ . \tag{2.18}$$

Equation (2.15) can be brought to the standard form (2.17) by changing ψ_n and η using the following transformations:

$$F_n = a_n\psi_n/(1+\eta\Delta)^n \tag{2.19}$$

$$y = \eta^2\Delta^2 - 1 \tag{2.20}$$

$$a_{n+1} = (1 + L_n\Delta)a_{n-1}/(1 - \tfrac{1}{2}L_n\Delta) \tag{2.21}$$

and

$$\Omega_n = (2 - k^2\Delta^2 W_n)a_{n-1}/(1 - \tfrac{1}{2}L_n\Delta)a_n \ . \tag{2.22}$$

Using these relations we find eq. (2.17), and hence its solution (2.18) where in the latter F_N/F_{N-1} is replaced by

$$F_N/F_{N-1} = a_N/[1 + (1+y)^{1/2}]a_{N-1} . \tag{2.23}$$

Thus denoting F_0/F_1 by $G(y,\omega)$, we have the infinite continued fraction

$$G(y,\omega) = F_0/F_1 = \Omega_1 + \frac{y}{\Omega_2 +} \cdots + \frac{y}{\Omega_{N-1} +} \frac{y}{2\left(\frac{a_{N-1}}{a_N}\right) +} \frac{y}{2\left(\frac{a_N}{a_{N-1}}\right) +} \cdots \tag{2.24}$$

which is closely related to $D(q,\omega)$ defined earlier. To establish this relationship, we observe that the finite difference analogue to (2.14), viz.,

$$D(q,\omega) \approx \frac{1}{2\Delta\psi_0}[\psi(\Delta) - \psi(-\Delta)] \tag{2.25}$$

yields the following expression for $G(y,\omega)$;

$$G(y,\omega) = \frac{a_0}{a_{-1}}[1 - \tfrac{1}{2}(1+y)^{1/2}L_0\Delta]/(1 + \tfrac{1}{2}L_0\Delta)\ \{D(y,\omega) +$$

$$+ (2 - k^2\Delta^2 W_0)/2[1 + (1+y)^{1/2}](1 - \tfrac{1}{2}L_0\Delta)\} \ . \tag{2.26}$$

Therefore the result of the continued fraction solution of (2.18) is the boundary value (2.26) given in terms of the parameters y and ω (or q and ω). Conversely if (2.26) is given as the boundary value of (2.17), then from its T-fraction expansion the coefficients Ω_n can be determined. We note that in (2.26), (a_0/a_{-1}) is an arbitrary normalization constant which can be set equal to one. A remarkable property of the representation (2.24), according to Thiele's expansion theorem, is that Ω_n's are expressible as the reciprocal derivatives of $G(y,\omega)$ about y=0, i.e. $G(y,\omega)$ can be expanded in terms of y as [5], [6]

$$G(y,\omega) = G_0 + \frac{y}{SG_0 +} \frac{y}{2SSG_0 +} \frac{y}{3SS_2G_0 +} \cdots . \tag{2.27}$$

In this relation $G_0 = G(0,\omega)$ and S_nG is the n-th reciprocal derivative of G which is defined by the recurrence relation

$$S_0G(y) = G(y)$$

$$SG(y) = 1/(dG/dy)$$

$$S_nG(y) = S_{n-2}G(y) + nSS_{n-1}G(y) \ . \tag{2.28}$$

By comparing (2.24) and (2.27) one can establish relations between Ω_n's and the reciprocal derivatives:

$$\Omega_1 = G(0,\omega)$$

and

$$\Omega_{n+1} = nSS_{n-1}G(0,\omega) \quad . \tag{2.29}$$

Since y and q are related to each other by

$$y = \left(q^2 - \frac{\omega^2}{c^2(d)}\right)\Delta^2 - 1 \tag{2.30}$$

therefore if $D(q,\omega)$ is known in terms of its reciprocal derivatives (or ordinary derivatives) about the point $q^2 \approx \omega^2/c^2(d) + 1/\Delta^2$, then Ω_n's and consequently W_n's and L_n's can be determined.

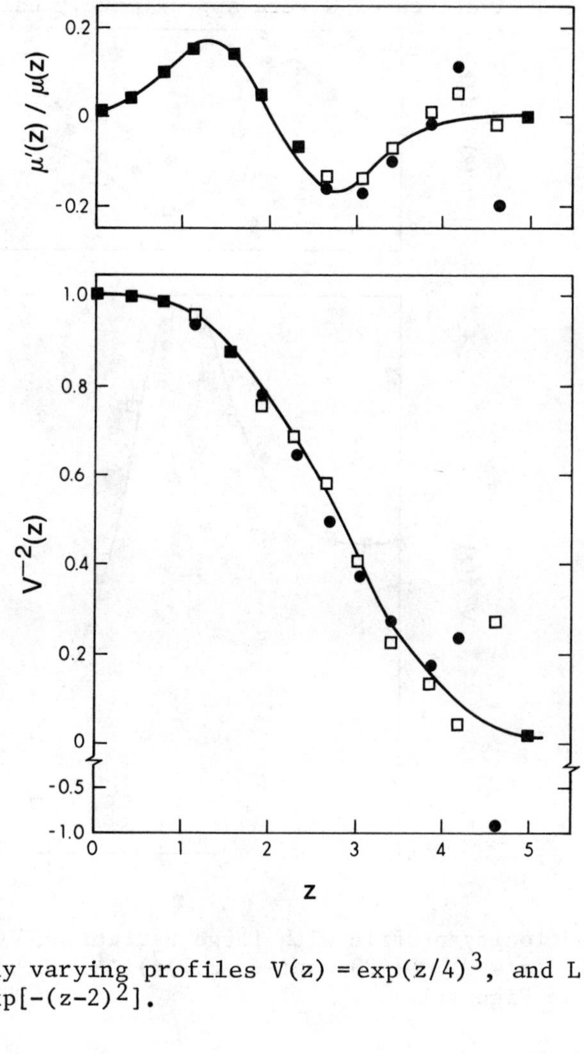

Figure 1. Smoothly varying profiles $V(z) = \exp(z/4)^3$, and $L(z) = 0.4 \times (z-2)\exp[-(z-2)^2]$.

3. Numerical Inversion. Model calculations in which the input data $D(q,\omega)$ is obtained from the exact solution of eq. (2.12) as a function of q is used as a test of reliability of the inverse method. We found that it is easier to transform (2.12) to a Riccati equation for the variable torsional impedance before carrying out the numerical integration. The results found in this way agree with those obtained by solving (2.15) to about one part in 10^5 when Δ is small (e.g. $\Delta \approx 0.02$), consistent with our error estimate for eq. (2.15). Both continuous and discontinuous velocity profiles and L(z) were used to obtain synthetic data for the boundary value of the torsional impedance. Although in an actual calculation, derivatives of G should be found from Hankel transforms of different orders of the experimental data, in this preliminary work we have assumed that the input data are given as the values of D about some value of q, say $q_0 > \omega/c(d)$. In other words $G(y,\omega)$ is given for different y's about $y = 0$. For calculation of derivatives, $G(y,\omega)$ was fitted by a polynomial in y and from this polynomial fit the derivatives of G were approximately calculated. From the

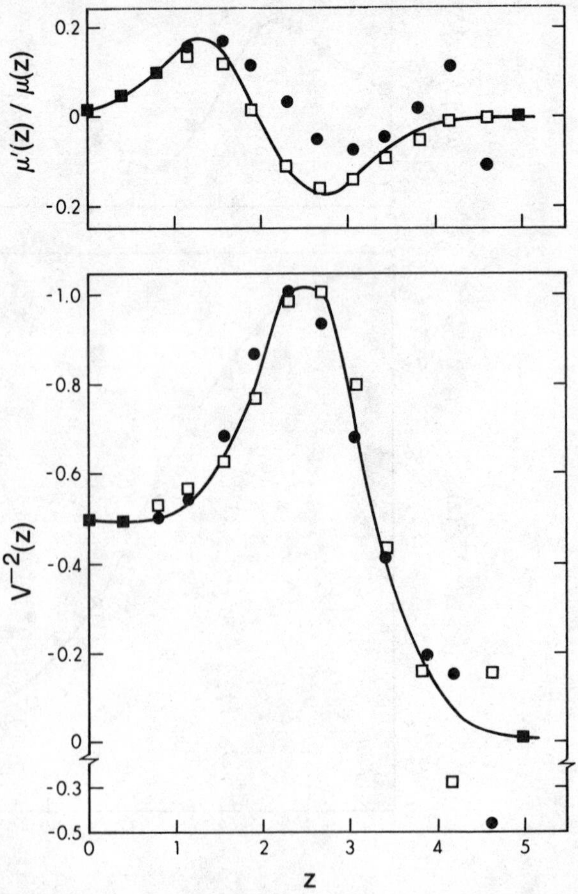

Figure 2. Velocity profile with large variations $V(z) = [0.707 \exp(-(z/4)^3) + 0.488 \exp(-(z-2.7)^2)]^{-1}$. L(z) is the same as in Figure 1.

derivatives of G its reciprocal derivatives were found by the following method due to Nörlund [6],

$$(n+1)SS_n G = (-1)^n \, p_n^2/p_{n-1}p_{n+1} \tag{3.1}$$

with

$$p_0 = 1\,, \quad p_1 = a_1\,, \quad p_2 = a_2$$

$$p_{2n} = p_{2,n}, \quad p_{2n+1} = p_{1,n+1} \tag{3.2}$$

where the quantities $p_{r,n+1}$ are defined by the determinant

$$p_{r,n+1} = \begin{vmatrix} a_r & a_{r+1} \cdots\cdots a_{r+n} \\ \vdots & \\ a_{r+n} & \cdots\cdots\cdots\cdots a_{r+2n} \end{vmatrix} \,. \tag{3.3}$$

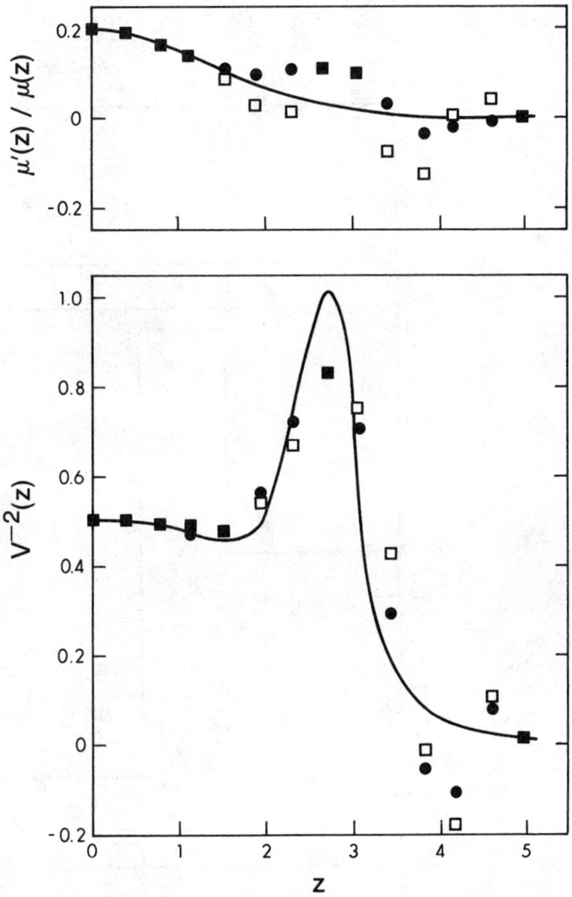

Figure 3. Localized variation in velocity function $V(z) = [0.707 \exp(-(z/4)^3) + 0.488 \exp(-(z-2.7)^2/0.3)]$ and $L(z) = 0.2 \exp(-(z/3)^2)$.

The elements of this determinant are related to the derivatives of G;

$$a_n = \frac{1}{n!}\left(\frac{d^nG(y,\omega)}{dy^n}\right)_{y=0} \quad . \tag{3.4}$$

These reciprocal derivatives are calculated at $y=0$, therefore if the data are given for a number of points about q_0, then the depth Δ can be related to q_0 by (2.30), i.e.

$$\Delta = (q_0^2 - \omega^2/c^2(d))^{-1/2} \quad . \tag{3.5}$$

Knowing Δ and the reciprocal derivatives we can calculate Ω_n's from eq. (2.29) and then find W_n and L_n from eqs. (2.21) and (2.22). In the numerical computation of various profiles we found that we have reasonably accurate results for the first six or seven values of $z=n\Delta$. To obtain better results and for larger values of z, we used the set of the found Ω_n's as the starting model for an iterative procedure of calculating W_n's and L_n's. For starting values of Ω_n for $n > 6$, we assumed that c(z) and L(z) tend to their asymptotic values at $z=d$ like

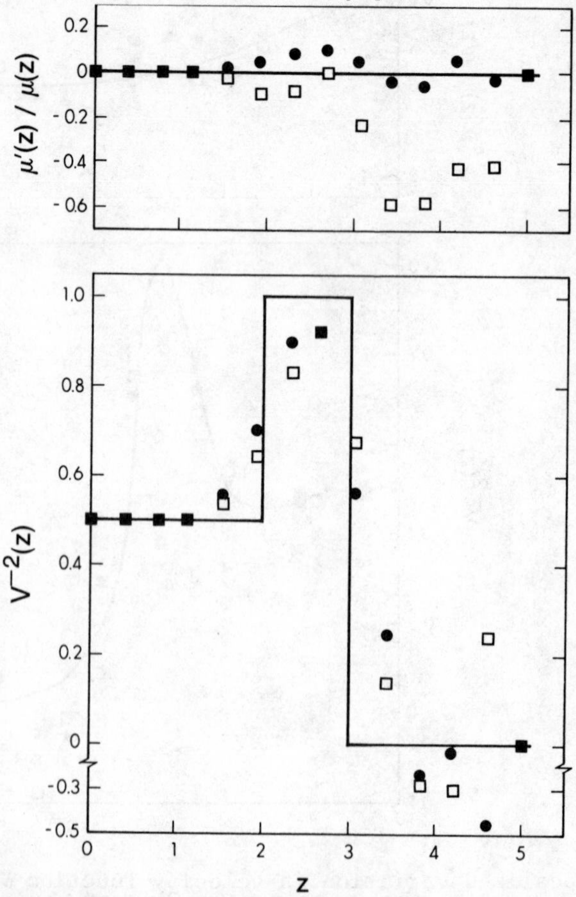

Figure 4. A discontinuous velocity profile with a thin low velocity zone in the deeper section.

$(z-d)^2$, and used this to calculate Ω_n for $n>6$. The resulting set of Ω_n's formed the starting model, which was subsequently used in the solution of simultaneous nonlinear equations routine, ZSCNT of IMSL to find a more accurate set of Ω_n's from eq. (2.24). It was found that this procedure can produce reasonably accurate results for values of n as high as 13, if a reliable starting model were used for Ω_n's. Therefore it seems that one needs to go through the steps outlined above, i.e. to solve eqs. (3.1)-(3.4) before using ZSCNT. But once this is done the solution of the nonlinear set of equations for Ω_n's (eq. (2.24)) reduces the effect of the errors made in the approximate evaluation of the reciprocal derivatives, and hence gives better results. Figs. 1-6 show the result of inversion for the model profiles used (drawn as solid lines). In these figures circles and squares show the results of inverting different types of input data, as was discussed in Section 2. Squares appearing in shear velocity (or L(z)) correspond to type a (or type b) information, whereas circles correspond to the type c data. The solid squares show the points where circles and squares overlap. For all these cases $N=13$, $d=5$, $2<q<3.5$

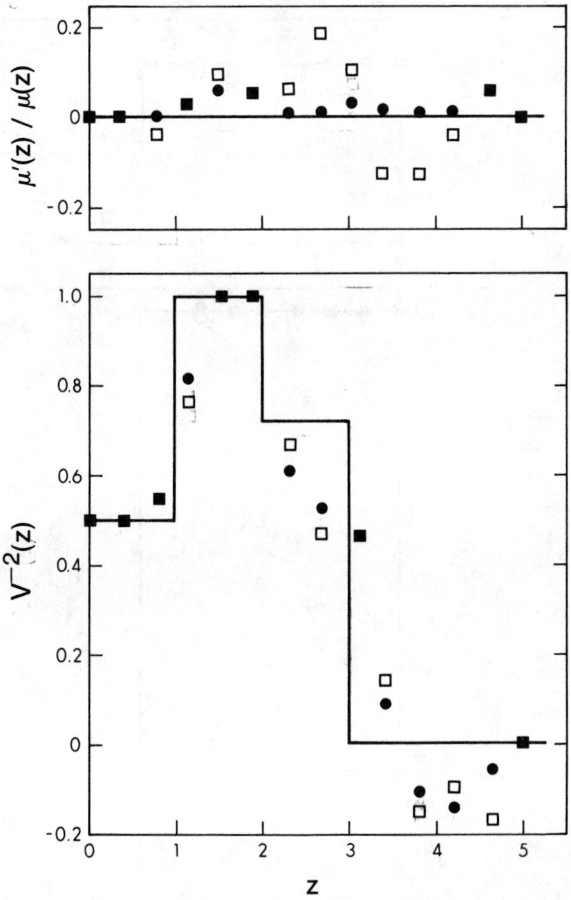

Figure 5. A discontinuous velocity profile with a low velocity zone between two high velocity zones.

and frequencies corresponding to $k_1 = 1.0$ and $k_2 = 1.1$ have been used. From the figures it is apparent that for smoothly varying profiles, the inversion specially for velocity function works very well, but as the changes in the profiles become more abrupt, the results to some extent depart from the actual profiles. In general the result of inversion for L(z) is not as reliable as that for the shear velocity, which indicates that round off errors play a more important role for L(z) than for velocity. For profiles with discontinuity the usual Gibbs' oscillation can also be noticed.

REFERENCES

[1] V.M. MARKUSHEVICH and E.L. REZNIKOV, Investigation of a Solid Symmetrical Medium by Standing SH-Waves on its Surface, Theoretical and Computational Geophysics (Moscow), 2 (1974), pp. 5-34.

[2] S. COEN, The inverse problem of the shear modulus and density profiles of a layered earth-torsional vibration data 22 (1981), pp. 2338-2341.

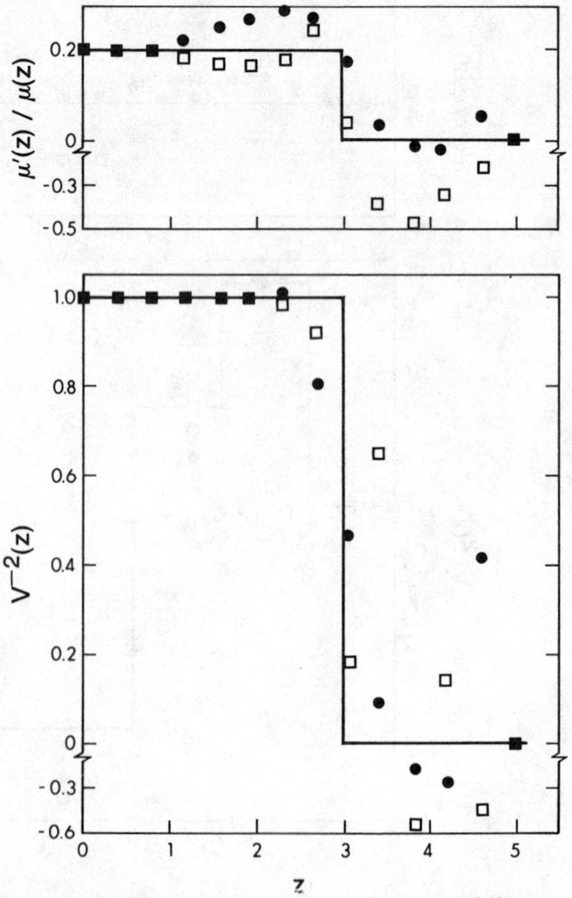

Figure 6. Results of inversion when both c(z) and L(z) are discontinuous.

[3] P. DALEY, V.M. MARKUSHEVICH and E.L. REZNIKOV, University of Alberta preprint (1983).

[4] W.B. JONES and W.J. THRON, Continued Fractions, Analytic Theory and Applications, in Encyclopedia of Mathematics and its Applications, Vol. 11 (Addison-Wesley Publishing Company, Reading, MA. 1980).

[5] L.M. MILNE-THOMSON, The Calculus of Finite Differences (Macmillan and Company, London, 1965) Chapter V.

[6] N.E. NÖRLUND, Differenzenrechnung (Springer-Verlag, Berlin, 1924) Chapter 15.

Appendix - Lagrangian Formulation of Torsional Vibration and Its Discrete Analogue. In replacing the differential equation (2.12) by the finite difference equation (2.15) some of the invariances or conservation properties of the solution may inadvertently be lost. Also eqs. (2.15) and (2.17) do not lend themselves to simple physical models. A Lagrangian formulation allows one to show that certain physical requirements such as the equality between action and reaction are satisfied, and at the same time it provides a simple mechanical model, i.e. a chain of massive particles connected by springs. We can find the Lagrangian for the function F(z) defined by

$$F(z,q,t) = \tilde{u}(z,q,t) \exp[\frac{1}{2} \int^{z} L(z)dz] \tag{A.1}$$

which satisfies the equation

$$\left(\frac{\partial^2}{\partial z^2} - q^2 - \frac{1}{4} L^2 - \frac{1}{2} L' - \frac{1}{c^2(z)} \frac{\partial^2}{\partial t^2}\right) F(z,q,t) = 0 . \tag{A.2}$$

This equation is derivable from the Lagrangian ;

$$\mathcal{L} = \int_0^d \frac{1}{2} dz \left(\frac{1}{c^2(z)} \left(\frac{\partial F}{\partial t}\right)^2 - \left(\frac{\partial F}{\partial z}\right)^2 - (q^2 + \lambda(z))F\right) \tag{A.3}$$

where

$$\lambda(z) = \frac{1}{4} L^2 + \frac{1}{2} L' \quad . \tag{A.4}$$

The integral in (A.3) can be replaced by the sum

$$\mathcal{L} = \sum_{j=1}^{N} \frac{1}{2} \Delta w_j \left(\frac{1}{c_j^2} \left(\frac{dF_j}{dt}\right)^2 - \frac{1}{\Delta^2} (F_j - \xi F_{j-1})^2 - (q^2 + \lambda_j) F_j^2\right) \tag{A.5}$$

where w_j is the weight function and ξ is a number. Both w_j and ξ are to be determined in such a way that (A.5) should approximate (A.3) at least to the order Δ^4. From the Lagrangian (A.5) we find the equations of motion to be

$$\frac{\Delta^2}{c_j^2}\frac{d^2F_j}{dt^2} = \xi\left(F_{j-1} + \frac{w_{j+1}}{w_j}F_{j+1}\right) - [1 + \Delta^2(q^2 + \lambda_j) + \frac{w_{j+1}}{w_j}\xi^2]F_j. \quad (A.6)$$

We solve this differential difference equation by taking

$$F_j(t) = F_j(0)e^{i\omega t} \quad (A.7)$$

which upon substitution in (A.6) yields

$$\xi\left(F_{j-1} + \frac{w_{j+1}}{w_j}F_{j+1}\right) - [1 + \Delta^2(q^2 + \lambda_j) + \frac{w_{j+1}}{w_j}\xi^2 - \frac{k^2}{V_j^2}]F_j = 0. \quad (A.8)$$

Defining Q^2 by

$$Q^2 = q^2 - \frac{k^2}{V_d^2} \quad (A.9)$$

we can write (A.8) as

$$\xi\left(F_{j-1} + \frac{w_{j+1}}{w_j}F_{j+1}\right) - [1 + \Delta^2 Q^2 + \Delta^2\lambda_j + \frac{w_{j+1}}{w_j}\xi^2 -$$

$$k^2\left(\frac{1}{V_j^2} - \frac{1}{V_d^2}\right)]F_j = 0 . \quad (A.10)$$

We choose the weight function w_j in such a way that the solution of (A.10) can be written as a T-fraction in q^2 (or Q^2), and at the same time approximates eq. (A.2) to the order Δ^4. To satisfy the first condition, we must remove the dependence of F_j on q^2 and make the coefficient of F_{j+1} dependent on q^2. This is simply achieved by letting w_j satisfy the relation

$$\frac{w_{j+1}}{w_j}\xi^2 = 1 - \Delta^2 Q^2$$

and choose ξ to be

$$\xi = (1 + \Delta Q)e^{-Q\Delta} . \quad (A.12)$$

Substituting these in (A.10) we find

$$\xi^{-1}(1 - \Delta^2 Q^2)F_{j+1} + \xi F_{j-1} - [2 + \Delta^2\lambda_j - k^2\left(\frac{1}{V_j^2} - \frac{1}{V_d^2}\right)]F_j = 0. \quad (A.13)$$

This equation can be transformed to an equation similar to (2.17) if we write

$$\mathcal{F}_j = F_j/\xi^j \quad (A.14)$$

and the resulting equation for $\mathfrak{F}_j$ differs from (2.17) by terms proportional to Δ^4. So either this transformed equation or (2.17) can be used for the purpose of inversion and both have the same degree of accuracy.

By rewriting (A.6) as

$$\frac{\Delta^2}{c_j^2}\frac{d^2F_j}{dt^2} = \xi\,\frac{W_{j+1}}{W_j}(F_{j+1} - F_j) + \xi(F_{j-1} - F_j) - \left[\Delta^2(q^2 + \lambda_j) + 1 + \frac{W_{j+1}}{W_j}(\xi^2 - \xi) - \xi\right] F_j \tag{A.15}$$

it becomes clear that the displacement of the oscillator j which is denoted by F_j is determined by three springs of spring constants $\xi\, W_{j+1}/W_j$, ξ and the quantity in the square bracket. All of these spring constants are positive for small Δ. Thus the discrete version of (A.3) can be described as a system of particles with masses proportional to Δ^2/c_j^2 and each coupled to a fixed point and to its nearest neighbours.

An Inverse Scattering Approach to the Pressure Transient Analysis of Petroleum Reservoirs

Weldon J. Wilson*

Abstract. The pressure transient analysis of petroleum reservoirs and groundwater aquifers is reviewed and then formulated as an inverse scattering problem. The inverse problem of determining the hydraulic conductivity profile of a reservoir from flow and pressure data is transformed into an equivalent inverse scattering problem for either the Schrodinger equation or the Zakharov-Shabat equation depending on whether one starts with the second-order or the first-order equations. The inverse scattering approach produces a direct inversion method that can complement the iterative modeling and parameter estimation techniques currently used throughout the industry.

1. Introduction. Pressure transients induced in petroleum reservoirs and groundwater aquifers have been used for many years as the standard method for the determination of the physical properties of these systems [1-4]. The essential idea of this technique is to create a disturbance in the system by flowing or pumping fluid from the reservoir at the well and monitoring the pressure at the well with time. From this flow versus time and pressure versus time data, which is collected at the well bore, one tries to infer various physical parameters of the reservoir in regions remote from the actual point of measurement.

The pressure transient data are generally interpreted by assuming a reservoir model with several free parameters which are in turn adjusted to the data either by curve fitting or analytic methods. The inverse problem posed by this approach is simply one of parameter estimation. In this technique one picks a model and makes initial guesses for its free parameters. The model is then used to calculate the pressure response. The calculated pressure response is compared to the actual observation, and if the two do not agree within a certain tolerance, a new guess for the parameters is made and the process is repeated.

*Department of Physics, University of Central Florida, Orlando, FL 3281

In cases where the spatial dependence of the model parameters is one dimensional (or reducible to an effective one dimensional problem), however, direct inversion without recourse to such iterative calculations becomes possible. The present paper is concerned with this alternative solution of the inverse problem which is essentially a modified version of the method of Gel'fand and Levitan [5] and Marchenko [6] for the solution of the inverse scattering problem.

2. Basic Equations. There are three simple geometries of importance in pressure transient testing which are used to model real reservoirs. The derivation of these models is developed in detail by Peaceman [7] and will only be summarized here.

a. One-Dimensional, Single Phase Flow. For linear flow the conservation of mass requires the continuity equation.

$$A \frac{\partial(\phi\rho)}{\partial t} + \frac{\partial(A\rho v)}{\partial x} = 0 \tag{1a}$$

where it is assumed that there are no sources and

$A = A(x)$ = Cross section area at x
$\phi = \phi(x)$ = Porosity of the reservoir rock
$v = v(x,t)$ = Fluid velocity
$\rho = \rho(x,t)$ = Fluid density.

This is coupled to the additional equation expressing D'arcy's Law for this geometry

$$v = -\frac{k}{\mu}\frac{\partial P}{\partial x} \tag{1b}$$

where

$P = P(x,t)$ = Fluid pressure
$k = k(x)$ = Permeability of the reservoir rock
$\mu = \mu$ = Fluid viscosity.

b. Two-Dimensional, Single-Phase Radial Flow. For a cylindrically symmetric reservoir and radial flow the mass conservation continuity equation becomes

$$h \frac{\partial(\phi\rho)}{\partial t} + \frac{1}{r}\frac{\partial(rh\rho v)}{\partial r} = 0 \tag{2a}$$

and D'arcy's Law becomes

$$v = -\frac{k}{\mu}\frac{\partial P}{\partial r} \tag{2b}$$

where now

$$r = (x^2 + y^2)^{1/2}$$

$v = v(r,t)$

$\phi = \phi(r)$

$\rho = \rho(r,t)$

$P = P(r,t)$

$k = k(r)$

and

$h = h(r)$ = Thickness of reservoir at a distance r from the well bore.

c. Three-Dimensional, Single-Phase Radial Flow. In this case the basic equations are

(3a) $$\frac{\partial(\phi\rho)}{\partial t} + \frac{1}{r^2}\frac{\partial(r^2\rho v)}{\partial r} = 0$$

and

(3b) $$v = -\frac{k}{\mu}\frac{\partial P}{\partial r}$$

where now

$r = (x^2 + y^2 + z^2)^{1/2}$

$v = v(r,t)$

$P = P(r,t)$

$\phi = \phi(r)$

$k = k(r)$.

d. General Equations. It is convenient to encompass all three of these special cases by introducing a geometrical factor α and a generic coordinate Z by

(4) $$Z = \begin{cases} x & \text{for } n = 1 \\ r = (x^2 + y^2)^{1/2} & \text{for } n = 2 \\ r = (x^2 + y^2 + z^2)^{1/2} & \text{for } n = 3 \end{cases}$$

and

(5) $$\alpha(Z) = \begin{cases} A(x) & \text{for } n = 1 \\ h(r) & \text{for } n = 2 \\ 1 & \text{for } n = 3 \end{cases}$$

for the n-dimension case. Doing this one can write equations (1), (2) or (3) in the general form

(6a) $$\alpha \frac{\partial(\phi\rho)}{\partial t} + \frac{1}{Z^{n-1}} \frac{\partial(Z^{n-1}\alpha\rho v)}{\partial Z} = 0$$

(6b) $$v = -\frac{k}{\mu}\frac{\partial P}{\partial Z}$$

where n = 1, 2, or 3 and

$$v = v(Z,t)$$

$$\rho = \rho(Z,t)$$

$$P = P(Z,t)$$

$$\alpha = \alpha(Z)$$

$$\phi = \phi(Z)$$

$$k = k(Z).$$

e. Constituitive Relations. In addition to specifying boundary conditions, it is necessary to specify porosity and fluid equations of states $\phi=\phi(P)$ and $\rho=\rho(P)$. It will be assumed here that these are given by

(7a) $$c_f = \frac{1}{\rho}\frac{d\rho}{dP} = \text{Fluid Compressibility}$$

and

(7b) $$c_r = \frac{1}{\phi}\frac{d\phi}{dP} = \text{Rock Compressibility}$$

where c_f and c_r are constant over the pressure range of interest. Using the relations (7), Eqs. (6) can be written in the form

(8a) $$\alpha\rho c \frac{\partial P}{\partial t} + \frac{1}{Z^{n-1}} \frac{\partial(Z^{n-1}\alpha\rho v)}{\partial Z} = 0$$

(8b) $$v = -\frac{k}{\mu}\frac{\partial P}{\partial Z}$$

where $c = c_r + c_f$. It will be convenient to define

(9) $$J(Z,t) = Z^{n-1}\alpha\rho v \equiv \text{Mass flow rate}$$

(10) $S = S(Z;P) = \alpha\rho c Z^{n-1} \equiv$ Storage coefficient

(11) $T = T(Z;P) = \alpha \dfrac{Z^{n-1}\rho k}{\mu} \equiv$ Transmissibility

so that Eqs. (8) can be written as

(12a) $$S \frac{\partial P}{\partial t} + \frac{\partial J}{\partial Z} = 0$$

(12b) $$J = - T \frac{\partial P}{\partial Z} .$$

In general, the system of equations (12) is nonlinear since S=S(Z;P) and T=T(Z;P); however, we shall restrict the discussion here to the case where S=S(Z) and T=T(Z) only. This is a standard linearization method for the flow problems encountered in the disciplines of reservoir engineering and groundwater hydrology [1, 2, 7].

d. Inverse Problem. The inverse problem of petroleum reservoirs or groundwater aquifers is to determine T(Z) and S(Z) given that the system evolves according to

(13a) $$S \frac{\partial P}{\partial t} + \frac{\partial J}{\partial Z} = 0$$

(13b) $$J = - T \frac{\partial P}{\partial Z}$$

and that at the well bore (Z=0)

(14a) $$P(Z=0,t) = f_1(t)$$

(14b) $$J(Z=0,t) = f_2(t)$$

are known for all time t with

(15a) $$P(Z\to\infty,t) = P_i$$

(15b) $$P(Z,t=0) = P_i$$

where P_i is the initial pressure of the reservoir. There is no loss of generality if the pressure P is gauged so that P_i=0 and this will be assumed to have been done. In addition, the storage and transmissibility are know at the well bore

(16a) $$T(Z=0) = T_o$$

(16b) $$S(Z=0) = S_o .$$

Since the system described by Eqs. (13) is diffusive, one thinks usually of the known flow $J(Z=0,t)$ producing the change in pressure $P(Z=0,t)$ that is observed. In any event, the two are causally related. The response of the reservoir is best measured by defining the response function

$$R(\omega) \equiv -\frac{P(Z=0,\omega)}{J(Z=0,\omega)} = \frac{P(0,\omega)}{T_o P_Z(0,\omega)} \tag{17}$$

where $P(Z=0,\omega)$ and $J(Z=0,\omega)$ are the time Fourier transforms of $P(Z=0,t)$ and $J(Z=0,t)$ respectively. This response function will effectively become the reflection amplitude at $Z=0$ in the reformulation of this problem into an equivalent scattering problem.

3. "Diffusion Time" Coordinates. To facilitate the analogy with the inverse seismic problem the "diffusion time" coordinate ξ is introduced by the change of variable

$$d\xi = [S(Z)/T(Z)]^{1/2}\, dZ \tag{18}$$

or

$$\xi = \xi(Z) = \int_{Z'=0}^{Z'=Z} [S(Z')/T(Z')]^{1/2}\, dZ' \tag{19}$$

Doing this Eqs. (13) become

$$\frac{\partial P}{\partial t} + \eta^{-2} \frac{\partial J}{\partial \xi} = 0 \tag{20a}$$

$$J = -\eta^2 \frac{\partial P}{\partial \xi} \tag{20b}$$

where

$$\eta^2 \equiv [S(\xi)\; T(\xi)]^{1/2}. \tag{21}$$

The inversion subsequently described will then recover η as a function of the "diffusion time" coordinate ξ.

4. Inverse Scattering Formulation for the Second-Order Equation. The field $J(\xi,t)$ may be eliminated from the Eqs. (20) giving the equivalent second order equation for $P(\xi,t)$

$$\eta^{-2} \frac{\partial}{\partial \xi}\left(\eta^2 \frac{\partial P}{\partial \xi}\right) = \frac{\partial P}{\partial t}. \tag{22}$$

If we change the dependent variable with a Liouville transformation

$$\psi(\xi,t) \equiv \eta(\xi)\; P(\xi,t), \tag{23}$$

the second order equation (22) becomes

$$\psi_{\xi\xi} - \frac{\eta_{\xi\xi}}{\eta}\psi = \frac{\partial\psi}{\partial t} \quad (24)$$

where $\frac{\partial f}{\partial \xi} \equiv f_\xi$. Taking the Fourier transform with respect to time reduces Eq. (24) to the time-independent Schrodinger equation in one dimension

$$\tilde{\psi}_{\xi\xi} - \frac{\eta_{\xi\xi}}{\eta}\tilde{\psi} = k^2\tilde{\psi} \quad (25)$$

where

$$\tilde{\psi}(\xi,\omega) \equiv \int_{-\infty}^{\infty} e^{-i\omega t}\psi(\xi,t)\,dt. \quad (26)$$

and $k^2 = i\omega$. The problem has now been transformed into an effective inverse scattering problem on the half-line $\xi>0$ with Eq. (25) as the Schrodinger equation to be inverted for the potential

$$V(\xi) = \frac{\eta_{\xi\xi}}{\eta}. \quad (27)$$

The response function (17) obtained from the $\xi = 0$ values of P and J can be transformed to ξ the corresponding ψ quantity using (23).

This inverse problem has been extensively studied and will not be disucssed here. The reader is referred to Chadan and Sabatier [8] and the references therein for a detailed exposition of the methods for obtaining $V(\xi)$. A similar system is also encountered in the geomagnetic induction inverse problem which is solved by P. Wiedelt [9] and Coen [10]. The methods used by those two authors would work equally well here.

5. Inverse Scattering Formulation for the First-Order Equations. While the pressure transient problem can be reformulated as an inverse scattering problem on the half-line using the second-order equation, there are advantages to using the first-order system of equations (20). The analogous case in seismic inversion has been discussed at length by Howard [11]. The differentiability requirements are relaxed somewhat by direct inversion of the first order equations. Returning to Eqs. (20), they can be rewritten after Fourier transforming as

$$\tilde{J}_\xi = -i\omega\eta^2\tilde{P} \quad (28a)$$

$$\tilde{P}_\xi = -\eta^{-2}\tilde{J} \quad (28b)$$

where again

$$\tilde{J}(\xi,\omega) = \int_{-\infty}^{\infty} e^{-i\omega t} J(\xi,t)\,dt$$

and

$$\tilde{P}(\xi,\omega) = \int_{-\infty}^{\infty} e^{-i\omega t} P(\xi,t)\, dt.$$

The system (28) can be written compactly in matrix form as

$$\tilde{\psi}_\xi = -k\underline{A}\tilde{\psi} \tag{29}$$

where $\tilde{\psi}$ is now a two component field

$$\tilde{\psi} = \begin{vmatrix} \tilde{\psi}_1 \\ \tilde{\psi}_2 \end{vmatrix}, \quad \tilde{\psi}_1 = \tilde{J}, \quad \tilde{\psi}_2 = k\tilde{P} \tag{30}$$

and $\underline{A}$ is a two by two matrix

$$\underline{A} = \begin{vmatrix} 0 & \eta^2 \\ \eta^{-2} & 0 \end{vmatrix} \tag{31}$$

and as before $k^2 = i\omega$.

The Eq. (29) can be put into Zakharov-Shabat form by a change of dependent variable with the matrix Liouville transformation:

$$\tilde{\psi} = \underline{M}(\xi)\psi, \quad \psi = M^{-1}(\xi)\,\tilde{\psi} \tag{32}$$

where

$$\underline{M}(\xi) = \begin{vmatrix} \eta & \eta \\ -\eta^{-1} & \eta^{-1} \end{vmatrix}, \quad \underline{M}^{-1}(\xi) = \frac{1}{2}\begin{vmatrix} \eta^{-1} & -\eta \\ \eta^{-1} & \eta \end{vmatrix}. \tag{33}$$

Making this transformation, (29) becomes

$$\psi_\xi + \sigma_x \frac{\eta_\xi}{\eta}\psi = k\,\sigma_z\,\psi \tag{34}$$

where σ_x and σ_z are the usual Pauli matrices

$$\sigma_x = \begin{vmatrix} 0 & 1 \\ 1 & 0 \end{vmatrix}, \quad \sigma_z = \begin{vmatrix} 1 & 0 \\ 0 & -1 \end{vmatrix}.$$

Multiplication of equation (34) by σ_z gives the standard Zakharov-Shabat form

$$(35) \qquad \hat{L}\psi = k\psi$$

where

$$(36) \qquad \hat{L} = \begin{vmatrix} \frac{\partial}{\partial \xi} & V(\xi) \\ -V(\xi) & -\frac{\partial}{\partial \xi} \end{vmatrix}, \quad V(\xi) = \frac{\eta_\xi}{\eta}.$$

The inverse scattering problem for the Zakharov-Shabat equation (35) has been extensively studied [12-15] and may be inverted for the potential $V(\xi)$.

The advantage of the first-order formulation lies in the fact that once $V(\xi)$ has been determined,

$$(37) \qquad \frac{\eta_\xi}{\eta} = V(\xi)$$

may be immdiately integrated to obtain

$$\eta(\xi) = \eta_o \exp[\int_o^\xi V(\xi')d\xi'].$$

The relation corresponding to (37) in the second order formulation is Eq. (27) or upon re-arranging

$$\eta_{\xi\xi} + V(\xi)\,\eta = 0.$$

The integration of this equation to obtain $\eta(\xi)$ is non-trivial.

6. Summary and Conclusions. It has been shown that the inverse problem arising in the pressure transient analysis of petroleum reservoirs or groundwater aquifers may be transformed and reformulated as an inverse scattering problem. Either the second order or the first order equations describing the phenomena may be used. In the first case the inverse problem is equivalent to the inverse scattering problem for the Schrodinger equation; in the second case it is equivalent to the inverse scattering problem for the Zakharov-Shabat equation. Both of these inverse scattering problems have been extensively studied and the methods developed for their inversion can be used to advantage in solving the pressure transient inverse problem.

Working directly with the first order equations rather than the second-order equation has the advantage of weakening the differentiability requirements. In either case the inversion gives less information than originally sought in that one obtains $\eta = (ST)^{1/2}$ as a function of diffusion time ξ rather than S and T as functions of distance.

The methods developed in this paper actually apply to a broad class of diffusion systems since the basic system of Eqs. (20) is representative of a generic diffusion problem in inhomogeneous media. Similar methods then could be applied in any diffusion dominated physical system. In particular the discussion here applies equally to thermal conductivity, geomagnetic induction, concentration-diffusion, neutron diffusion, and many other physical problems governed by a parabolic system such as Eqs. (20).

REFERENCES

[1] C. S. Matthews and D. G. Russell, Pressure Buildup and Flow Tests in Wells, SPE Monograph No. 1, Society of Petroleum Engineers, Dallas, 1967.

[2] R. C. Earlougher, Jr., Advances in Well Test Analysis, SPE Monograph No. 5, Society of Petroleum Engineers, Dallas, 1976.

[3] C. C. Kisiel and L. Duckstein, Ground-Water Models, In A. K. Biswas, Systems Approach to Water Management, McGraw-Hill, New York, 1976, pp. 80-155.

[4] P. A. Domenico, Concepts and Models in Groundwater Hydrology, McGraw-Hill, New York, 1972.

[5] I. M. Gel′fand and B. M. Levitan, On the Determination of a Differential Equation by its Spectral Function, Am. Math. Soc. Transl., 2 (1955), pp. 253-304.

[6] Z. S. Agranovich and V. A. Marchenko, The Inverse Scattering Problem, Gordon and Breach, New York, 1963.

[7] D. W. Peaceman, Fundamentals of Numerical Reservoir Simulation, Elsevier, Amsterdam, 1977, pp. 1-14.

[8] K. Chadan and P. C. Sabatier, Inverse Problems in Quantum Scattering Theory, Springer-Verlag, New York, 1977.

[9] P. Weidelt, The Inverse Problem of Geomagnetic Induction, J. Geophys., Band 38 (1972), pp. 257-289.

[10] S. Coen and M. W. Yu, The Inverse Problem of the Direct Current Conductivity Profile of a Layered Earth, Geophys. 46 (1981), pp. 1702-1713.

[11] M. S. Howard, Inverse Scattering for a Layered Acoustic Medium Using the First-Order Equations of Motion, Geophys. 40 (1983), pp. 163-170.

[12] H. M. deCastro and W. F. Wreszinski, Inverse Scattering Theory for Systems of the Zakharov-Shabat Type, J. Math. Phys. 24 (1983), pp. 1502-1508.

[13] G. Eilenberger, Solitons: Mathematical Methods for Physicists, Springer-Verlag, Berlin, 1981, pp. 58-74.

[14] G. L. Lamb, Jr. Elements of Soliton Theory, Wiley, New York, 1980, pp. 99-107.

[15] R. K. Dodd, J. C. Eilbeck, J. D. Gibbon, and H. C. Morris, Solitons and Nonlinear Wave Equations, Academic, London, 1982, pp. 269-387.

Computational Methods for Estimation of Parameters in Hyperbolic Systems

H. T. Banks,* K. Ito† and K. A. Murphy*

Abstract. We discuss approximation techniques for estimating spatially varying coefficients and unknown boundary parameters in second order hyperbolic systems. Methods for state approximation (cubic splines, tau-Legendre) and approximation of function space parameters (interpolatory splines) are outlined and numerical findings for use of the resulting schemes in model "1-D seismic inversion" problems are summarized.

1. Introduction. We discuss here some of our continuing efforts on the development of computational techniques for estimation or "identification" of parameters in second order hyperbolic systems (e.g., the acoustic wave equation). The parameters of interest include boundary parameters such as coefficients of elasticity and source terms in elastic boundary conditions as well as spatially varying moduli of elasticity in the partial differential equation itself. Among the features of our approach are the following: We do not require an impulse or delta function for the source term; indeed the source term need not even be parameterized a priori (although it is in the numerical examples presented below). Furthermore, the elastic moduli in the system equations can be estimated with or without a priori parameterization (i.e., assumption of a specific form or shape class). Our ideas are, in principle, applicable to vector systems in appropriately defined multidimensional domains.

We combine results from the theory of dissipative operators, linear semigroups, approximation theory (splines, spectral methods), and

*Division of Applied Mathematics, Brown University, Providence, RI and Department of Mathematics, Southern Methodist University, Dallas, TX. Part of this research was carried out while the first author was a visitor at the Institute for Computer Applications in Science and Engineering (ICASE), NASA Langley Research Center, Hampton, VA, which is operated under NASA contracts NAS1-15810 and NAS1-16394. This research was also supported in part by NSF grant MCS-8205335, by AFOSR contract 81-0198, and ARO contract ARO-DAAG-29-79-C-0161.
†Institute for Computer Applications in Science and Engineering, NASA Langley Research Center, Hampton, VA. This research was supported in part by NASA under contracts NAS1-17070 and NAS1-17130.

optimization techniques in our attempts to develop theoretically sound and numerically attractive procedures. While our long term goals include development of efficient methods for use in 2-D and 3-D problems such as those that arise in "surface seismic" and "bore hole" inversion (we have made progress in this direction), we illustrate some of our ideas here with a scalar "model problem" in 1-D. The system in this model problem is given by

$$(1) \quad \rho(x)u_{tt} = \frac{\partial}{\partial x}\left(E(x)\frac{\partial u}{\partial x}\right), \qquad 0 \le x \le 1, \quad t > 0$$

$$(2) \quad u_x(t,0) + k_1 u(t,0) = S(t,\tilde{q}),$$

$$(3) \quad u_t(t,1) + k_2 u_x(t,1) = 0,$$

$$(4) \quad u(0,x) = 0, \quad u_t(0,x) = 0.$$

Here ρ is the medium mass density and E is an elastic modulus in (1) while the boundary condition (2) is an elastic surface $(x=0)$ condition involving a restoring force parameter k_1 as well as a parameter $(\tilde{q})$ dependent source term S. This source term is assumed to be the result of a perturbing shock to the medium which occurs on the surface at some distance from the point of observation. The medium is initially at rest (initial conditions (4)) and it is assumed that no waves are reflected at a finite lower boundary $(x=1)$; this is given by the absorbing boundary condition (3)--(this condition can be obtained formally by factoring the equation (1) at $x=1$ and taking $k_2 = \sqrt{E(1)/\rho(1)}$). We make the physically motivated assumptions $k_1 < 0$, $k_2 > 0$ throughout.

Our model problem consists of using observations of the system (1) - (4) to estimate the parameters $q = (\rho, E, k_1, k_2, \tilde{q})$. More precisely we consider the mathematical problem of minimizing the fit-to-data criterion

$$(5) \quad J(q) = \sum_{i,j} |u(t_i,x_j;q) - \hat{y}_{ij}|^2$$

over a given admissible parameter set Q. Here we assume we have observations $\hat{y}_{ij}$ for $u(t_i,x_j)$--(the "bore hole" problem)--or for $u(t_i,0)$--(the "surface seismic" problem), where u is the solution to (1) - (4) corresponding to q.

It is convenient for our theoretical discussions to reformulate this problem in terms of an abstract evolution equation in a Hilbert space.

To do this we first assume that the system (1) - (4) has been transformed to a system with homogeneous boundary conditions

$$\rho v_{tt} = \frac{\partial}{\partial x}\left(E \frac{\partial v}{\partial x}\right) + g(t,x,q)$$

$$(6) \quad \begin{aligned} &v_x(t,0) + k_1 v(t,0) = 0 \\ &v_t(t,1) + k_2 v_x(t,1) = 0 \end{aligned}$$

$$v(0,x) = \phi(x,q), \ v_t(0,x) = \psi(x,q) .$$

This can be done in a straightforward fashion (see [11]).

As our state space we choose $Z = H^1(0,1) \times H^0(0,1)$ with parameter dependent inner product

$$\langle z,w\rangle_q = \int_0^1 E z_1' w_1' dx - E(0)k_1 z_1(0) w_1(0) + \int_0^1 \rho z_2 w_2 dx ,$$

for $z = (z_1,z_2)$, $w = (w_1,w_2)$ in Z. Under reasonable assumptions on ρ, E and k_1, this yields a Hilbert space $Z = Z(q)$ with topology equivalent to the usual $H^1 \times H^0$ topology. The transformed system (6) can then be written in abstract form as (we don't distinguish between a vector and its transpose)

$$(7) \quad \begin{aligned} &\dot{z}(t) = A(q)z(t) + G(t,q) \\ &z(0) = \Phi(q) \end{aligned}$$

where $z = (v,v_t)$, $\Phi = (\phi,\psi)$, $G = (0,g)$, and the operator A(q) defined on $\text{dom}(A(q)) = \{z \in H^2 \times H^1 \mid z_1'(0) + k_1 z_1(0) = 0,\ z_2(1) + k_2 z_1'(1) = 0\}$ is given by

$$A(q) = \begin{pmatrix} 0 & 1 \\ \frac{1}{\rho}\frac{\partial}{\partial x}\left(E \frac{\partial}{\partial x}\right) & 0 \end{pmatrix} .$$

It can then be shown that under boundedness assumptions on Q, there exists a constant ω independent of q in Q such that $A(q) - \omega I$ is dissipative in Z (i.e., $\langle A(q)z,z\rangle \leq \omega\langle z,z\rangle$). Furthermore A(q) generates a strongly continuous semigroup $S(t;q)$, $t \geq 0$, that is the family of solution operators for (7).

This framework provides a convenient setting for discussion of semidiscrete approximation schemes (and their convergence properties) for solving the problem of minimizing (5) over Q. In the case under consideration here both the state space for (1) - (4) and the parameter set Q are infinite dimensional. We first turn to a description of state approximation ideas that we have employed.

Abstractly, one approximates (7)--at least in its state variable--by choosing a sequence of finite dimensional subspaces Z^N, $N = 1,2,\dots$, of the state space Z. Letting P^N be the projection of Z onto Z^N and $A^N : Z^N \to Z^N$ be a family of approximating operators for A, one can define the sequence of approximating systems in Z^N by

$$(8)\qquad \begin{aligned} \dot{z}^N(t) &= A^N(q)z^N(t) + P^N G(t,q) \\ z^N(0) &= P^N \Phi \end{aligned}$$

and the corresponding fit-to-data criterion

$$(9)\qquad J^N(q) = \sum_{i,j} |z_1^N(t_i)(x_j) - \hat{y}_{ij}|^2 .$$

The problem of minimizing J^N over Q is then a finite dimensional state problem which can in some cases (e.g., when the functional parameters are assumed in parameteric form) be readily solved for approximate parameters $\bar{q}^N$, $N = 1,2,\dots$. In this situation one then desires to argue that the sequence $\{\bar{q}^N\}$ (or some subsequence) converges to a parameter q^* in Q that provides a minimum for (5). However, in other cases where the parameter functions (such as ρ and E in (1)) are not assumed to possess a priori finite dimensional parameterizations, the problems involving (8), (9) still entail optimizations over an infinite dimensional set and thus a parameter approximation scheme must further be introduced before the approximating problems are easily solved. We defer discussion of this aspect of our methods until section 4 below. Instead we first discuss two state approximation schemes (cubic spline and tau-Legendre) that we have used with some success.

2. Cubic spline state approximations. These methods are founded on ideas given in [1],[3],[9] where cubic B-splines $\hat{B}_j^N$ (see [13] for general concepts and discussions) are used to generate basis elements for subspaces Z^N in which the elements satisfy the boundary conditions inherent in the problem. For the problems under consideration in this note, this results in parameter dependent basis elements $B_j^N = B_j^N(q)$. Thus the dependence of $Z^N = Z^N(q)$ on q is not only because of the parameter dependent inner product but also through the explicit

dependence of the basis elements B_j^N on the parameters. This aspect leads to nontrivial technical difficulties (from both a theoretical and a numerical viewpoint) in extending the ideas of [3]. One can however overcome these difficulties to obtain a theoretically sound and computationally feasible scheme (see [8], [11] for more detailed discussions).

To give a brief idea of the theoretical aspects of this method, we first observe that the above considerations lead to subspaces $Z^N = Z^N(q)$ in the context of the Galerkin approach of [3], [7]. One then desires to define Galerkin approximations $A^N = A^N(q^N) = P^N(q^N)A(q^N)P^N(q^N)$ associated with a given sequence of parameter estimates $\{q^N\}$. Here $P^N(q)$ is the orthogonal projection of $Z(q)$ onto $Z^N(q)$. To establish a state convergence theory for (8), it suffices to argue stability and consistency for the schemes (see [3], [7]). Stability follows readily from the uniform dissipativeness of the operators $A(q) : \langle A^N(q)z,z\rangle = \langle P^N(q)A(q)P^N(q)z,z\rangle = \langle A(q)P^N(q)z,P^N(q)z\rangle \leq \omega\langle P^N(q)z,P^N(q)z\rangle \leq \omega\langle z,z\rangle$. Consistency is somewhat more delicate since one wishes to argue that for $q^N \to q^*$ in Q one has $A^N(q^N)z \to A(q^*)z$. More generally in the process of discussing consistency and state convergence one must deal with statements involving the convergence of elements z^N in $Z^N(q^N)$--which satisfy boundary conditions involving q^N--to elements z^* in $\mathrm{dom}(A(q^*))$. Hence one must construct some device to express convergence of the boundary condition parameters as well as that of the parameters defined directly in the operators $A^N(q^N)$. With care this can be done and one can employ the Trotter-Kato approximation theorem from linear semigroup theory [12] along with estimates from spline approximation theory [13] to establish consistency and state convergence (see [8], [11] for details).

These spline based schemes have proven quite satisfactory in numerical computations with test examples as we shall see in the numerical section below.

3. <u>Tau-Legendre state approximations</u>. The tau method (due to Lanczos) is a special case (see p. 11 of [10]) of the spectral methods discussed in [10] and involves use of eigenfunctions that are in general <u>not</u> related to the natural modes of the system being approximated. As outlined above, one again rewrites the system (6) as an abstract system in the state space $Z = Z(q)$ defined in section 1. The system (7) is written in the form

$$\begin{aligned} \dot{z}(t) &= L(q)z(t) + G(t,q) \\ z(0) &= \Phi(q) \end{aligned} \tag{10}$$

(11) $\mathcal{B}(q)z(t) = 0$,

where L(q) is the same as the operator A(q) in (7) except that we do not include the boundary conditions in defining the domain of L(q); i.e., $\text{dom}(L(q)) = H^2 \times H^1$. Instead the boundary operations are imbedded in an operator $\mathcal{B}$ and we impose the side conditions (11).

The approximating subspaces Z^N are then defined in terms of an orthonormal family that is complete in $H^0(0,1)$. Members in this family are not required to individually satisfy the boundary conditions; these are imposed on the approximations to the solution of (10), (11) by requiring that the approximations satisfy exactly the conditions (11). To be more specific, suppose we begin with N+1 elements $\{\phi_1,\ldots,\phi_{N+1}\}$ (e.g., Legendre functions) to generate the appropriate subspaces $Z^N(q)$ of Z(q)--(the $Z^N(q)$ have dimension $2N = (N+1) + (N-1)$ in this case--the analogous cubic spline approximating subspaces have dimension $2N+3$). Then we assume that the first components of solutions $z = (v, v_t)$ of (10)--i.e., of (6)--are approximated by $v^N(t,x) = \sum_{j=1}^{N+1} w_j(t)\phi_j(x)$ where the first N - 1 coefficients w_j are determined by imposing the equation (10) and the remaining coefficients are determined by imposing the boundary conditions (11).

We observe that the tau method is not a Galerkin procedure. It also differs from the cubic spline method described above in that the approximating subspaces satisfy $Z^N \subset Z^{N+K}$, $K > 0$.

Our efforts have been devoted to the use of the tau-Legendre method in the model problem of section 1. In this case, we chose $\phi_j(x) = P_{j-1}(2x-1)$, $0 \leq x \leq 1$, $j = 1,2,\ldots,N+1$, where P_j is the Legendre polynomial of degree j. For a convergence analysis, one can employ the same Hilbert space framework described in discussing the cubic spline schemes. In this operator formulation one again establishes convergence via demonstrating stability and consistency. The arguments involve dissipative estimates, the Gronwall inequality, and approximation properties of Legendre polynomials.

One interesting (and potentially highly advantageous) aspect of the tau-Legendre methods involves their use in layered media problems (e.g., see Example 4 below) where the coefficients ρ, E in (1) possess discontinuities. In this case one can include (in addition to the boundary conditions) in the conditions (11) the continuity conditions $v^N(t,x_j^-) = v^N(t,x_j^+)$--on displacement--and $E(x_j^-)v_x^N(t,x_j^-) = E(x_j^+)v_x^N(t,x_j^+)$--on stress--at interfaces x_j in the medium. This could lead to methods that are computationally superior to methods in which these interface continuity conditions are imposed directly on the basis elements for Z^N.

4. Parameter approximations. As we have noted above, the problem of minimizing J^N of (9) over Q subject to the state approximation equations (8) is still a difficult infinite dimensional optimization problem in cases where Q has nonparameterized function space components (e.g., in situations where we estimate ρ and/or E in (1) choosing from some infinite dimensional function classes). In such situations it is useful to introduce a family of finite dimensional parameter sets Q^M that approximate, in some sense, the original parameter set Q--i.e., "$Q^M \to Q$" as $M \to \infty$. We may then consider the problem of minimizing J^N of (9) over Q^M, which is finite dimensional in both the states and parameters and may be easily solved for judicious choices of Q^M, producing estimates $\bar{q}_M^N$.

We have, with some success, used such double approximation procedures to estimate functional coefficients in parabolic transport equations [4], [5], [6] and in higher order equations of elasticity [2]. In these efforts we employed approximating sets Q^M consisting of either linear or cubic interpolatory splines. Under reasonable assumptions on Q and on the approximation properties of Q^M (e.g., see [2], [4], [6] where theoretical results are also given for the systems mentioned above), one can prove a double limit convergence result: Given any sequence of estimates $\{\bar{q}_M^N\}$ as defined above, there exists a subsequential limit $q^* = \lim \bar{q}_{M_j}^{N_k}$ in Q that provides a minimum for J of (5) over Q.

In the next section we shall present a sample of some of our numerical results using such procedures.

5. Numerical examples. We present here a summary of some of our numerical findings for the methods described above when used with the model problem involving (1) - (5). The estimation schemes were tested on examples in the following manner. First, known "true" values (denoted by q^* in the tables below) of the parameters to be estimated were chosen and a numerical method independent of the one being tested was used to solve the forward problem for a solution $u = u(q^*)$. Values of this numerical solution were used for "observations" or data for the inverse algorithm. The minimization problems were solved iteratively (with "start-up" or initial guess q^0 listed in each example) employing an IMSL version (ZXSSQ) of the Levenberg-Marquardt algorithm. The ordinary differential equations for the approximate states were

solved using either DVERK or DGEAR in the IMSL packages. The test calculations were carried out on an IBM 370 at Brown University, a CDC 6600 at Southern Methodist University, and CDC Cyber 170 at NASA Langley Research Center. In the first two examples we compare the cubic spline state approximation scheme with the one based on tau-Legendre state approximations. In the third example we give a sample of our findings on a problem where the double approximation ideas of section 4 were used while in the last example we detail results for a multilayered media problem.

Example 1. In this example we considered (1)-(4) with $E/\rho = q_1$ constant, source $S(t,\tilde{q}) = q_2(1-e^{-5t})e^{q_3 t}$ and k_1, k_2 to be estimated. The "true" values q^*, start-up values q^0, along with findings for the cubic spline state approximations and the tau-Legendre state schemes are given below in tabular form. Observations included values $u(t_i,x_j;q^*)$ for t_i values .5, 1 and 1.5, x_j values 0, .5, and 1. The residual $(J^N(\bar{q}^N))$ for the converged parameter values along with CPU time in seconds is listed for each level (N) of state approximation.

	$\bar{q}_1^N$	$\bar{q}_2^N$	$\bar{q}_3^N$	$\bar{k}_1^N$	$\bar{k}_2^N$	$J^N(\bar{q}^N)$	CPU
CUBIC SPLINES							
N = 4	3.014	2.001	-1.084	-1.883	.992	$.6\text{x}10^{-5}$	124
N = 8	2.992	2.017	- .958	-2.082	.999	$.17\text{x}10^{-5}$	108
TAU-LEGENDRE							
N = 4	2.940	2.098	-1.026	-2.034	.994	$.7\text{x}10^{-3}$	31
N = 8	3.017	1.957	-1.001	-1.979	1.008	$.6\text{x}10^{-5}$	40
TRUE VALUES (q^*)	3.0	2.0	-1.0	-2.0	1.0		
START UP (q^0)	2.0	1.5	- .5	-1.0	2.0		

Example 2. We considered the transformed system (6) with $\rho = 1$, $g = 0$, parameterized modulus $E(x) = 1.5 + \frac{1}{\pi}\,\text{Arctan}\,(q_1(x - q_2))$ and initial data $\phi(x) = e^x$, $\psi(x) = -3e^x$. Observations at values $t_i = .16, .33, .5, .66, .83, 1$ and $x_j = 0, .5, 1$ were used. The following converged values were obtained.

	$\bar{q}_1^N$	$\bar{q}_2^N$	$\bar{k}_1^N$	$\bar{k}_2^N$	$J^N(\bar{q}^N)$	CPU
CUBIC SPLINES						
N = 4	2.964	.487	-.990	3.006	$.8\text{x}10^{-4}$	60
N = 8	3.051	.501	-.999	2.996	$.28\text{x}10^{-5}$	54
N = 16	3.012	.5002	-.9999	2.999	$.19\text{x}10^{-6}$	146
TAU LEGENDRE						
N = 4	3.191	.516	-1.028	3.015	$.12\text{x}10^{-2}$	14
N = 8	2.942	.496	-1.001	2.997	$.8\text{x}10^{-4}$	57
N = 16	2.991	.4992	- .9998	2.999	$.15\text{x}10^{-5}$	520
TRUE VALUES (q^*)	3.0	.5	-1.0	3.0		
START UP (q^0)	5.0	1.0	-2.0	2.0		

<u>Example 3.</u> We considered the system (6) with $\rho = 1$, $g = 0$, $\phi(x) = e^x$, $\psi(x) = -3e^x$ and parameters to be estimated $E^*(x) = 1.5 + \tanh(6(x-.5))$, $k_1^* = -1.0$, $k_2^* = 3.0$. We did not assume an a priori parameterization for E, but used linear interpolatory splines for the parameter approximation procedure as described in section 4. Cubic spline state approximations were used. Observations were taken at the same t_i, x_j as in Example 2. The initial guesses were $E^0(x) = 1.0$ (a constant function), $k_1^0 = -2.0$, $k_2^0 = 2.0$. Graphs for $\bar{E}_M^N$ are given in the figures below for N = 4 (2N + 3 = 11 cubic elements in the basis for Z^N) and N = 16 with parameter approximations corresponding to M = 3 (M + 1 = 4 linear elements to approximate E). For N = 4, the results obtained were $\bar{k}_1^4 = -1.054$, $\bar{k}_2^4 = 3.357$, $J^4(\bar{q}^4) = .25\text{x}10^{-2}$, $|E^* - \bar{E}_3^4| = .81\text{x}10^{-1}$, CPU = 38 sec., while for N = 16 the results were $\bar{k}_1^{16} = -1.100$, $\bar{k}_2^{16} = 3.070$, $J^{16}(\bar{q}^{16}) = .47\text{x}10^{-4}$, $|E^* - \bar{E}_3^{16}| = .29\text{x}10^{-1}$, CPU = 118 sec.

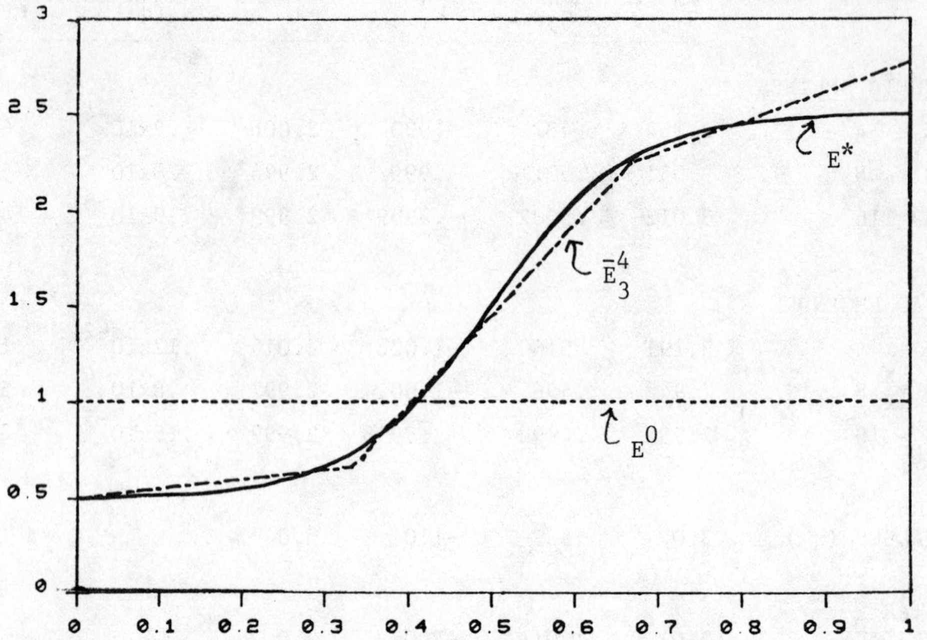
3
2.5
2
1.5
1
0.5
0
0
0.1
0.2
0.3
0.4
0.5
0.6
0.7
0.8
0.9
1
E*
$\bar{E}_3^4$
E^0

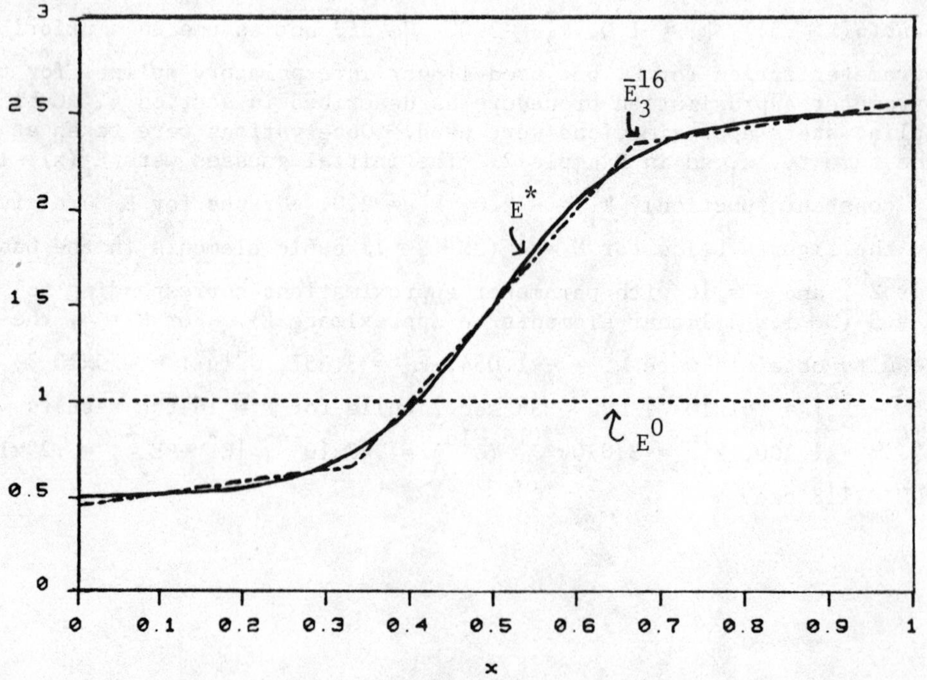
3
2.5
2
1.5
1
0.5
0
0
0.1
0.2
0.3
0.4
0.5
0.6
0.7
0.8
0.9
1
x
$\bar{E}_3^{16}$
E*
E^0

Example 4. We considered system (1) - (4) for a multilayered medium (i.e., a discontinuous elastic modulus). We chose $\rho = 1$, E piecewise constant (E^* given below) and $S = 2(1 - e^{-5t})e^{-t}$ and used the tau-Legendre method for the state approximations as described in section 3 to estimate E, k_1, k_2. Observations consisted of surface observations ($x_j = 0$) at 40 evenly spaced times t_i in $[0,2]$ (i.e., $t_i = .05, .1, .15, \ldots$). For N = 4, we obtained the estimates listed below with $J^4(\bar{q}^4) = .3 \times 10^{-3}$, CPU time = 172 sec.

INITIAL GUESS

$$E^0(x) = \begin{cases} 1.5 & 0 \le x \le .2 \\ 1.5 & .2 < x \le .8 \\ 1.5 & .8 < x \le 1.0 \end{cases} \qquad k_1^0 = -2.0 \qquad k_2^0 = 2.0$$

TRUE VALUES

$$E^*(x) = \begin{cases} 2.0 & 0 \le x \le .3 \\ 3.0 & .3 < x \le .7 \\ 1.0 & .7 < x \le 1.0 \end{cases} \qquad k_1^* = -1.0 \qquad k_2^* = 3.0$$

ESTIMATES (N = 4)

$$\bar{E}^4(x) = \begin{cases} 1.996 & 0 \le x \le .299 \\ 2.986 & .299 < x \le .7006 \\ .996 & .7006 < x \le 1.0 \end{cases} \qquad \bar{k}_1^4 = -.998 \qquad \bar{k}_2^4 = 2.987$$

Concluding remarks. As we have outlined above, a convergence theory can be developed for both the state and parameter approximation schemes described in this note. We have tested the methods on a number of examples in addition to the ones presented here. The schemes perform well on both "bore hole" and "surface seismic" type model problems. In some cases (see Example 1) the tau-Legendre state approximations perform slightly better than the cubic spline approximations. In others (see Example 2), the cubic spline schemes appear to be more desirable.

While our test examples are clearly very simple, they do serve the purpose of illustrating the potential for use of the methods and ideas in estimating variable (continuous and/or discontinuous) coefficients and unknown boundary parameters in second order hyperbolic systems.

REFERENCES

[1] H.T. BANKS and J.M. CROWLEY, Parameter estimation for disbributed systems arising in elasticity, Symp. on Engineering Sciences and Mechanics, National Cheng Kung Univ., Taiwan, Dec. 28-31, 1981, pp. 158-177; LCDS Rep. No. 81-24, Brown Univ., Providence RI, Nov., 1981.

[2] H.T. BANKS and J.M. CROWLEY, Parameter identification in continuum models, LCDS rep. No. M-83-1, Brown Univ., Providence, RI, March, 1983; in Proc. Amer. Control Conf., IEEE, June 22-24, 1983, San Francisco, pp. 997-1001.

[3] H.T. BANKS, J.M. CROWLEY, and K. KUNISCH, Cubic spline approximation techniques for parameter estimation in distributed systems, IEEE Trans. Auto. Control 28 (1983), to appear.

[4] H.T. BANKS and P.L. DANIEL, Estimation of variable coefficients in parabolic distributed systems, LCDS Rep. No. 82-22, Sept. 1982, Brown Univ., Providence, RI; IEEE Trans. Auto. Control, to appear.

[5] H.T. BANKS, P.L. DANIEL, and P. KAREIVA, Estimation of temporally and spatially varying coefficients in models for insect dispersal, LCDS Rep. No. 83-14, Brown Univ., Providence, RI, Juen 1983; J. Math. Biology, to be submitted.

[6] H.T. BANKS, P.L. DANIEL, and P. KAREIVA, Estimation techniques for transport equations, Proc. Intl. Conf. on Mathematics in Biology and Medicine, July 18-22, 1983, Bari, Italy, to appear.

[7] H.T. BANKS and K. KUNISCH, An approximation theory for nonlinear partial differential equations with applications to identification and control, SIAM J. Control and Optimization 20 (1982), pp. 815-849.

[8] H.T. BANKS and K.A. MURPHY, Inverse problems for hyperbolic systems with unknown boundary parameters, in Control Theory for Distributed Parameter Systems and Applications, F. Kappel et al, editors, Springer Lecture Notes in Control and Info. Sci., 54 (1983), pp. 35-44.

[9] J.M. CROWLEY, Numerical Methods of Parameter Identification for Problems Arising in Elasticity, Ph.D. Dissertation, Brown Univ., Providence, RI, May, 1982.

[10] D. GOTTLIEB and S. ORSZAG, Numerical Analysis of Spectral Methods: Theory and Applications, Vol. 26, CBMS-NSF Reg. Conf. Series in Applied Math, SIAM, Philadelphia, 1977.

[11] K.A. MURPHY, A Spline-Based Approximation Method for Inverse Problems for a Hyperbolic System Including Unknown Boundary Parameters, Ph.D. Dissertation, Brown Univ., Providence, RI, May, 1983.

[12] A. PAZY, Semigroups of Linear Operators and Applications to Partial Differential Equations, Lecture Notes 10, Univ. of Maryland, College Park, 1974.

[13] M.H. SCHULTZ, Spline Analysis, Prentice-Hall, Englewood Cliffs, N.J., 1973.

An Approximation Technique for Estimating Discontinuous Coefficients in Distributed Systems

Patricia Daniel Lamm*

Abstract. We discuss the problem of estimating spatially-varying coefficients (related to porosity, permeability, etc.) that appear in distributed pressure or flow equations for porous media problems. A special feature of our approach is the formulation of a relatively simple spline-based numerical algorithm that not only determines the shape of the coefficients but locates points of spatial discontinuity as well. Theoretical results and representative numerical findings are presented.

Introduction. We present here our efforts related to the estimation of discontinuous spatially-varying coefficients in parabolic distributed systems. Although our work is motivated by an inverse problem in reservoir simulation known as "history matching," we believe that our ideas are applicable to a wide class of problems governed by distributed systems. In particular, the approximation methods discussed here should have straightforward extension to seismic problems and to other applications for which hyperbolic model equations (with discontinuous coefficients) are appropriate.

The problem in "history matching" involves determining unknown parameters (such as permeability, porosity) that appear in model reservoir equations and which provide the best match between the observed and simulated production history at one or more wells. Information about these coefficients (their shape and location of discontinuities) provides insight into the physical properties of the reservoir and can indicate the location of abrupt structural changes; in addition, precise determination of these parameters is essential to the process of accurately simulating and predicting reservior behavior.

*Department of Mathematics, Southern Methodist University, Dallas, Texas 75275. Part of this research was carried out while the author was a visitor at the Institute for Computer Applications in Science and Engineering, NASA Langley Research Center, Hampton, VA, which is operated under NASA contracts NAS1-15810 and NAS1-16394. This research was also supported in part by the National Science Foundation under grant #NSF-MCS-8200883.

The governing reservoir equations describe mathematically the physical and chemical processes occurring during primary hydrocarbon recovery or during enhanced recovery efforts. Mathematical models, which vary widely depending on the physical process being described and the types of observations available, are typically distributed in nature and of parabolic type [11][12]. Unknown parameters quite often include the porosity of surrounding rock, or the ratio of pore volume to total volume, and (relative) permeability, which is the ability of the rock to transmit fluid [12]. Due to spatial changes in underground structure, it is highly likely that these parameters will vary spatially and contain numerous discontinuities.

In order to solve the inverse problem, data in the form of fluid pressure (or flow rate) is collected at the wells and used in a numerical parameter estimation process. One numerical approach commonly taken involves subdividing the reservoir into a grid of smaller blocks; constant-valued parameters (which are allowed to vary independently from block to block) are then estimated numerically. Unfortunately, if accurate solutions are desired, it is not surprising that the grid size often must be quite small and thus the number of parameters, as well as the dimension of the state space, can be very large (as many as 50,000 parameters or more) [11]. Our goal is to avoid this difficulty by separating the problem of state approximation from that of parameter estimation so that the need for an approximate state space of large dimension does not impose similar restrictions on the dimension of an approximation space for the parameters. In order to focus attention on the problems associated with estimating spatially-varying discontinuous coefficients in this context, we consider a model of parabolic distributed type that admittedly is a simplified version of the equations associated with reservoir simulation (see [11], [12] and the references therein); nevertheless the model selected here is a prototype that contains the essential parameter-dependent terms for which we may begin our investigations.

The Parameter Estimation Problem. We consider the following model equation with Dirichlet boundary conditions:

$$
(1) \quad \begin{cases} \frac{\partial u}{\partial t}(t,x) = \frac{\partial}{\partial x}\left(q(x)\frac{\partial u}{\partial x}(t,x)\right) + f(t,x,r(x)), & (x,t) \in (0,1) \times (0,T) \\ u(0,x) = u_0(x) \\ u(t,0) = u(t,1) = 0. \end{cases}
$$

Here q and r are unknown functional parameters which are to be estimated through a numerical identification scheme. The mapping f not only represents external sources/sinks but may also include terms that arise from transforming a similar problem with nonzero boundary conditions to a system in the present form (with homogeneous boundary conditions); thus r may contain unknown constants that were previously part of the boundary conditions as well as unknown components of the forcing term f. We remark here that it is also possible to consider u_0 as an unknown functional parameter. This rather complicated case is handled in [10] and is not presented here in order to keep technical detail to a minimum.

We assume that the discontinuous function q may be represented by

$$(2) \qquad q = \phi_0 + \sum_{i=1}^{\nu} \phi_i H_{\xi_i}$$

where $0 < \xi_1 < \xi_2 < \dots < \xi_\nu < 1$, $\phi_i \in C[0,1]$, $0 \le i \le \nu$, and H_ξ denotes the usual Heaviside function given by $H_\xi = 0$ on $[0,\xi)$, $H_\xi = 1$ on $[\xi,1]$. Given this parameterization for q it is hardly surprising that the parameter set of interest, Γ, is defined in terms of ϕ_0, ϕ_i, and ξ_i, $1 \le i \le \nu$, and r. Indeed Γ is assumed to be a compact subset of $\tilde{\Gamma}$, where

$$\tilde{\Gamma} \equiv \{\gamma = (\xi_1,\dots,\xi_\nu,\phi_0,\phi_1,\dots,\phi_\nu,r) \in R^\nu \times \prod_{i=1}^{\nu+1} C[0,1] \times L_2(0,1) \mid 0 < \xi_1 < \dots < \xi_\nu < 1,\ \phi_i \text{ is sufficiently smooth and bounded, } 0 \le i \le \nu\}.$$

The parameter estimation problem associated with (1) and Γ is the following: Given distributed observations $\hat{u}_i \in L_2(0,1)$ at times $t_i \in [0,T)$, $i = 1,\dots,n$, find $\gamma^* \in \Gamma$ that minimizes the least squares fit-to-data criterion

$$(3) \qquad J(\gamma) = \sum_{i=1}^{n} |(u(t_i,\cdot;\gamma) - \hat{u}_i)\omega_i|^2$$

over all $\gamma \in \Gamma$. Here $|\cdot|$ denotes the usual norm on $L_2(0,1)$ and $\omega_i \in L_\infty(0,1)$ has support in the spatial regions corresponding to observed wells.

Our goal is to construct a scheme to estimate γ^* and at the same time approximate the corresponding solution $u(\gamma^*)$ to (1). To this end we examine properties of (1) for arbitrary values of γ in Γ. We thus fix $\gamma \in \Gamma$, define q using (2) and γ, and reformulate (1) in an abstract setting by defining the new state variable $z(t) \equiv u(t,\cdot;\gamma) \in L_2(0,1)$. Equation (1) may then be rewritten

$$(4)\quad \begin{cases} \dot{z}(t) = A(q)z(t) + F(t;r), & t \in (0,T) \\ z(0) = u_0 \end{cases}$$

where $F(t;r) \equiv f(t,\cdot;r)$ and $A(q)\psi = D(qD\psi)$ for all $\psi \in \mathrm{dom}A(q)$ (D denotes the spatial differentiation operator, $D \equiv \frac{\partial}{\partial x}$). Here

$$(5)\quad \mathrm{dom}A(q) \equiv \{\psi \in H_0^1(0,1) \mid qD\psi \in H^1(0,1)\}$$

where $H^1(0,1)$ denotes the usual Sobolev space of "functions" in $L_2(0,1)$ with first "derivatives" in $L_2(0,1)$; similarly $H_0^1(0,1)$ denotes those $H^1(0,1)$ functions that are zero at the endpoints $x = 0$ and $x = 1$. We note that by requiring that $z(t) \in \mathrm{dom}A(q)$ for $t > 0$ we are simply ensuring that all spatial derivatives in (1) may legitimately be taken. In addition, $z(t) = u(t,\cdot) \in \mathrm{dom}A(q)$ also provides for the continuity of the mapping $x \to q(x)Du(t,x)$; this yields in particular, a physically meaningful conservation-type property,

$$(6)\quad q(\xi_i^-)Du(t,\xi_i^-) = q(\xi_i^+)Du(t,\xi_i^+), \quad i = 1,\ldots,\nu,$$

for solutions at points $x = \xi_i$ of "structural discontinuity."

Appealing to the theory of semigroups [13], [15], it is not difficult to establish [10] that $A(q)$ generates an analytic semigroup on $L_2(0,1)$ and that, for f, u_0 sufficiently smooth, there exists a unique "strong" solution z to (4) that exhibits a number of desirable regularity properties. Among these properties is the continuity of the mapping $\gamma \to z(t;\gamma) : \Gamma \to L_2(0,1)$ for each $t \in [0,T)$. It is then easy to see that $\gamma \to J(\gamma)$ is continuous over the compact set Γ, so that the existence of a minimizer γ^* for J over Γ is assured.

A Spline-based Approximation Scheme. We consider now the problem of estimating γ^* numerically. To employ any of a number of standard optimization packages to minimize J over Γ it is necessary to compute the value of $J(\gamma)$ (i.e., solve (1) for $u(\gamma)$) for various choices of γ. It is thus desirable to combine numerical estimation of a minimizer γ^* with approximation schemes for solving (1). To this end we describe a spline-based approximation theory similar to that detailed in [1], [3], [4], [5], [7], [8], [9], [14], to name only a few of the related references in this area. The approach we take here is complicated by the fact that the approximation spaces change with every choice of the parameter vector γ and the fact that these spaces are not, in general, contained in $\mathrm{dom}A(q)$ (where it is assumed throughout that q is constructed using γ and (2)).

For any $\gamma = (\xi_1,\ldots,\xi_\nu,\phi_0,\phi_1,\ldots,\phi_\nu,r) \in \Gamma$, $\xi_j \in (0,1)$, $1 \leq j \leq \nu$, we construct parameter-dependent approximating spaces and operators as follows (for ease of presentation we take $\nu = 1$): For $N = 1,2,\ldots$, let $X^N(\gamma) \equiv \text{span}\{B_i^N(\gamma),\ i = 1,\ldots,2N-1\}$, where $B_i^N(\gamma)$ denotes the ith continuous piecewise-linear B-spline basis element satisfying $B_i^N(x;\gamma) = 0$ for $x = 0,1$; knots for $B_i^N(\gamma)$ are parameter-dependent and given by $\{t_k^N(\gamma),\ k = 0,\ldots,2N\}$ where $t_k^N(\gamma) = k\xi_1/N$, $k = 0,\ldots,N$, and $t_k^N(\gamma) = \xi_1 + (k-N)(1-\xi_1)/N$, for $k = N+1,\ldots,2N$. See Figures 1-3.

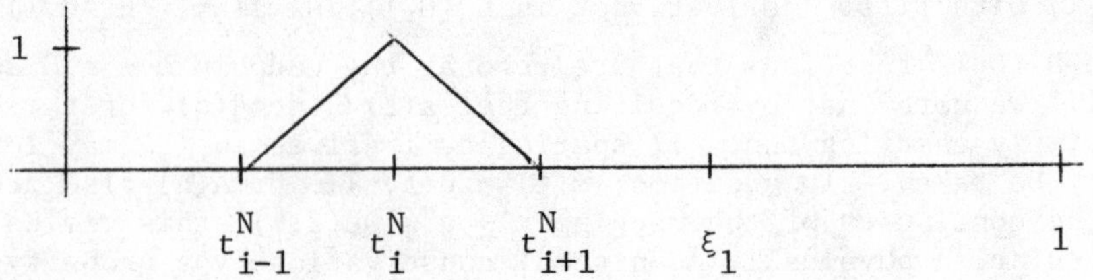

Figure 1. B_i^N, $i = 1,\ldots,N-1$.

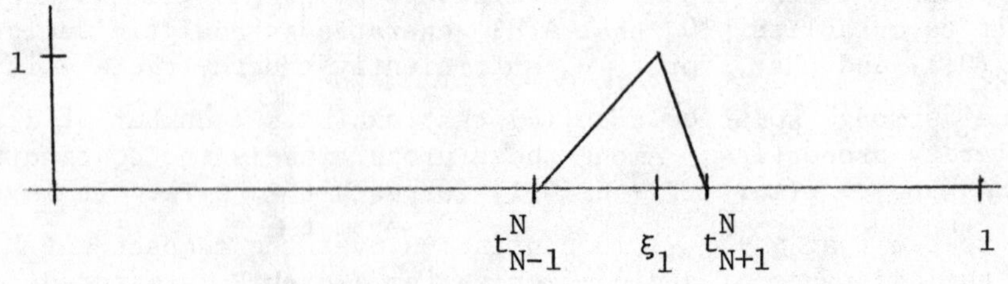

Figure 2. B_N^N.

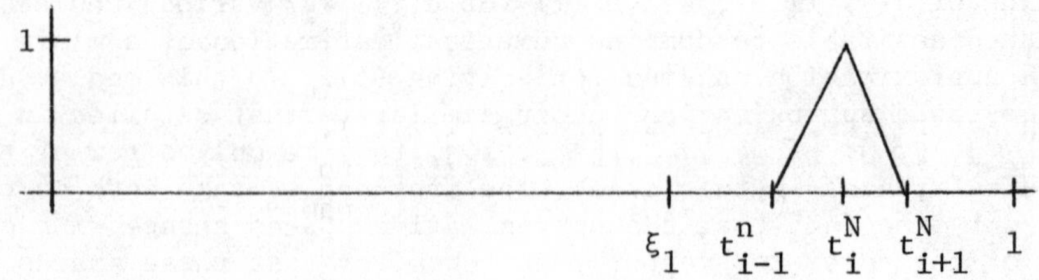

Figure 3. B_i^N, $i = N+1,\ldots,2N-1$.

We remark that if γ, $\tilde{\gamma} \in \Gamma$, in general we do not have $X^N(\gamma) \subseteq X^N(\tilde{\gamma})$ nor do we have $X^N(\gamma) \subseteq \mathrm{dom}A(q)$, where q is constructed from γ. It is for this reason that we do not seek an approximation scheme based on approximations of A(q) by operators of the form $P^N A(q) P^N$ (where $P^N = P^N(\gamma) : L_2(0,1) \to X^N(\gamma)$ is a projection type operator) although such ideas have been used with success in related efforts using spline-based approximations [1], [2], [3], [6], [8], [9]. Instead we propose a Galerkin-type scheme that has the advantage of being quite simple and inexpensive from a computational standpoint.

For each $\gamma \in \Gamma$, we shall seek an approximation to $z(s;\gamma)$ (the solution to (4)) of the form

$$(7) \qquad z^N(s;\gamma) = \sum_{i=1}^{2N-1} w_i^N(s;\gamma) B_i^N(\gamma)$$

where the coefficients w_i^N are determined by solving the following system of ordinary differential equations (ODEs):

$$(8) \qquad \begin{cases} \langle \dot{z}^N(s;\gamma), B_i^N(\gamma)\rangle = -\langle qDz^N(s;\gamma), DB_i^N(\gamma)\rangle \\ \qquad\qquad + \langle F(s;r), B_i^N(\gamma)\rangle, \quad s \in (0,T) \\ \langle z^N(0;\gamma), B_i^N(\gamma)\rangle = \langle u_0, B_i^N(\gamma)\rangle, \quad i = 1,\ldots,2N-1. \end{cases}$$

For fixed N, there is associated with (8) an approximate estimation problem, namely that of minimizing J^N over Γ where

$$(9) \qquad J^N(\gamma) = \sum_{i=1}^{n} |(\hat{u}_i - z^N(t_i;\gamma))\omega_i|^2$$

and z^N is a solution to (8) corresponding to $\gamma \in \Gamma$. Applying standard results from ODE theory and suitable regularity assumptions on f, one may easily show that there exists a unique solution z^N to (8) for a given choice of $\gamma \in \Gamma$ and that the mapping $\gamma \to z^N(t;\gamma)$ is continuous for $t \in [0,T)$. We are thus assured that there exists, for each N, $\bar{\gamma}^N \in \Gamma$ that minimizes J^N over the compact set Γ.

Our goal, of course, is to demonstrate the convergence, in an appropriate sense, of $\bar{\gamma}^N$ to γ^* where γ^* is a solution to the original estimation problem associated with (1) and (3); in addition, we seek state variable convergence, namely that $z^N(t;\bar{\gamma}^N) \to z(t;\gamma^*)$ as $N \to \infty$. The proof of state variable convergence involves variational-type arguments (see, for example, pp. 128-131 of [16]) and spline-based estimates that are modifications of standard linear spline interpolation estimates [16, p. 17]. The interested reader should consult [10] for these rather technical calculations. Once it has been established that $z^N(t;\gamma^N) \to z(t;\gamma)$ for any sequence $\{\gamma^N\}$ in Γ that satisfies $\gamma^N \to \gamma \in \Gamma$, our fundamental parameter convergence result follows immediately [10] from the compactness of Γ and the minimizing properties of $\bar{\gamma}^N$. Our findings are summarized below.

Theorem 1. For each N let $\bar{\gamma}^N$ denote a solution to the problem of minimizing J^N over Γ. There exists $\gamma^* \in \Gamma$ and a subsequence $\{\bar{\gamma}^{N_k}\}$ of $\{\bar{\gamma}^N\}$ such that, as $N_k \to \infty$,

(i) $\bar{\gamma}^{N_k} \to \gamma^*$,

(ii) $z^{N_k}(t;\bar{\gamma}^{N_k}) \to z(t;\gamma^*)$ in $L_2(0,1)$ for each $t \in [0,T)$,

(iii) $J^{N_k}(\bar{\gamma}^{N_k}) \to J(\gamma^*)$, and,

(iv) γ^* is a solution to the original parameter estimation problem (namely, that of minimizing J over Γ).

Therefore, to approximate γ^* numerically we need only fix N (sufficiently large) and employ standard optimization techniques to solve the Nth parameter estimation problem (associated with (8) and (9)) for $\bar{\gamma}^N$. Of course, Theorem 1 only guarantees subsequence convergence to γ^*; fortunately, it has been our experience in this and related efforts that we actually appear to obtain convergence of the entire sequence and that $\bar{\gamma}^N \approx \gamma^*$ for fairly small N (N = 8 for example). Some representative numerical examples demonstrating this behavior are found in [10] and in the section that follows.

Implementation and Numerical Examples. An important feature of the work presented here is the ease of implementation of the spline-based approximation scheme, particularly in the case where the points of discontinuity, ξ_i, $i = 1,\ldots,\nu$, are to be estimated. We shall discuss briefly some of the features of the approximating ODE (8) on $X^N(\gamma)$ for given $\gamma \in \Gamma$, and then indicate our experience with the numerical aspects of the parameter estimation problem.

For a given $\gamma = (\xi_1,\phi_0,\phi_1,r) \in \Gamma$, $q = \phi_0 + H_{\xi_1}\phi_1$, (again we let $\nu = 1$ for the sake of simplicity) we may use the expansion (7) for $z^N(t)$ to rewrite (8) in terms of $w^N(t;\gamma) \equiv (w_1^N(t;\gamma), \ldots, w_{2N-1}^N(t;\gamma))^T$;

here $\{w_i^N\}$ are the coefficients appearing in (7). The ODE in $w^N(t) \in R^{2N-1}$ is then

$$\text{(10)} \quad \begin{cases} Q^N \dot{w}^N(t) = - K^N w^N(t) + G^N(t), & t \in (0,T) \;, \\ w^N(0) = w_0^N \;, \end{cases}$$

where the (2N-1)-square matrices $Q^N = Q^N(\gamma)$ and $K^N = K^N(\gamma)$ have entries

$$\text{(11)} \quad Q_{i,j}^N = (\langle B_j^N(\gamma),\ B_i^N(\gamma)\rangle)$$

and

$$\text{(12)} \quad K_{i,j}^N = (\langle qDB_j^N(\gamma),\ DB_i^N(\gamma)\rangle).$$

Further,

$$\text{(13)} \quad G^N(t) = G^N(t;\gamma) = (\langle F(t;r),\ B_1^N(\gamma)\rangle,\ \ldots,\ \langle F(t;r),\ B_{2N-1}^N(\gamma)\rangle)^T,$$

and

$$\text{(14)} \quad w_0^N = w_0^N(\gamma) = (Q^N)^{-1}(\langle u_0, B_1^N(\gamma)\rangle,\ \ldots,\ \langle u_0, B_{2N-1}^N(\gamma)\rangle)^T.$$

We remark that, due to the parameter-dependent nature of the basis elements $\{B_i^N(\gamma)\}$, the $L_2(0,1)$ inner product entries in Q^N, K^N, G^N, and w_0^N must be recomputed (via numerical quadratures) every time that γ is updated. Since numerical optimization packages generate numerous γ iterates, it would appear that the ideas proposed here are not advantageous from a computational standpoint. In fact, the methods developed here are quite simple and relatively inexpensive (especially in the case of ϕ_0, ϕ_1 constant) because many of the inner products may be easily computed by hand in advance of the iterative process. Thus, during the optimization process, one need only substitute the current values of N, ξ_1, ϕ_0, and ϕ_1 into the resulting matrices. These ideas are made precise in [10]; we also discuss there implementation problems when ϕ_0 and ϕ_1 are unknown, truly spatially-varying, functions. In the latter case, we separate state variable approximation (of order N) from the approximation of these functional parameters (we use for example an approximate parameter space, Γ^M, of order M); we then investigate the convergence of $\bar{\gamma}^{M,N}$ (a minimizer for J^N over Γ^M) to γ^* as $M,N \to \infty$.

We consider here a numerical example where γ^* is known and data is generated synthetically so that we may test our ideas. Both γ^* and $u(\gamma^*)$ are selected in advance while the appropriate forcing function f is determined by substituting γ^*, $u(\gamma^*)$ into (1). For chosen sample times t_i, $i = 1,\ldots,n$, and sampling locations x_j, $j = 1,\ldots,m$ (discrete data is used for these examples), data is generated by setting $\hat{u}_{ij} = u(t_i,x_j;\gamma^*)$, $1 \le i \le n$, $1 \le j \le m$. For the example presented here, $\nu = 2$ and $\gamma^* \equiv (.2, .6, 1., 6., .5)$ so that

$$q^* \equiv \begin{cases} 1., & 0 \le x < .2, \\ 6., & .2 \le x < .6, \\ .5\ , & .6 \le x \le 1\ . \end{cases}$$

In addition, the mapping $u(t,\cdot;\gamma^*) \in \mathrm{dom}A(q^*)$, defined by

$$u(t,x;\gamma^*) \equiv \begin{cases} 30(t+4)x & , \quad 0 \le x < .2\ , \\ (5x+5)(t+4) & , \quad .2 \le x < .6\ , \\ 100(t+4)(-2x^2+3x-1), & .6 \le x \le 1\ , \end{cases}$$

is used to generate sample data at times t_i, given by .5, 1.0, 1.5, and 2.0, and at sampling locations $x_j = j/10$, $j = 1, \ldots, 9$. We then begin the parameter estimation process by supplying an initial guess of γ^0 to IMSL's minimization routine ZXSSQ (a Levenberg-Marquardt algorithm) which numerically attempts to determine a minimum, for given N, to

$$J^N(\gamma) = \sum_{i=1}^{n} \sum_{j=1}^{m} |\hat{u}_{ij} - z^N(t_i,x_j;\gamma)|^2$$

over a fixed constraint set $\Gamma \subseteq R^5$. Here $z^N(\gamma)$ is the solution to (8) (i.e., (7) and (10)) calculated using IMSL's DGEAR, an ODE solver, and the known values of u_0 and f. In Table 1 we summarize our findings for N = 8 and N = 16 where our initial guess for $(\xi_1, \xi_2, \phi_0, \phi_1, \phi_2)$ is (.3, .7, 5., 2., 1.5) in the case of N = 8 ($\bar{\gamma}^8$ is used as an initial guess in the case of N = 16). In Table 2 we repeat the example, this time using start-up values of (.05, .8, 5., 5., 5.), so that the initial guess, q^0, for q is given by $q^0 \equiv 5$. We note that although this corresponds to a situation where no knowledge whatsoever is available about the location of discontinuities, our scheme has the disadvantage of having to specify the number, ν, of expected discontinuities in advance. Fortunately, it is possible to both underestimate and overestimate this number and still obtain excellent results. These and other related findings are included in [10], where a more thorough treatment of our numerical experience may be found.

Table 1. Example 1

N	$\bar{\xi}_1^N$	$\bar{\xi}_2^N$	$\bar{\phi}_0^N$	$\bar{\phi}_1^N$	$\bar{\phi}_2^N$	CP time (sec)
8	.2001	.6114	1.061	5.973	.4736	294.
16	.2003	.6060	1.029	6.016	.4866	512.

Table 2. Example 2

N	$\bar{\xi}_1^N$	$\bar{\xi}_2^N$	$\bar{\phi}_0^N$	$\bar{\phi}_1^N$	$\bar{\phi}_2^N$	CP time (sec)
8	.2084	.5960	.9971	7.399	.4975	512.
16	.2000	.6000	1.0000	6.000	.5000	341.

For cases with nonconstant ϕ_i, numerous test examples exist and may be found in [10]; the reader may also find examples where f and u_0 do not contain discontinuities at ξ_i^*, $i = 1,\ldots,\nu$, and where random noise has been added to the data.

Acknowledgment. The author would like to express appreciation to Prof. H. T. Banks for numerous insightful discussions during the course of this work.

REFERENCES

[1] H.T. BANKS, J.M. CROWLEY, and K. KUNISCH, Cubic spline approximation techniques for parameter estimation in distributed systems, IEEE Trans. Auto. Control 28 (1983), to appear.

[2] H.T. BANKS and P.L. DANIEL, Estimation of delays and other parameters in nonlinear functional differential equations, SIAM J. Control and Optimization 21 (1983), to appear.

[3] H.T. BANKS and P.L. DANIEL, Estimation of variable coefficients in parabolic distributed systems, LCDS Rep. No. 82-22, Sept. 1982, Brown University, Providence, RI 02912; IEEE Trans. Auto. Control, to appear.

[4] H.T. BANKS, P.L. DANIEL, and E.S. ARMSTRONG, A spline-based parameter and state estimation technique for static models of elastic surfaces, ICASE Tech. Rep. 83-25, NASA Langley Research Center, Hampton, VA 23665, June, 1983.

[5] H.T. BANKS, P.L. DANIEL, and P. KAREIVA, Estimation of temporally and spatially varying coefficients in models for insect dispersal, LCDS Rep. No. 83-14, Brown University, Providence, RI 02912, June, 1983; J. Math. Biology, to be submitted.

[6] H.T. BANKS and F. KAPPEL, Spline approximations for functional differential equations, J. Differential Equations 34 (1979), pp. 496-522.

[7] H.T. BANKS and P. KAREIVA, Parameter estimation techniques for transport equations with applications to population dispersal and tissue bulk flow models, LCDS Rep. No. 82-13, Brown University, Providence, RI 02912, July, 1982; J. Math Biology, to appear.

[8] H.T. BANKS and K. KUNISCH, An approximation theory for nonlinear partial differential equations with applications to identification and control, SIAM J. Control and Optimization 20 (1982), pp. 815-849.

[9] H.T. BANKS and K.A. MURPHY, Inverse problems for hyperbolic systems with unknown boundary parameters, in Control Theory for Distributed Parameter Systems and Applications, F. Kappel et al editors, Springer Lecture Notes in Control and Info. Sci., 54 (1983), pp. 35-44.

[10] P.L. DANIEL, Estimation of discontinuous spatially-varying coefficients in parabolic systems with applications to reservoir simulation problems, SIAM J. Control and Optimization, to be submitted.

[11] R.E. EWING, Determination of coefficients in reservoir simulation, Numerical Treatment of Inverse Problems in Differential and Inregral Equations, P. Deuflhard and E. Hairer, editors, Birkhäuser, Boston, 1983, pp. 206-226.

[12] R.E. EWING, The Mathematics of Reservoir Simulation, Ch. I, SIAM Frontiers in Appl. Math. 1 (1983), to appear.

[13] A. FRIEDMAN, Partial Differential Equations, Robert E. Krieger Publishing Co., Huntington, N.Y., 1976.

[14] K. KUNISCH and L. WHITE, The parameter estimation problem for parabolic equations in multidimensional domains in the presence of point evaluations, March, 1983, preprint.

[15] A. PAZY, Semigroups of Linear Operators and Applications to Partial Differential Equations, Lecture Notes 10, Univ. of Maryland, College Park, 1974.

[16] M.H. SCHULTZ, Spline Analysis, Prentice-Hall, Englewood Cliffs, N.J., 1973.

The Seismic Inverse Problem as a Sequence of Before Stack Migrations

Patrick Lailly*

Abstract. We are interested in 2 D or 3 D inversion of before stack seismic data. In fact the inverse problem is linearized about a reference medium which is space varying. Roughly speaking, this reference medium contains the available information about mean propagation velocities. We therefore want to find the difference between the actual medium and the reference medium. The inverse problem is formulated as an optimization problem. It is shown that the first iteration of the gradient algorithm applied to this problem can be interpreted as a "before stack migration". Following iterations appear to be residual "before stack migrations".

1. Introduction. An exploration seismology experiment is described on figure 1. A seismic source is located at a point S1, near the surface of the earth and is fired at time t = 0. The seismic waves propagate from the source into the earth and are reflected, transmitted, diffracted, ... when they meet the interfaces between geologic layers. The upgoing wave field (for instance the pressure in offshore exploration) is measured at different points $G_1, \dots G_N$ (G stands for geophone) on the time interval $[0,T]$ and we obtain the data $p_{S1}^{obs}(\vec{r}_G,t)$ (**) for $t\in[0,T]$ and $\vec{r}_G$ (vector defining the location of one receiver) $\in R_G(S1)$ which is defined as the set of receiver locations for a source in S1. This was shot number 1.

Then the source and the receivers are moved to other places and shot number 2 is run in the same way : it gives the data $p_{S2}^{obs}(\vec{r}_G,t)$ for $t\in[0,T]$ (***) and $\vec{r}_G \in R_G(S2)$ (S2 defines the source location for shot # 2). And so on for the following shots.

* Institut Français du Pétrole, 1-4, avenue de Bois Préau, 92500 Rueil-Malmaison, France.

** The subscript S1 indicates that these data have been obtained for a source located in S1.

*** for each shot, the time t = 0 is the time when the source is fired.

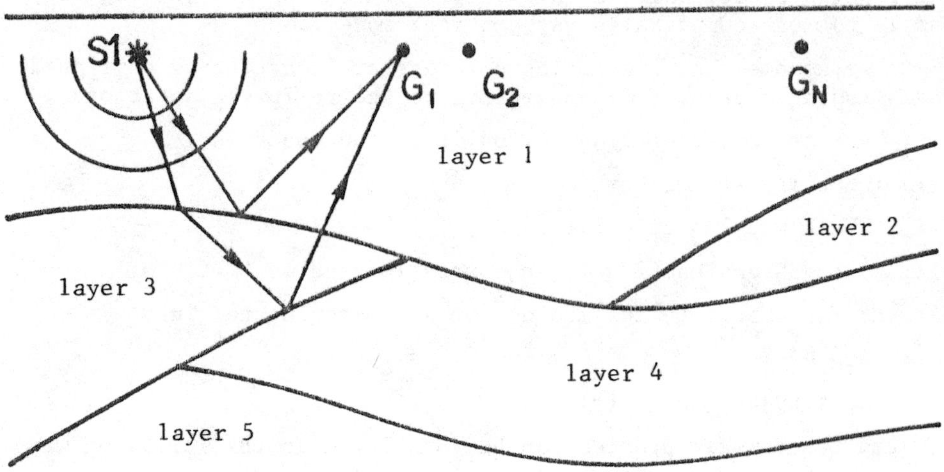

Figure 1. An exploration seismology experiment.

We introduce the set of source locations :

$$R_S = \{S_j, \ j = 1, 2, \ldots \}$$

In the following, we deal with the inverse problem which can be roughly stated as follows :

To find some parameters of the earth from the records $p_S^{obs}(\vec{r}_G, t)$, $t \in [0,T]$, $\vec{r}_G \in R_G(S)$ obtained for each S in R_S (the source functions are supposed to be known for simplicity).

Our aim is to make the link between some solutions of the inverse problem and the classical "before stack migration". In order to do so, we shall mainly study the linearized inverse problem in a similar way to Clayton and Stolt's approach [3].

Before dealing with the inverse problem, we are interested in the forward problem which is :

For a given earth and given source functions, to find, for each source location S in R_S, the seismograms $p_S(\vec{r}_G, t)$ for $\vec{r}_G \in R_G(S)$ and $t \in [0,T]$.

2. A simple modeling of the forward problem : the acoustic wave equation. For sake of simplicity we deal with a simple mathematical model for the forward problem : the classical acoustic wave equation. The results concerning the inverse problem can be generalized very easily to more complicated mathematical models.

So we assume that the geologic layers are constituted of liquid media (shear modulus = 0) and introduce the following notations :

$\vec{r}$: vector characterizing one point in the space R^3

$\rho(\vec{r})$: density at point $\vec{r}$

$K(\vec{r})$: bulk modulus at point $\vec{r}$

$f_S(\vec{r},t)$: source function for a source located in S

$p_S(\vec{r},t)$: pressure in the medium for a source located in S

z : depth

Ω : half space $z > 0$ (*)

Then the forward problem can be formulated in the following way :

K,ρ,f_S being given, to find $p_S(\vec{r},t)$ solution of :

$$\text{(1.a)} \quad \frac{1}{K}\frac{\partial^2 p_S}{\partial t^2} - \operatorname{div}\left(\frac{1}{\rho}\,\overrightarrow{\text{grad}}\, p_S\right) = f_S(\vec{r},t) \text{ in } \Omega \times [0,T]$$

$$\text{(1.b)} \quad p_S = 0 \quad \text{for } t \le 0 \text{ (initial conditions)}$$

$$\text{(1.c)} \quad p_S = 0 \quad \text{for } z = 0 \text{ (free surface boundary condition)}$$

To model the data acquisition along a seismic profile we need to solve the problem (1.a) (1.b) (1.c) for each S in R_S.

The linearized forward problem. In order to make the link between inversion and "before stack migration" we linearize the forward problem. This (classical) linearization can be also very useful, from a practical point of view, to simplify the solution of the inverse problem.

This linearization (about a reference medium defined by the density ρ^o and the bulk modulus K^o) consists of splitting the density and the bulk modulus in the following way :

$$\text{(2.a)} \quad \rho(\vec{r}) = \rho^o(\vec{r}) + \delta\rho(\vec{r})$$

$$\text{(2.b)} \quad K(\vec{r}) = K^o(\vec{r}) + \delta K(\vec{r})$$

where the functions $\delta\rho$ and δK are sufficiently small to allow the approximation (linearization) :

$$\text{(3)} \quad p_S(\vec{r},t) \simeq p^o{}_S(\vec{r},t) + \delta p_S(\vec{r},t)$$

for each S in R_S, where $p^o{}_S(\vec{r},t)$ and $\delta p_S(\vec{r},t)$ are defined as the solutions of the problems :

* for sake of simplicity we assume the surface of the earth to be plane

Equation for primary waves $p^o_S(\vec{r},t)$:

(4.a) $$\frac{1}{K^o}\frac{\partial^2 p^o_S}{\partial t^2} - \operatorname{div}\left(\frac{1}{\rho^o}\,\overrightarrow{\text{grad}}\; p^o_S\right) = f_S(\vec{r},t) \text{ in } \Omega \times [0,T]$$

(4.b) $p^o_S = 0$ for $t \le 0$ (initial conditions)

(4.c) $p^o_S = 0$ for $z = 0$ (boundary condition)

Equation for scattered waves $\delta p_S(\vec{r},t)$:

(5.a) $$\frac{1}{K^o}\frac{\partial^2 \delta p_S}{\partial t^2} - \operatorname{div}\left(\frac{1}{\rho^o}\,\overrightarrow{\text{grad}}\;\delta p_S\right) = \frac{\delta K}{(K^o)^2}\frac{\partial^2 p^o_S}{\partial t^2} - \operatorname{div}\left(\frac{\delta \rho}{(\rho^o)^2}\,\overrightarrow{\text{grad}}\; p^o_S\right) \text{ in } \Omega \times [0,T]$$

(5.b) $\delta p_S = 0$ for $t \le 0$ (initial conditions)

(5.c) $\delta p_S = 0$ for $z = 0$ (boundary condition)

Some remarks.

i) Physical interpretation of the wave fields p^o_S and δp_S. If we suppose that the functions ρ^o and K^o are very smooth (*), there will be no reflexion along the propagation of p^o_S. Then the wave field p^o_S may be called the direct waves or the downgoing waves. When p^o_S meets a perturbation in the medium (i.e. a point $\vec{r}$ where $\delta K(\vec{r})$ or $\delta\rho(\vec{r})$ is different from 0), this gives rise to a secondary source (right hand side of equation (5.a)) : the wave field δp_S may be called the scattered waves resulting from the incidence of the wave field p^o_S on the pertubations in the medium. This justifies the name given to problems (4) and (5).

ii) To model the data acquisition along a seismic profile we need to solve problems (4) and (5) for each S in R_S.

Before studying the (linearized) inverse problem we introduce the

Definitions

We define the *set* $\mathcal{L}$ *of perturbations* which are small enough to allow approximation (3)(**) and, on this set, we define, for a given S the *operator* :

(6) $$\mathcal{A}_S : \begin{pmatrix}\delta\rho(\vec{r})\\ \delta K(\vec{r})\end{pmatrix} \longrightarrow \delta p_S(\vec{r}_G,t) \text{ for } t\in[0,T] \text{ and } \vec{r}_G \in R_G(S)$$

perturbations in the medium — scattered wave field (solution of problem (5)) observed at the different receiver locations $\vec{r}_G$

*This will be the case when we shall compare inversion and "before stack migration".

** of course the set $\mathcal{L}$ depends on the desired accuracy for approximation (3).

According to a terminology used in automatic control we call $\mathcal{A}_S(\delta\rho,\delta K)$ the *response* of the perturbations $(\delta\rho,\delta K)$ to a source located in S.

The operators $\mathcal{A}_S$ are linear. Consequently, we have :

$$\mathcal{A}_S\,(\delta\rho,\delta K) = \mathcal{A}_S(\delta\rho,0) + \mathcal{A}_S(0,\delta K)$$

To separate the dependency of the response on $\delta\rho$ and δK we introduce the following notations :

$$A_S^{\rho}(\delta\rho) = \mathcal{A}_S(\delta\rho,0) \qquad (6.a)$$

$$A_S^{K}(\delta K) = \mathcal{A}_S(0,\delta K) \qquad (6.b)$$

3. Formulation of the (linearized) inverse problem. If we denote by $\hat{\rho}(\vec{r})$ and $\hat{K}(\vec{r})$ the actual density and bulk modulus, our problem is to find - for a given reference medium (i.e. given $\rho^o(\vec{r})$ and $K^o(\vec{r})$ (*)) - the perturbation $\widehat{\delta\rho}(\vec{r})$ and $\widehat{\delta K}(\vec{r})$ defined by :

$$\hat{\rho}(\vec{r}) = \rho^o(\vec{r}) + \widehat{\delta\rho}(\vec{r}) \qquad (7.a)$$

$$\hat{K}(\vec{r}) = K^o(\vec{r}) + \widehat{\delta K}(\vec{r}) \qquad (7.b)$$

from the observations that we are going to describe more precisely.

The space of observations. Our measurements have been corrupted by noise. So, we may write :

$$p_S^{obs}(\vec{r}_G,t) = p^o{}_S(\vec{r}_G,t) + \mathcal{A}_S(\widehat{\delta\rho},\widehat{\delta K}) + \text{noise}.$$

As the direct wave field $p^o{}_S$ can be computed (ρ^o, K^o and f_S are given) we can substract it from the observation p_S^{obs}. We shall still denote p_S^{obs} the result, so that we may write :

$$p_S^{obs}(\vec{r}_G,t) = \mathcal{A}_S(\widehat{\delta\rho},\widehat{\delta K}) + \text{noise}. \qquad (8)$$

This observation, obtained for a given S, can be viewed as a vector (denoted P_S^{obs}), the components of which are the values $p_S^{obs}(\vec{r}_G,t)$ corresponding to a given $\vec{r}_G$ in $R_G(S)$ and to a given t in [0,T]. We shall call P_S^{obs} the *observed vector* for a source in S.

*Let us recall that these functions must be sufficiently close to the actual (and unknown !) functions $\hat{\rho}(\vec{r})$ and $\hat{K}(\vec{r})$. This condition may be satisfied by using information available from velocity analysis and standard geophysical data processing, geology, well logs,...

Considering the vector space of possible observations for a source in S, we can introduce the (canonical) *scalar product* $(\, , \,)_S$:

$$(9) \quad (P_S^{obs}, P'^{obs}_S)_S = \sum_{\vec{r}_G \in R_G(S)} \int_0^T P_S^{obs}(\vec{r}_G, t)\, P'^{obs}_S(\vec{r}_G, t)\, dt$$

This scalar product allows a quantitative comparison of seismograms which will be useful for the formulation of the inverse problem.

A natural (least-squares) formulation of the inverse problem. Basically, we want to find the perturbations $(\delta\tilde{\rho}, \delta\tilde{K})$ whose responses are, on average in R_S, as close (for the distance defined by (9)) as possible to the observations P_S^{obs}. The aim of such a formulation is to take account of the noise-corrupted nature of the observations ; in this way it should be compared to methods based on direct inversion. It should be noticed that, due to the redundancy in our data set, such a formulation is expected to provide us with a means of separating the noise and the signal.

Mathematically the problem can be formulated in the following way :

$$(10) \quad \begin{cases} \text{To find } (\delta\tilde{\rho}, \delta\tilde{K}) \text{ which minimizes over } \mathcal{L} \text{ the functional} \\ J(\rho, K) = \sum_{S \in R_S} (\mathcal{A}_S(\rho, K) - P_S^{obs}, \mathcal{A}_S(\rho, K) - P_S^{obs})_S \end{cases}$$

We expect the solution $(\delta\tilde{\rho}, \delta\tilde{K})$ to be not too far from the actual $(\delta\hat{\rho}, \delta\hat{K})$ if the noise level is low. Unfortunately this might not be the case, as can be seen from the study of the continuity of the operators $\mathcal{A}_S$ (cf. Lions [6], theorem 3.1, chapter 4 for instance) : very different perturbations (*) may have very close responses. This trouble is the classical instability of the inverse problem.

We give now, very shortly, two techniques (among others) which are able to overcome this difficulty. For further detail one can refer to the given references.

A regularized formulation of the least-squares inverse problem. This formulation has been used by Bamberger, Chavent, Lailly [1] to solve the 1 D seismic inverse problem.

The regularized formulation is :

$$(P.1) \quad \begin{cases} \text{To find } (\delta\tilde{\rho}, \delta\tilde{K}) \text{ which minimizes the functional} \\ J \text{ defined in (10) over a set } \mathcal{L}_{ad} \text{ of admissible perturbations.} \end{cases}$$

The set $\mathcal{L}_{ad}$ must be chosen :

i) sufficiently small (compact of $L^2(\Omega)$ for instance) to ensure the stability

* It should be noticed that the set $\mathcal{L}$ contains perturbations which are small when they are measured by a very special distance !

ii) sufficiently large to allow a good fit of $\mathcal{A}_S(\delta\rho,\delta K)$ on P_S^{obs}, for each S when the noise level is low.

Remark : if the actual solution $(\delta\hat{\rho},\delta\hat{K})$ is not in $\mathfrak{L}$ we have only found a regular representation of the solution. From this representation, it is possible to describe the whole set of possible solutions.

Utilization of a generalized least-squares criterion and of a priori information on the solution

This approach is suggested by Tarantola and Valette [10] if we dispose of an a priori estimate of the solution.

The inverse problem is formulated in the following way :

(P.2) $\left\{ \begin{array}{l} \text{To find } (\delta\tilde{\rho},\delta\tilde{K}) \text{ which minimizes over } \mathfrak{L} \text{ the functional} \\ I(\rho,K) : \end{array} \right.$

$$(11)\left\{ \begin{array}{l} I(\rho,K) = \sum\limits_{S\in R_S} (\mathcal{A}_S(\rho,K) - P_S^{obs}, C_p^{-1}[\mathcal{A}_S(\rho,K) - P_S^{obs}]) \\ \\ + ((K-\delta K^{est}, C_K^{-1}[K - \delta K^{est}])) + ((\rho - \delta\rho^{est}, C_\rho^{-1}[\rho-\delta\rho^{est}])) \end{array} \right.$$

where (*) :

- C_p is a covariance operator which takes account of the nature of the noise on the record P_S^{obs}
- $\delta\rho^{est}$ and δK^{est} (which are functions of space) are a priori estimates of the solution (a good estimate might be zero !)
- C_ρ and C_K are covariance operators describing the uncertainties on the a priori estimates $\delta\rho^{est}$ and δK^{est}
- $((\ ,\ ))$ is the scalar product in $L^2(\Omega)$

4. Computation of the solution of the inverse problem by gradient methods. We exhibit the solution given by a gradient method applied to problem (P1). This will allow us to make the link between the solution of the (linearized) inverse problem and the classical "before stack migration". Similar results can be readily obtained for the problem (P2) as well as for more general inverse problems (non linear inverse problem, cf. Tarantola [8], non linear inverse problem for the elastic wave equation, cf. Tarantola [9], ...).

We have chosen the gradient method in order not to be too technical. Of course we do not recommend such an algorithm for practical applica-

* For sake of simplicity, we suppose that the uncertainties we have on the a priori estimates $\delta\rho^{est}$ and δK^{est} are independent from each other.

tion. However similar results can be obtained for other gradient type algorithms.

The gradient algorithm. We recall the principle of the gradient method. For a detailed presentation, one can refer to classical books on optimization (cf. Fletcher [4] for instance).

A gradient method is an iterative method which constructs, starting from an initial guess $\begin{pmatrix} \delta\rho_o \\ \delta K_o \end{pmatrix}$, a sequence defined by :

$$(12) \quad \begin{pmatrix} \delta\rho_{n+1} \\ \delta K_{n+1} \end{pmatrix} = \begin{pmatrix} \delta\rho_n \\ \delta K_n \end{pmatrix} - \lambda_n \text{ grad } J(\delta\rho_n, \delta K_n)$$

where λ_n is a positive number which is chosen such that :

$$(13) \quad J(\delta\rho_{n+1}, \delta K_{n+1}) < J(\delta\rho_n, \delta K_n) \quad (*)$$

We know that such a λ_n exists, as far as the minimum of J is not reached, since the direction opposite to the gradient gives a local descent direction.

Remark. The constraint for $(\delta\rho, \delta K)$ to belong to $\mathcal{L}_{ad}$(cf. formulation of problem (P1)) can easily be introduced by classical penalization or duality techniques. This will only modify the algorithm (12) when it leads one iterate outside $\mathcal{L}_{ad}$. It will not be the case for the first iterations in practical applications.

In introducing the ρ and K components (denoted grad_ρ J and grad_K J) of the gradient of the functional $J(\rho,K)$, we can rewrite (12) in the following way :

$$(14.a) \quad \delta\rho_{n+1} = \delta\rho_n - \lambda_n \text{ grad}_\rho J(\delta\rho_n, \delta K_n)$$

$$(14.b) \quad \delta K_{n+1} = \delta K_n - \lambda_n \text{ grad}_K J(\delta\rho_n, \delta K_n)$$

The problem is now to calculate the ρ and K components of the gradient evaluated at some point $(\delta\rho, \delta K)$.

Calculation of the gradient of J (ρ,K). Let us give a perturbation $\delta\rho$ and δK to ρ and K (which are already perturbations). There results a perturbation δJ on the functional J which is given, to the first order, by :

* Applied to our problem, this property means that the synthetic seismograms associated to the earth model obtained at iteration n+1 will be, on average in R_S, closer to the observed seismograms than the synthetic seismograms associated to the earth model obtained at iteration n.

$$\delta J = \sum_{S \in R_S} (A_S^\rho(\delta\rho) + A_S^K(\delta K),\ A_S^\rho(\rho) + A_S^K(K) - P_S^{obs})_S$$

$$+ \sum_{S \in R_S} (A_S^\rho(\rho) + A_S^K(K) - P_S^{obs},\ A_S^\rho(\delta\rho) + A_S^K(\delta K))_S$$

$$= 2 \sum_{S \in R_S} (A_S^\rho(\delta\rho),\ \mathcal{A}_S(\rho,K) - P_S^{obs})_S$$

$$+ 2 \sum_{S \in R_S} (A_S^K(\delta K),\ \mathcal{A}_S(\rho,K) - P_S^{obs})_S$$

Introducing the adjoint (or transposed) operators $A_S^{*\rho}$ and A_S^{*K} of operators A_S^ρ and A_S^K, we can write (*) :

$$\delta J = 2 \sum_{S \in R_S} ((\delta\rho,\ A_S^{*\rho}[\mathcal{A}_S(\rho,K) - P_S^{obs}]))$$

$$+ 2 \sum_{S \in R_S} ((\delta K,\ A_S^{*K}[\mathcal{A}_S(\rho,K) - P_S^{obs}]))$$

so that the components of the gradient are given by :

(15.a) $$\text{grad}_\rho\ J(\rho,K) = 2 \sum_{S \in R_S} A_S^{*\rho}[\mathcal{A}_S(\rho,K) - P_S^{obs}]$$

(15.b) $$\text{grad}_K\ J(\rho,K) = 2 \sum_{S \in R_S} A_S^{*K}[\mathcal{A}_S(\rho,K) - P_S^{obs}]$$

<u>Transposition of operators A_S^ρ and A_S^K</u>. So, to calculate the gradient, we need to make explicit the image by operators $A_S^{*\rho}$ and A_S^{*K} of some vector Y defined by :

(16) $$Y = \mathcal{A}_S(\rho,K) - P_S^{obs}$$

We give the classical (cf. Lions [6] for instance) principle of this calculation for operator A_S^{*K}. To do so, let us recall the way we have constructed the operator A_S^K.

First, from the function $\delta K(\vec{r})$ we construct the function :

* Note that we use here the identification of $L^2(\Omega)$ and of the (Hilbert) space of observations with their duals which is allowed by the Riesz theorem.

(17) $$\delta f_S\ (r,t) = \frac{\delta K}{(K^o)^2}\ \frac{\partial^2 p^o{}_S}{\partial t^2}$$

and we denote by B_S the operator :

(18) $B_S : \delta K \to \delta f_S$ defined by (17) .

Second, from the function δf_S, we construct the solution δp_S of :

(19) $$\frac{1}{K^o}\ \frac{\partial^2 \delta p_S}{\partial t^2} - \mathrm{div}\left(\frac{1}{\rho^o}\ \overrightarrow{\mathrm{grad}}\ \delta p_S\right) = \delta f_S$$

with the boundary condition (5.c) and the initial conditions (5.b).

We denote by C^{-1} the operator :

(20) $C^{-1} : \delta f_S \to \delta p_S$

C is actually the (restriction to regular functions having a compact support (*) in Ω on the time interval $[0,T]$ and satisfying the conditions (5.b) and (5.c) of the) operator :

$$\frac{1}{K^o}\ \frac{\partial^2}{\partial t^2} - \mathrm{div}\left(\frac{1}{\rho^o}\ \overrightarrow{\mathrm{grad}}\quad\right)$$

At last from the function $\delta p_S(\vec{r},t)$, we construct the observed vector P_S :

$$P_S = \{\delta p_S(\vec{r}_G,t)\}\quad \vec{r}_G \in R_G(S),\ t\in[0,T]$$

We denote by H_S the (observation) operator :

(21) $H_S : \delta p_S\ (\vec{r},t) \to P_S$

So, the operator A_S^K appears to be :

$$A_S^K = H_S\ C^{-1}\ B_S$$

Basically, the principle of the calculation of $A_S^{*K}(Y)$ is the following. Let δK be an arbitrary perturbation and $<\ ,\ >$ denote different duality products. To calculate $< A_S^{*K}(Y),\ \delta K >$ we write :

$$\begin{aligned} < A_S^{*K}(Y),\ \delta K > &= <\ Y,\ H_S\ C^{-1}\ B_S\ \delta K > \\ &= < H_S^*\ Y,\ C^{-1}\ B_S\ \delta K > \end{aligned}$$

* the compact support results from the zero initial conditions, the compact support of the source and the bounded velocity of propagation.

Now we use a mathematical device : we define the function $q_S(\vec{r},t)$ (adjoint state) as the solution of :

$$C^* q_S = H_S^* Y \tag{22}$$

So, we shall have :

$$< A_S^{*K}(Y), \delta K > = < C^* q_S, C^{-1} B_S \delta K >$$
$$= < B^*_S q_S, \delta K >$$

and finally :

$$A_S^{*K}(Y) = B_S^* q_S \tag{23}$$

where q_S is defined by (22).

Then it remains to make explicit the adjoint of operators B_S, C and H_S.

<u>Transposition of H_S</u>. Let $x(\vec{r},t)$ be an arbitrary function and $y(\vec{r}_G,t)$ be the components of vector Y. We can write (*) :

$$< Y, H_S x > = \sum_{\vec{r}_G \in R_G(S)} \int_0^T y(\vec{r}_G,t)\, x(\vec{r}_G,t)\, dt$$

$$= \sum_{\vec{r}_G \in R_G(S)} \int_0^T y(\vec{r}_G,t)\, \delta(\vec{r}-\vec{r}_G)\, x(\vec{r},t)\, d\vec{r}dt$$

where $\delta(\vec{r}-\vec{r}_G)$ denotes the Dirac delta function in $\vec{r}_G$.

Hence (**)

$$H^*_S\ Y = \sum_{\vec{r}_G \in R_G(S)} y(\vec{r}_G,t)\, \delta(\vec{r}-\vec{r}_G) \tag{24}$$

<u>Transposition of C</u>. The transposition of C is obtained by integration by parts. Again let $x(\vec{r},t)$ be an arbitrary function which has a compact support in Ω on [0,T] and satisfies the conditions (5.b) and (5.c). We evaluate (**) :

$$< Cx, q > = \int_0^T \int_\Omega [\frac{1}{K^o} \frac{\partial^2 x}{\partial t^2} - \mathrm{div}(\frac{1}{\rho o}\, \vec{\mathrm{grad}}\ x)]\ q\ d\vec{r}dt$$

*Again we use here the identification of the (Hilbert) space of observations with its dual.

**we use here the identification of the Hilbert space $L^2(\Omega x]0,T[)$ with its dual. This identification is consistent with the previous identifications.

We integrate by parts, using the conditions (5.b) (5.c) and the compactness of the support of x :

$$< Cx,q > = \int_0^T \int_\Omega [\frac{1}{k^o} \frac{\partial^2 q}{\partial t^2} - \mathrm{div}(\frac{1}{\rho^o} \vec{\mathrm{grad}}\ q)]\ x d\vec{r} dt$$

$$(25) \qquad + \int_0^T \int_{z=0} \frac{1}{\rho^o} \frac{\partial x}{\partial z}\ q\ d\vec{r} dt + \int_\Omega \frac{1}{K^o} \frac{\partial x}{\partial t} (T)\ q\ (T)\ d\vec{r}$$

$$- \int_\Omega \frac{1}{K^o}\ x(T) \frac{\partial q}{\partial t} (T)\ d\vec{r}$$

Hence, as q_S satisfies for any x (cf. (22)) :

$$< C^*_{q_S}, x > = \sum_{\vec{r}_G \in R_G(S)} \int_0^T \int_\Omega y(\vec{r}_G, t)\ \delta(\vec{r}-\vec{r}_G)\ x(\vec{r},t) d\vec{r} dt$$

q_S appears to be the solution of :

$$(26.a) \quad \frac{1}{K^o} \frac{\partial^2 q_S}{\partial t^2} - \mathrm{div}(\frac{1}{\rho^o} \vec{\mathrm{grad}}\ q_S) = \sum_{\vec{r}_G \in R_G(S)} y(\vec{r}_G, t)\ \delta(\vec{r}-\vec{r}_G) \quad \text{in } \Omega \times [0,T]$$

$$(26.b) \quad q_S = 0 \quad \text{for } t \geq T \text{ (final conditions)}$$

$$(26.c) \quad q_S = 0 \quad \text{for } z = 0 \text{ (boundary condition)}$$

Equations (26.a) (26.b) (26.c) characterize the adjoint state formally defined by (22).

Transposition of B_S. Let us consider now an arbitrary perturbation $\delta K(\vec{r})$. We evaluate :

$$< q_S, B_S\ \delta K > = \int_0^T \int_\Omega q_S\ (\vec{r},t) \frac{\delta K(r)}{(K^o(\vec{r}))^2} \frac{\partial^2 p^o_S}{\partial t^2} (\vec{r},t)\ d\vec{r} dt$$

Hence $B^*_S\ q_S$ is the function of $\vec{r}$ defined by :

$$(27) \qquad B^*_S\ q_S = \frac{1}{(K^o(\vec{r}))^2} \int_0^T q_S(\vec{r},t) \frac{\partial^2 p^o_S}{\partial t^2} (\vec{r},t)\ dt$$

Summary (solution of the inverse problem for δK). We assume here that $\delta\rho = 0$. It amounts to assuming that the density is known or that we neglect the perturbations $\delta\rho$ with respect to the perturbations δK as is often done.

So one iteration of the gradient algorithm consists in computing :

$$\delta K_{n+1}(\vec{r}) = \delta K_n(\vec{r}) + \frac{\lambda n}{(K^o(\vec{r}))^2}\, g(\vec{r}) \tag{28}$$

where $g(\vec{r})$ is defined by :

$$g(\vec{r}) = \sum_{S \in R_S} \int_0^T \frac{\partial^2 p_S^o}{\partial t^2}(\vec{r},t)\, q_S(\vec{r},t)\, dt \tag{29}$$

with q_S solution of the adjoint equations (26) in which $y(\vec{r}_G,t)$ are the components of the vector Y equal to $P_S^{obs} - \mathcal{A}_S(0,\delta K_n)$ (cf. (16)).

Interpretation of the first iteration. We are now going to interpret the algorithm in the case of a smooth reference medium. To compute $\frac{\partial^2 p_S^o}{\partial t^2}$ (which appears in (29)) we can solve equations (4) using, as a second member in equation (4.a), the second time derivative of the source function : as previously said this is just the calculation of the downgoing waves generated by the (second time derivatives of the) sources.

If we choose the initial guess δK_o to be zero, then solving the adjoint equations (26) is the so called "downward extrapolation", for each shot, of the observed seismograms in "before stack migration".

The calculation of $g(\vec{r})$ defined by (29) consists in stacking, in both time and source location, the events when there is a time coincidence (*) of the downgoing wavefield and downward extrapolated wave field: this is the "imaging principle" (**) as formulated by Claerbout [2]. In conclusion, the first iteration of the gradient algorithm applied to problem (P1) is the classical before stack migration applied with a slightly modified "imaging principle".

Interpretation of the following iterations. Following iterations appear to consist in a downward extrapolation of the residual seismograms (i.e. the difference between the responses of $\mathcal{A}_S(0, \delta K_n)$ to the sources and the observed seismograms) which the previous "imaging principle" is applied to. In other words the following iterations are a sequence of before stack migration of the residuals.

*it is the only case which makes the product $\frac{\partial^2 p^o_S}{\partial t^2}\, q_S$ different from 0.

** The classical formulation of the "imaging principle" requires to stack the ratio between the amplitude of the upgoing and downgoing wave fields which is understandable from amplitude considerations. So the first iteration mainly takes account of the time arrivals and we need the following iterations to obtain a correct amplitude processing. On the other hand, inversion does not assume an impulse wavelet.

Simultaneous calculation of the perturbations $\delta\rho$ and δK. Similarly it can be shown that one iteration of the gradient algorithm to solve the inverse problem for both $\delta\rho$ and δK consists in computing :

$$\delta K_{n+1}(\vec{r}) = \delta K_n(\vec{r}) + \frac{\lambda_n}{(K^o(\vec{r}))^2} g(\vec{r}) \tag{28}$$

$$\delta\rho_{n+1}(\vec{r}) = \delta\rho_n(\vec{r}) + \frac{\lambda_n}{(\rho^o(\vec{r}))^2} h(\vec{r}) \tag{30}$$

where $g(\vec{r})$ and $h(\vec{r})$ are defined respectively by (29) and :

$$h(\vec{r}) = \sum_{S\in R_S} \int_0^T \vec{\text{grad}}\, p_S^o(\vec{r},t) \cdot \vec{\text{grad}}\, q_S(\vec{r},t)\, dt \tag{31}$$

with q_S solution of the adjoint equations (26) in which Y is equal to $p_S^{obs} - \mathcal{A}_S(\delta\rho_n, \delta K_n)$.

5. Conclusions. We have given a mathematical basis to the commonly used "before stack migration" technique. In this way, we have checked, provided that the underlying assumptions are verified, the interest of such a technique.

On the other hand, we have also seen the limitations of this technique and we suggest an actual inversion to replace (and improve !) before stack migration. For instance we can expect the possibility for the inversion to use the redundancy in the data to separate nearly completely the noise from the signal, as it has been checked for the 1 D VSP inverse problem (cf. Lailly and Macé [5]) where the data are also redundant. This improvement of the signal to noise ratio was very partial in the before stack migration approach.

The main weakness of the linearized inverse problem is the necessity to dispose of a good approximation of the actual medium (which will be the reference medium). It is also the main weakness of before stack migration. For many field examples, such an accurate knowledge will not be available. In this case we can only suggest the use of a non linear inversion algorithm which is (theoretically) very similar to the one described here : to calculate the gradient at iteration n, we linearize the forward problem about the earth model obtained at iteration n (for further detail, cf. Tarantola [8]).

The previous results can also be generalized to more complicated (and more realistic) mathematical models (for instance, the elastic wave equation, cf. Tarantola [9]).

We are convinced that, using the new generations of computers, it will be possible to solve such complicated inverse problems in a few years and then significant progress will be made beyond the stage "before stack migration."

Acknowledgements. I would like to thank Albert Tarantola from Institut de Physique du Globe (Paris) who suggested that I try a generalization of the results he has obtained in [7] and Samuel Gray from Amoco Production Company (Tulsa, Oklahoma) for very fruitful discussions on this subject.

REFERENCES

[1] A. BAMBERGER, G. CHAVENT and P. LAILLY, About the stability of the inverse problem in a 1-D wave equation - Application to the interpretation of seismic profiles, Journ. Appl. Math. Optim. 5 (1979), pp. 1-47.

[2] J.F. CLAERBOUT, Toward a unified theory of reflector mapping, Geophysics 36 (1971), pp. 467-481.

[3] R.W. CLAYTON and R.M. STOLT, A Born WKBJ inversion method for acoustic reflection data, Geophysics 46 (1981), pp. 1559-1568.

[4] R. FLETCHER, Practical methods of optimization, John Wiley and Sons, New-York, 1980.

[5] P. LAILLY and D. MACE, The solution of the 1 D VSP inverse problem, Paper presented at the 45th annual EAEG Meeting, Oslo, 1983.

[6] J.L. LIONS, Contrôle optimal de systèmes gouvernés par des équations aux dérivées partielles, Dunod, Paris, 1968, English translation, Springer-Verlag, New-York, 1972.

[7] A. TARANTOLA, Iterative migration = inversion, Part 1 : linearized problem for a homogeneous reference model, Submitted to Geophysical Prospecting.

[8] A. TARANTOLA, Iterative migration = inversion, Part 2 : non linear inverse problem for a heterogeneous acoustic medium, Submitted to Geophysics.

[9] A. TARANTOLA, Communication at the Workshop meeting on "seismic waves in laterally inhomogeneous media", Liblice near Prague, 1983.

[10] A. TARANTOLA and B. VALETTE, Generalized non linear inverse problems solved using the least-squares criterion, Reviews of Geophysics and Space Physics, 20 (1982), pp. 219-232.

Inversion of the 2.5 – D Acoustic Equation

Shimon Coen*, Margaret Cheney** and Arthur Weglein†

Abstract. An inverse acoustic scattering theory and algorithm is presented for the reconstruction of a two dimensional inhomogeneous acoustic medium from surface measurements. The measurements of the surface pressure due to a harmonically oscillating surface point source at two arbitrary frequencies allows the separate reconstruction of the density and velocity of the subsurface. The solution of the inverse acoustic scattering problem is obtained by a transformation to an inverse quantum scattering problem in two dimension, the solution of which has been obtained recently by Cheney, who was inspired by Newton's solution in three dimensions. The solution presented is a generalization of Coen's and Stickler and Deift's solutions of the three dimensional acoustic problem for a plane stratified acoustic medium.

1. Introduction The problem we consider is that of reconstructing the subsurface velocity and density from surface measurements of pressure waves emanating from an oscillating point source on the surface. A natural approach to this problem is to transform the acoustic equation into the Schrödinger equation in order to take advantage of the great body of knowledge on inverse scattering. Ware and Aki(1) for example, did this for the one-dimensional inverse elastic scattering problem; Coen(2) similarly transformed the two and three dimensional acoustic and elastic inverse scattering problems for the cases of plane and spherically stratified media. In particular he showed that the density and velocity profiles of a plane stratified acoustic medium are uniquely determined from point source surface data at any two distinct frequencies.

Recently the inverse scattering techniques of Marchenko(3) and Gel'fand-Levitan(4) have been extended to three dimensions by Newton(5)

* Engineering Geoscience, Department of Materials Science and Mineral Engineering, University of California, Berkeley, CA 94720
** Department of Mathematics, Stanford University, Stanford, CA 94305
† Geophysical Research, Sohio Petroleum Company, 1 Lincoln Center, 5400 LBJ Freeway, Dallas, TX 75240

and to two dimensions by Cheney[6]. (For other multidimensional approaches, see references in (5) and (6).) This has suggested the possibility of applying inverse scattering techniques to the multi-dimensional acoustic equation; however, for a number of years attempts to transform the higher dimensional acoustic equation into the Schrödinger equation have been unsuccessful. This paper overcomes this difficulty and goes on to apply inverse scattering techniques to the "2½ dimensional" acoustic equation.

We transform the three dimensional acoustic inverse scattering problem for a two dimensional acoustic medium into an equivalent inverse quantum scattering problem in two dimensions with a potential which is real, independent of energy, and which has compact support. The solution procedure contains 4 parts: 1) Transformation of the acoustic equation to the two dimensional Schrödinger equation. 2) Transformation of the acoustic data into equivalent quantum scattering data - the scattering amplitude. 3) Reconstruction of the potential from the scattering amplitude via Cheney's procedure. 4) Reconstruction of the velocity and density of the acoustic medium from the potential.

Transformation of the Acoustic Equation into the Schrödinger Equation. The pressure $p(\vec{r},\vec{r}_s,\omega)$ in a fluid with density $\rho(\vec{r})$ and local wave velocity $c(\vec{r})$, due to a harmonically oscillating point source at $\vec{r}_s$ with frequency ω, is governed by the inhomogeneous acoustic equation

$$(1) \qquad \{\nabla^2 - \frac{\nabla\rho}{\rho}\cdot\nabla + \frac{\omega^2}{c^2}\}\, p(\vec{r},\vec{r}_s,\omega) = \delta(\vec{r}-\vec{r}_s) .$$

Let (x,y,z) denote the cartesian coordinates of $\vec{r}$. We assume that:
I) The density and local wave velocity are uniform in the y direction, that $\rho = \rho(x,z)$ and $c = c(x,z)$.
II) The density and velocity are uniform exterior to the circle $x^2 + z^2 = a^2$ so that $\rho = \rho_0$ and $c = c_0$ for $x^2+z^2 \geq a^2$, a being a finite constant.
III) The exterior velocity c_0 satisfies $c_0 \leq c(x,z)$ for all x and z. (This condition excludes bound states.)

We also assume either of the two following geometries:
IV) The point sources are placed on a circle at positions $r_s = (x_s,0,z_s)$ with $x_s^2+z_s^2 = a^2$.
(IV') The point sources are placed on two planes at positions $\vec{r}_s = (x_s,0,a)$ and $\vec{r}_s = (x_s,0,-a)$.

The transformation

$$\Phi(\vec{r}_t,\vec{r}_s,k,\omega) = \frac{1}{\sqrt{2\pi}}\, g(\vec{r}_t) \int_{-\infty}^{\infty} p(\vec{r},\vec{r}_s,\omega)e^{-iky}dy$$

(2)

$$g(\vec{r}_t) = \left[\frac{\rho(\vec{r}_t)}{\rho_0}\right]^{-\frac{1}{2}} , \quad \vec{r}_t = (x,o,z)$$

transforms eq. (1) into

(3) $$(\nabla_t^2+\xi^2)\psi(r_t,r_s,\xi) = v(\vec{r}_t;\omega)\psi(\vec{r}_t,\vec{r}_s,\xi) + \delta(\vec{r}_t-\vec{r}_s)$$

where

(4) $$\xi^2 = \frac{\omega^2}{c_0^2} - k^2$$

(5) $$v(\vec{r}_t;\omega) = \frac{\omega^2}{c_0^2}\left[1 - \frac{c_0^2}{c^2(\vec{r}_t)}\right] + \frac{\nabla_t^2 g(\vec{r}_t)}{g(\vec{r}_t)}$$

$$\psi(\vec{r}_t,\vec{r}_s,\xi) = \Phi(\vec{r}_t,\vec{r}_s,k,\omega)$$

and $\nabla_t^2 = \frac{\partial^2}{\partial x^2} + \frac{\partial^2}{\partial z^2}$ is the transverse Laplacian. Equation (3) for $\vec{r}_t \neq \vec{r}_s$ is a two dimensional Schrödinger equation where ξ plays the role of energy and v plays the role of potential which in this case is <u>energy independent</u> with ω being a <u>fixed</u> parameter.

To obtain data for the inverse problem under assumption IV, we measure the pressure at the boundary of the cylinder of radius a, thus obtaining $p(\vec{r},\vec{r}_s,\omega)$ for all $\vec{r}$ of the form $\vec{r} = (x,y,z)$ with $x^2+z^2 = a^2$ and for all $\vec{r}_s$ satisfying assumption IV above. To obtain data under assumption IV', we measure the pressure at $\vec{r} = (x,y,a)$ for sources at $(x_s,0,a)$ and $(x_s,0,-a)$, and at $\vec{r} = (x,y,-a)$ for sources at $(x_s,0,-a)$. In either case, the transformation (4) transforms these data into $\psi(\vec{r}_t,\vec{r}_s,\xi)$ for equation (3), which is known for all $\vec{r}_t$ and $\vec{r}_s$ as above and for ξ of the form $\xi^2 = \frac{\omega^2}{c_0^2} - k^2$ for all real k. In the ξ variable, we therefore have data on the positive imaginary axis and on the interval $(0,\omega/c_0)$ of the real axis.

Transformation to Plane Wave Incidence Equation (3) may be cast into the Lippmann-Schwinger integral equation

$$(6)\quad \psi(\vec{r}_t,\vec{r}_s,\xi) = G(\vec{r}_t,\vec{r}_s,\xi) + \int_{|\vec{r}'|<a} v(\vec{r}';\omega)\psi(\vec{r}',\vec{r}_s,\xi)G(\vec{r}_t,\vec{r}',\xi)d^2\vec{r}'$$

where

$$G(\vec{r}_t,\vec{r}',\xi) = -\frac{i}{4}H_0^{(1)}(\xi|\vec{r}_t-\vec{r}'|)$$

is the two dimensional Green's function. We rewrite eq. (6) as

$$\psi(\vec{r}_t,\vec{r}_s,\xi) = G(\vec{r}_t,\vec{r}_s,\xi) + \psi^{sc}(\vec{r}_t,\vec{r}_s,\xi)$$

where ψ^{sc} denotes the scattered wave function.

If the incident field were the plane wave $e^{i\vec{\xi}\cdot\vec{r}_t}$ with $|\vec{\xi}| = \xi$ rather than the two dimensional Green's function $G(\vec{r}_t,\vec{r}_s,\xi)$, then eq. (3) would be

$$(7)\quad (\nabla_t^2+\xi^2)\phi(\vec{r}_t,\vec{\xi},\xi) = v(\vec{r}_t;\omega)\phi(\vec{r}_t,\vec{\xi},\xi)$$

with a corresponding Lippmann-Schwinger integral equation

$$(8)\quad \phi(\vec{r}_t,\vec{\xi},\xi) = e^{i\vec{\xi}\cdot\vec{r}_t} + \int_{|\vec{r}'|<a} v(\vec{r}';\omega)\phi(\vec{r}',\vec{\xi},\xi)G(\vec{r}_t,\vec{r}',\xi)d^2\vec{r}'$$

which may be rewritten as

$$(9)\quad \phi(\vec{r}_t,\vec{\xi},\xi) = e^{i\vec{\xi}\cdot\vec{r}_t} + \phi^{sc}(\vec{r}_t,\vec{\xi},\xi)\ .$$

For geometry IV, an argument modelled on that of Berezanskii[7] allows us to relate ϕ^{sc} to ψ^{sc} by means of the formula

$$(10a)\quad \phi^{sc}(\vec{r}_t,\vec{\xi},\xi) = \sum_{n=0}^{\infty}{}' \frac{4i^{n+1}}{\pi H_n^{(1)}(\xi a)} \int_0^{2\pi} \psi^{sc}(\vec{r}_t,\vec{r}_s,\xi)\cos(n\theta_{s\xi})d\theta_s$$

for $|\vec{r}_t| = a = |\vec{r}_s|$. The prime on the summation sign in (10a) indicates that the $n = 0$ term is multiplied by 1/2.

For geometry IV', for reflection from the upper plane $z = a$, we use

(10b) $$\phi^{sc}(\vec{r},\vec{\xi},\xi) = i\xi \cos\theta_\xi \int_{-\infty}^{\infty} \psi^{sc}(\vec{r},\vec{r}_s,\xi)\exp(ix_s\xi \sin\theta_\xi)dx_s ,$$

where θ_ξ is the angle between $\vec{r}_s$ and $\vec{\xi}$; for reflection from the lower plane $z = -a$ and for transmission there are similar formulae.

The transformation (10) allows us to transform our point source data into plane-wave-incident data; however, we still have the problem that our data are known on the imaginary axis and not on the whole real axis. Following Stickler and Deift[8], we deal with this problem as follows.

We know from the Lippmann-Schwinger equation (Eq. (8)) that in the absence of bound and half-bound states $\Phi = \exp(-i\vec{\xi}\cdot\vec{r})\phi^{sc}$ is analytic in the upper half ξ plane. Moreover, a generalization of a proof in Cheney[6] shows that Φ is in the Hardy space H^{2+}, which is the space of functions analytic in the upper half-plane that are uniformly square-integrable on each horizontal line. In order to obtain Φ on the real axis, we now apply a theorem of Van Winter's[9]. Her theorem allows us to determine Φ for real ξ by means of two successive transforms. We first form the Mellin transform

$$\tilde{\Phi}(\vec{r}_t,\vec{\xi},t) = \exp(-\pi t/2 + i\pi/4) \int_0^{\infty} \Phi(\vec{r}_t,\vec{\xi},is)s^{it-\frac{1}{2}}ds ;$$

then we perform the inverse Mellin transform

(11) $$\exp(-i\vec{\xi}\cdot\vec{r})\phi^{sc}(\vec{r}_t,\vec{\xi},\xi) = (2\pi)^{-1} \int_{-\infty}^{\infty} \tilde{\Phi}(\vec{r}_t,\vec{\xi},t)\xi^{-it-\frac{1}{2}}dt .$$

We have noted that the applicability of this formula depends on the absence of bound states. The presence or absence of bound states, however, can be ascertained from the data, because bound states give rise to poles of $\phi(\vec{r}_t,\vec{\xi},\xi)$ that are located precisely on the imaginary axis.

<u>The Scattering Amplitude</u> The scattering amplitude $A(\xi,\hat{\alpha},\hat{\beta}) = A_1(\xi,\vec{\xi}',\vec{\xi})$, corresponding to plane wave incidence in the $\vec{\xi} = \hat{\beta}\xi$ direction and scattered cylindrical wave in direction $\vec{\xi}' = \hat{\alpha}\beta$, must next be determined from $\phi^{sc}(\vec{r}_t,\vec{\xi},\xi)$ for $|\vec{r}_t| = a$ (for assumption IV) or $\vec{r}_t = (x,0,a)$ and $\vec{r}_t = (x,0,-a)$ (for assumption IV'). First

we consider the case of assumption IV. Because ϕ^{sc} for $|\vec{r}_t| \geq a$ satisfies the Schrödinger equation with zero potential and also satisfies the radiation condition at $|\vec{r}_t| \to \infty$, we can immediately write the solution for $|\vec{r}_t| \geq a$,

$$\phi^{sc}(\vec{r}_t,\vec{\xi},\xi) = \sum_{m=-\infty}^{\infty} \frac{H_m^{(1)}(\xi|\vec{r}_t|)e^{-im}}{2\pi H_m^{(1)}(\xi a)} \int_0^{2\pi} \phi^{sc}(\vec{r}_t,\vec{\xi},\xi)\Big|_{|\vec{r}'_t|=a} e^{im\theta'_t} d\theta'_t$$

from which, by using the asymptotic expansion of the Hankel functions for large argument, we conclude that

$$\text{(12)} \quad A_1(\xi,\vec{\xi}',\vec{\xi}) = \sum_{m=-\infty}^{\infty} \frac{4e^{-im(\theta'+\pi/2)}}{2\pi H_m^{(1)}(\xi a)} \int_0^{2\pi} \phi^{sc}(\vec{r}_t,\vec{\xi},\xi)\Big|_{|\vec{r}_t|=a} e^{im\theta_t} d\theta_t$$

where $\vec{\xi}' = (\xi \sin\theta', \xi\cos\theta')$.

Now, under assumption IV', and for the case of reflection from above,

$$A(\xi,\hat{\alpha},\hat{\beta}) = -i\xi\cos\theta_\beta \int_{-\infty}^{\infty} \phi^{sc}(\vec{r},\vec{\xi},\xi)e^{-ix\xi\sin\theta_\beta}\,dx$$

where $\hat{\beta} = (\cos\theta_\beta, \sin\theta_\beta)$. The results for reflection from below and transmission are similar. Weglein, Boyse and Anderson[10a], Weglein and Silvia[10b] and Stolt and Jacobs[11] provided various equivalent methods for extracting $A(\xi,\hat{\alpha},\hat{\beta})$ from ψ^{sc} for situations such as IV and IV'.

<u>Reconstruction of the Potential from the Scattering Amplitude via Cheney's Procedure</u> We now use $A(\xi,\hat{\alpha},\hat{\beta})$ as input into the two-dimensional inverse scattering machinery of Cheney[6]. We compute the kernel G of the Marchenko equation,

$$G_{\vec{r}}(s,\hat{\alpha},\hat{\beta}) = -2(2\pi)^{3/2} i \int_{-\infty}^{\infty} \exp[i\xi(s+(\hat{\alpha}-\hat{\beta})\cdot\vec{r})]\overline{(\operatorname{sgn}\xi)A(\xi,\hat{\alpha},\hat{\beta})d\xi} ,$$

where the bar denotes complex conjugate. We insert $G_{\vec{r}}$ into the Marchenko equation

$$\text{(13)} \quad \eta(s,\hat{\alpha},\vec{r}) = \int_0^{\infty}\!\!\int_{S^1} G_{\vec{r}}(s+q,\hat{\alpha},\hat{\beta})\eta(q,-\hat{\beta},\vec{r})d\hat{\beta}dq + \int_{S^1} G_{\vec{r}}(s,\hat{\alpha},\hat{\beta})d\hat{\beta}$$

where S^1 denotes the unit circle and $s > 0$. For each $\vec{r}$, we must then solve (13) for $\eta(s,\hat{\alpha},\vec{r})$, from which the potential $V(\vec{r};\omega)$ can be computed via

$$(14) \qquad V(\vec{r};\omega) = -2\hat{\alpha}\cdot\nabla_{\vec{r}}\, \eta(s,\hat{\alpha},\vec{r})\Big|_{s=0^+} .$$

We remark that this solution must be miraculous, i.e., the right side of (14) must be independent of $\hat{\alpha}$. It is for this reason that we are limited to solving the reconstruction problem; in other words we must assume that we begin not with arbitrary data but rather with data that is known to correspond to an acoustic medium with twice differentiable velocity and four times differentiable density.

An alternative method is to use the Born approximation to reconstruct the potential from the large ξ behavior of $A(\xi,\hat{\alpha},\hat{\beta})$; see Cheney[6].

Reconstruction of the Velocity and Density from the Potential If, as in Coen[2], we perform the acoustic experiment with any two distinct frequencies, ω_1 and ω_2, the procedure described above will reproduce the two potentials $V(\vec{r}_t;\omega_\ell)$, $\ell = 1,2$. The velocity is then given by

$$\frac{c^2(\vec{r}_t)}{c_0^2} = \frac{\omega_1^2-\omega_2^2}{\omega_1^2-\omega_2^2-c_0^2[V(\vec{r}_t;\omega_1)-V(\vec{r}_t;\omega_2)]}$$

and the density is found by solving the following Dirichlet problem:

$$(15) \qquad \{\nabla_t^2 - \varepsilon(\vec{r}_t;\omega_1)\}\, g(\vec{r}_t) = 0 , \qquad g(\vec{r}_t)\Big|_{|\vec{r}_t|=a} = 1$$

where $$\varepsilon(\vec{r}_t;\omega_1) = V(\vec{r}_t;\omega_1) - \frac{\omega_1^2}{c_0^2}\left(1 - \frac{c_0^2}{c^2(\vec{r}_t)}\right)$$

and $$\frac{\rho(\vec{r}_t)}{\rho_0} = g^{-2}(\vec{r}_t) .$$

General facts about elliptic equations imply that the solution g of (15) is unique if it is positive; it is guaranteed to be positive if we are doing a reconstruction problem.

Numerical Implementation There are a number of difficulties connected with numerical implementation of the foregoing inversion algorithm. The first difficulty is the necessity of making an analytic continuation of the data. Analytic continuations are notoriously unstable. Nevertheless, this process can be completely avoided by using only the data we have on the real axis, namely $\phi^{sc}(\vec{r}_t,\vec{\xi},\xi)$ for $0 \le \xi \le \frac{\omega}{c_0}$. Use of this data alone should lead to an answer with limited resolution. For the one-dimensional inverse scattering case, a theory of inversion using limited data has been worked out by Mel'nikov[12]; the higher dimensional version has yet to be investigated.

A second difficulty in numerical implementation occurs in solving the Marchenko equation. First of all, in order to have a hope of a unique solution, all bound and half-bound states must be absent. The main computational difficulty, however, is that the Marchenko equation (13) must be solved for each $\vec{r}$. This involves an enormous amount of calculation. It is possible that a two-dimensional Gel'fand-Levitan method would be more tractable, but a two-dimensional version of Newton's Gel'fand-Levitan method has not yet been worked out.

A third difficulty with practical implementation is that imperfectly known data may lead to a non-miraculous solution of the Marchenko equation. The meaning and relevance of such a solution is unknown at present.

REFERENCES

[1] J. A. Ware and K. Aki, Continuous and discrete inverse scattering problems in a stratified elastic medium. I. Plane waves at normal incidence. J. Acoust. Soc. of America, 45 (1969), pp. 911-921.

[2] S. Coen, On the elastic profiles of a layered medium from reflection data. Part I: Plane wave sources, J. Acoust. Soc. of America, 70 (1981), pp. 172-175, The inverse problem of the shear modulus and density profiles of a layered earth, J. Geophys. Res., 86 (1981), pp. 6052-6056, Density and compressibility profiles of a layered acoustic medium from precritical incidence data, Geophysics, 46 (1981), pp. 1244-1246, The inverse problem of the shear modulus and density profiles of a layered earth - torsional vibration data, J. Math. Phys., 10 (1981), pp. 2338-2341, On the elastic profiles of a layered medium from reflection data. Part II: Impulsive point source, J. Acoust. Soc. of America, 70 (1981), pp. 1473-1479, Velocity and density profiles of a layered acoustic medium from common source point data, Geophysics 47 (1982), pp. 898-905, The inverse problem of the density and bulk modulus profiles of a layered fluid, Bull. Seis. Soc. of America, 72 (1982), pp. 809-820, The inverse problem of a spherically symmetric fluid earth, J. Geophys. Res., 88 (1983), pp. 4299-4303.

[3] V. A. Marchenko, The construction of the potential energy from the phases of the scattered waves, Math. Rev. 17, 740 (1956).

[4] I. M. Gel'fand and B. M. Levitan, On the determination of a differential equation from its spectral function, AMS Transl. ser. 2 (1955), p. 253.

[5] R. G. Newton, (5a) Inverse Scattering II. Three dimensions, J. Math. Phys. 21 (1980), pp. 1698-1715, (5b) Inverse Scattering III. Three dimensions, continued, 22 (1981), pp. 2191-2200, and (5c) Inverse Scattering IV. Three dimensions: generalized Marchenko construction with bound states, and generalized Gel'fand Levitan equations, 23 (1982), pp. 594-604.

[6] M. Cheney, "Quantum Mechanical Scattering and Inverse Scattering in Two Dimensions", Ph.D. thesis, Indiana University (1982), and submitted to J. Math. Phys. under titles "Two dimensional scattering: number of bound states from scattering data" and "Inverse scattering in dimension two".

[7] Ju. M. Berezanskii, The Uniqueness theorem in the inverse problem of spectral analysis for the Schrödinger equation, A,S Transl. ser. 2, 35 (1964), pp. 167-235.

[8] D. C. Stickler and P. A. Deift, Inverse problem for a stratified ocean and bottom, J. Acoust. Soc. of America, 70 (1981), pp. 1723-1727.

[9] C. Van Winter, Fredholm equations on a Hilbert space of analytic functions, Trans. AMS, 162 (1971), pp. 103-139.

[10a] A. B. Weglein, W. E. Boyse, and J. E. Anderson, Obtaining three-dimensional velocity information directly from reflection seismic data: An inverse scattering formalism, Geophysics, 48 (1981), pp. 1116-1120.

[10b] A. B. Weglein and M. T. Silvia, "Scattering theory approach to the identification of the Helmholtz equation: a near-field solution," J. Acoust. Soc. Am., Vol. 69 (1981), pp. 483-488.

[11] R. H. Stolt and B. Jacobs, "Inversion of seismic data in a laterally heterogeneous media," paper presented at the 1980, S.E.G. meeting, Houston, Texas.

[12] V. K. Mel'nikov, On Approximate methods in the inverse problem of the quantum theory of scattering, Ser. 2, 25, pp. 271-282.

** Research was supported by the National Science Foundation, the Army Research Office, the Office of Naval Research and the Air Force Office of Scientific Research.

Some Transmutation Methods in Geophysics

Robert Carroll* and Fadil Santosa**

Abstract. A model one dimensional inverse problem is studied with initial impulse disturbance at the origin $x = 0$, $t = 0$ and transmission readout $H(t)$ at $x = \tilde{x}$ sufficiently large. Using the transmutation machine of [9] one connects $H(t)$ with the impulse response $G(t)$ at $x = 0$. This leads to a formula for the spectral measure as the Fourier transform of an autocorrelation function $\mathcal{H}(t)$ involving H' and thence to a formula $G'(t) = A_\infty \mathcal{H}(t)$. From this the inverse problem for the acoustic impedance A as a function of travel time y can be solved and stability estimates obtained. Finite domain dependence of G, H, and A is indicated and a new type of extended Gelfand-Levitan (G-L) equation is obtained involving H, G, and the G-L kernel K.

1. Basic constructions. We consider the inverse problem for $\rho(x)v_{tt} = (\mu(x)v_x)_x$ ($v = 0$ for $t < 0$) where some initial disturbance is supplied at (0,0) and from the readout or response at some point $x = \tilde{x}$ (transmission data) one wants to find the acoustic impedance $A = (\rho\mu)^{\frac{1}{2}}$ as a function of travel time $y = \int_0^x (\rho/\mu)^{\frac{1}{2}} d\xi$. One can think here of SH waves in a vertically stratified earth, where ρ = density and μ is a shear modulus, and with readout $G(t) = v(0,t)$ (reflection data) this kind of problem has been treated in various ways (cf. [1;2;4-6;8-11; 16-22;24;27;31-33;36-39]). We are motivated by certain problems of wave propagation in a spherically symmetric medium with impulse disturbance at the origin and readout at $r = \tilde{r}$ for example (cf. [1-3;12-14;26-30]). With the change of variables to travel time y our equation becomes

$$v_{tt} = (Av_y)_y/A = Q(D_y)v; \; v = 0 \text{ for } t < 0 \tag{1.1}$$

and we assume $\rho, \mu \in C^1$ with ρ and μ constant for large $x \geq \tilde{x}$. Hence

* Mathematics Dept., University of Illinois, Urbana, Illinois 61801
** Dept. of Theoretical and Applied Mechanics, Cornell University, Ithaca, New York 14853
Work partially supported by ONR contract #N00014-83-K0051

$A' = 0$ and $A = A_\infty$ (known) eventually with $0 < a \le A(y) \le A < \infty$. By rescaling if necessary we assume $A(0) = 1$ and let us note that as x increases so does $y(x)$. We will show that (with impulse input at (0, 0) the readout $H(t)$ at sufficiently large $x = \tilde{x}$ determines the spectral measure $d\omega = \omega(\lambda)d\lambda$ in a striking manner. Indeed one has $\omega(\lambda) = (2A_\infty/\pi)|\mathcal{F}H'|^2$ where $\mathcal{F}$ denotes Fourier transform and $|\mathcal{F}H'|^2$ is of course the Fourier transform of an autocorrelation type function $\mathcal{H}$ for H'. The connection here to strings and prediction theory etc. will be examined at another time (cf. [15;20-23;25]). Once ω is known we can recover A by the techniques of [9-11;31] and in fact (cf. Theorem 3.2) $G'(t) = A_\infty\mathcal{H}(t)$ where $G(t) = v(0,t)$ is the impulse response readout at $x = 0$ (reflection data).

<u>Example 1.1.</u> Take $A = 1$ and start with input data $v_y(0,t) = -\delta(t)$ as in [10;31]. The solution of (1.1) is then $v(y,t) = Y(t-y)$ (for $y,t \ge 0$) where Y denotes the Heavyside function. Thus $v_y = -\delta(t-y) \to -\delta(t)$ as $y \to 0$ and $v(0,t) = Y(t)$ with say $v(1,t) = Y(t-1)$. We note that the solution could also arise from an impulse $v_t(y,0) = \delta(y)$ or from a nonhomogeneous equation with a forcing term as in [36] - cf. [9] for the connections. The Fourier transform is $\mathcal{F}T = \int_{-\infty}^{\infty} T(t)\exp(i\lambda t)dt$ and (1.1) becomes ($\hat{v}(y,\lambda) = \mathcal{F}v(y,t)$), $\hat{v}_{yy} + \lambda^2\hat{v} = 0$. Since $v = 0$ for $t < 0$ we must have $\hat{v} = A(\lambda)\exp(i\lambda y)$ and with input $\hat{v}_y(0,\lambda) = -1$ it follows that $A = -(1/i\lambda)$ so $\hat{v} = -\exp(i\lambda y)/i\lambda$. Now (cf. [7]) $\mathcal{F}\{Y(t) - Y(-t)\} = -2/i\lambda$ ($\mathcal{F}Y = \pi\delta(\lambda) - 1/i\lambda$) and $\mathcal{F}\delta(t-y) = \exp(i\lambda y)$ so via the full Fourier theory one is led to $v = \frac{1}{2}\{Y(t-y) - Y(-t-y)\}$; $v_y = -\frac{1}{2}\{\delta(t-y) - \delta(-t-y)\}$; $v_t = \frac{1}{2}\{\delta(t-y) + \delta(-t-y)\}$. However working only from the quadrant $y,t \ge 0$ we multiply by 2 and drop $Y(-t-y) = 0$ to get $v_y \to -\delta(t)$ as $y \to 0$ and $v_t \to \delta(y)$ as $t \to 0$ (note $\delta(y) \equiv \delta(-y)$ and cf. [9]). This Fourier picture also shows how a natural odd and even extension in t of v is associated with the situation.

In any event we will deal now with (1.1) and impulse data (♦) $\delta(y) = v_t(y,0)$ whose solution in the model case $A = 1$ is $v(y,t) = Y(t-y)$ $(y,t \ge 0)$. We refer now to [9] (cf. also [35;37]) and will discuss various aspects of solving this problem. Thus let φ_λ^Q denote "spherical functions" satisfying (*) $Q\varphi = -\lambda^2\varphi$ with $\varphi_\lambda^Q(0) = 1$ and $D_y\varphi_\lambda^Q(0) = 0$. One can express Riemann functions for example in terms of transmutation kernels (cf. [9]) and we write first

$$S(y,t,\eta) = \langle \varphi_\lambda^Q(y)\varphi_\lambda^Q(\eta), \text{Cos}\lambda t\rangle_\omega; \qquad (1.2)$$

$$R(y,t,\eta) = \langle \varphi_\lambda^Q(y)\varphi_\lambda^Q(\eta), \text{Sin}\lambda t/\lambda\rangle_\omega$$

where ω denotes the Q-spectral pairing. For general A of the type treated here one has $d\omega = d\omega_Q = \omega_Q(\lambda)d\lambda = \omega d\lambda$ with $\omega = 1/2\pi|c_Q(\lambda)|^2$ (in [9;10;31] a factor A_∞ appeared in the denominator of ω because of the way the Jost solutions were normalized). In this connection let us define the Jost solutions of (*) by $\Phi^Q_{\pm\lambda}(y) \sim A_\infty^{-\frac{1}{2}}\exp(\pm i\lambda y)$ as $y \to \infty$ and one has $\varphi^Q_\lambda = c_Q(\lambda)\Phi^Q_\lambda + c_Q(-\lambda)\Phi^Q_{-\lambda}$ (A_∞ can be assumed known). Now for the solution of (1.1) with Cauchy data $v(y,0) = f(y)$ and $v_t(y,0) = F(y)$ one has $v(y,t) = \langle S(y,t,\eta),A(\eta)f(\eta)\rangle + \langle R(y,t,\eta),A(\eta)F(\eta)\rangle$ and in particular for $f(\eta) = 0$ and $F(\eta) = \delta(\eta)/A_o = \delta(\eta)$ (cf. (♦)) we obtain

$$v(y,t) = R(y,t) = \langle \varphi^Q_\lambda(y), \mathrm{Sin}\lambda t/\lambda\rangle_\omega \tag{1.3}$$

For y = 0 one obtains the readout $G(t) = \langle 1, \mathrm{Sin}\lambda t/\lambda\rangle_\omega$ from which the spectral density ω is determined by

$$\omega(\lambda) = (2\lambda/\pi)\int_0^\infty G(t)\mathrm{Sin}\lambda t dt \tag{1.4}$$

From this one obtains A by use of the G-L machine (cf. [9;10;31]) and the nature of the map $G \to A$ is fairly well understood.

Now pick some sufficiently large $\tilde{y}$ (discussed later) and write

$$H(t) = v(\tilde{y},t) = \langle \varphi^Q_\lambda(\tilde{y}), \mathrm{Sin}\lambda t/\lambda\rangle_\omega \tag{1.5}$$

so that $\varphi^Q_\lambda(\tilde{y})\omega/\lambda = (2/\pi)\int_0^\infty H(t)\mathrm{Sin}\lambda t dt$ and from (1.4)

$$\varphi^Q_\lambda(\tilde{y})\int_0^\infty G(t)\mathrm{Sin}\lambda t dt = \int_0^\infty H(t)\mathrm{Sin}\lambda t dt \tag{1.6}$$

The function $\varphi^Q_\lambda(\tilde{y})$ is an even entire function of exponential type $\tilde{y}$ and the expression of G in terms of H in (1.6) can be regarded in the context of deconvolution (cf. [25;34]). Indeed by Paley-Wiener ideas we can write ($\Phi(t)$ even)

$$\varphi^Q_\lambda(\tilde{y}) = \int_{-\tilde{y}}^{\tilde{y}} \Phi(t)e^{i\lambda t}dt = \hat{\Phi}(\lambda) = 2\int_0^{\tilde{y}} \Phi(t)\mathrm{Cos}\lambda t dt \tag{1.7}$$

(where $\hat{\Phi}$ denotes the Fourier transform). Similarly if we take $\tilde{G}$ and $\tilde{H}$ to be odd extensions of G and H then it follows that $\hat{\Phi}(\lambda)\tilde{G}\hat{} = \tilde{H}\hat{}$ and

Theorem 1.2. The readouts G at y = 0 and H at $y = \tilde{y}$ are related by $\Phi * \tilde{G} = \tilde{H}$.

Example 1.3. We note for A = 1 as in Example 1.1 we have $v = Y(t-y)$ $(y,t \geq 0)$, $G(t) = Y(t)$, and $H(t) = Y(t-\tilde{y}) = \delta(t-\tilde{y}) * Y(t)$. Since $\delta(t+\tilde{y}) * \delta(t-\tilde{y}) = \delta(t)$ the deconvolution here is expressed by $G(t) = \delta(t+\tilde{y}) * H(t) = H(t+\tilde{y})$. However working from Theorem 1.2 is not too productive. We can write (taking $\tilde{y} = 1$ for convenience) $\varphi^Q_\lambda(1) = \mathrm{Cos}\lambda$,

$\Phi = \frac{1}{2}\{\delta(t-1) + \delta(-t-1)\}$, $\tilde{G} = Y(t) - Y(-t)$, $\tilde{H} = Y(t-1) - Y(-t-1)$, and in fact $\Phi * \tilde{G} = \tilde{H}$. However a natural splitting involving $\delta(t-1) * Y(t) = Y(t-1)$ is not visible. Indeed $\Phi * Y(t) = \frac{1}{2}\{Y(t-1) + Y(t+1)\}$ so $\Phi * G \neq H$ while to deconvolute $\Phi * \Gamma = Y(t-1)$ one obtains (using a z-transform method as in [25], $\Gamma = 2\sum(-1)^{k+1}Y(t-2k)$ $(k = 1 \to k = \infty)$ which is step function of no apparent physical meaning. Thus the need to split $\tilde{G}$ and $\tilde{H}$ simultaneously so that G and H are involved directly presents some difficulties and in §2 below we will proceed a little differently.

Remark 1.4. Again taking $\tilde{y} = 1$ for convenience let us write out the convolution in Theorem 1.2 as follows (Φ is even with supp$\Phi \subset [-1,1]$, $\tilde{G}$ and $\tilde{H}$ are odd), $\tilde{H}(t) = \frac{1}{2}\int_{-1}^{1}\Phi(\tau)\tilde{G}(t-\tau)d\tau = \int_0^1 \Phi(\tau)\frac{1}{2}\{\tilde{G}(t-\tau) + \tilde{G}(t+\tau)\}d\tau$ and this is seen to represent a classical type domain of dependence situation for the sideways Cauchy problem. The value of $\tilde{H}(t)$ depends only on $\tilde{G}(\xi)$ in the region $t-1 \leq \xi \leq t+1$ and evidently one may remove the $\sim$ in $\tilde{H}$ and $\tilde{G}$ for $t > 1$. Note $H(t) = 0$ for $0 \leq t < 1$. One can also derive this sort of formula directly by working with the sideways Cauchy problem and constructing appropriate Riemann functions as before.

2. Splitting techniques. Let us use the transmutation machine to split up everything as we go along. Recall that $\omega(\lambda) = 1/2\pi|c_Q(\lambda)|^2$ is even and $\varphi_\lambda^Q(y)$ is even in λ. Also for calculation it will be convenient to remove the $1/\lambda$ factor in (1.5). Thus

$$(2.1) \qquad H'(t) = \langle \varphi_\lambda^Q(y), \mathrm{Cos}\lambda t\rangle_\omega = \int_0^\infty \varphi_\lambda^Q(y)\omega \mathrm{Cos}\lambda t d\lambda = \frac{1}{2}\int_{-\infty}^{\infty} \varphi_\lambda^Q(y)\omega e^{i\lambda t}d\lambda$$

Further $\omega(\lambda)\varphi_\lambda^Q(y) = (1/2\pi)\{\Phi_\lambda^Q(y)/c_Q(-\lambda) + \Phi_{-\lambda}^Q(y)/c_Q(\lambda)\} = (1/2\pi)\{\Psi_\lambda^Q(y) + \Psi_{-\lambda}^Q(y)\}$ where $\Psi_\lambda^Q(y) = \Phi_\lambda^Q(y)/c_Q(-\lambda)$ is analytic in the upper half plane etc. (cf. [9;10;31]). Hence set

$$(2.2) \qquad H_1(t) = (1/4\pi)\int_{-\infty}^{\infty} \Psi_{-\lambda}^Q(y)e^{i\lambda t}d\lambda = (1/4\pi)\int_{-\infty}^{\infty} \Psi_\lambda^Q(y)e^{-i\lambda t}d\lambda$$

and it follows that $H'(t) = H_1(t) + H_1(-t)$. Again we remark (cf. Example 1.1) that in using the Fourier theory, or equivalently in representing H by (1.5) and H' by (2.1) etc., one automatically introduces various odd and even extensions of the quantities G, H, etc. (cf. also (1.4)). We note that by formal contour integral arguments $H_1(t) = 0$ in (2.2) for $t < \tilde{y}$. Indeed by [9;10;31] $\Psi_\lambda^Q(\tilde{y}) \sim c\exp(i\lambda\tilde{y})$ for $\mathrm{Im}\lambda > 0$ so $\Psi_\lambda^Q(y)\exp(-i\lambda t) \sim c\exp(i\lambda(\tilde{y}-t))$ on a large semicircular contour in the half plane $\mathrm{Im}\lambda > 0$ so for $\tilde{y} > t$ this vanishes strongly and the integral in (2.2) is zero - see [9] for details. Thus $H_1(t)$ provides the readout H' for $t > \tilde{y}$ (and $H_1(-t)$ is simply tagging along for $t < -\tilde{y}$

because of the representation (2.1) - it contributes nothing to H' for $t > 0$). Now from (2.2) we can write

$$(2.3) \qquad \tfrac{1}{2}\Psi_\lambda^Q(y) = \tfrac{1}{2}\Phi_\lambda^Q(y)/c_Q(-\lambda) = \int_{\tilde{y}}^{\infty} H'(t)e^{i\lambda t}dt$$

Further let us take our readout point $\tilde{x}$ large enough so that ρ and μ are constant for $x \geq \tilde{x}$ and consequently $A(y) = A_\infty$ (known) for $y \geq \tilde{y}$ ($\tilde{y} = y(\tilde{x})$). But $\Phi_\lambda^Q(\tilde{y})$ is the Jost solution $\Phi_\lambda^Q(y) \sim A_\infty^{-\frac{1}{2}}\exp(i\lambda y)$ as $y \to \infty$ and for $\tilde{y}$ as indicated we must have then $\Phi_\lambda^Q(\tilde{y}) = A_\infty^{-\frac{1}{2}}\exp(i\lambda\tilde{y})$. Therefore we have proved

<u>Theorem 2.1</u>. <u>Under the hypotheses indicated, for $\tilde{y}$ suitably large</u>

$$(2.4) \qquad 1/c_Q(-\lambda) = 2A_\infty^{\frac{1}{2}}e^{-i\lambda\tilde{y}}\int_{\tilde{y}}^{\infty} H_1(t)e^{i\lambda t}dt = 2A_\infty^{\frac{1}{2}}e^{-i\lambda\tilde{y}}\,\hat{H}'(\lambda)$$

Note here that $H_1(t)$ will usually have a delta function component $A_\infty^{-\frac{1}{2}}\delta(t-\tilde{y})$ as in Example 1.1 and the integration symbol in (2.4) is intended to take this into account. We see that the location of $\tilde{y}$ only introduces a phase factor into the readout (for $\tilde{y}$ suitably large). Now since $c_Q(-\lambda) = \bar{c}_Q(\lambda)$ for λ real one obtains

<u>Corollary 2.2</u>. <u>Under the hypotheses above it follows that</u> $\omega(\lambda) = 1/2\pi|c_Q(\lambda)|^2 = (2/\pi)A_\infty|\hat{H}'(\lambda)|^2$ <u>from which one can recover A by the methods of [9;10;11;31]</u>.

<u>Remark 2.3</u>. This formula seems "striking" because it directly exhibits the spectral measure in terms of the Fourier transform of an autocorrelation type function $\mathcal{H}(t) = \int_{-\infty}^{\infty} H'(t+\tau)H'(\tau)d\tau$. One knows of course that there is an intimate and profound connection between vibrating string problems and problems of extrapolation and interpolation for stationary time series (cf. [2;15;20-23;40]) and the results above fit into that context very neatly. In fact they seem to provide a new link directly connected with the geophysical problem and thus perhaps will lead in some new directions connecting the traditional time series analysis in geophysics with exact techniques for the inverse problem.

In the same spirit as the transition (2.1)-(2.2) we write now (cf. (1.3), (1.4), and recall $\varphi_\lambda^Q(0) = 1$)

$$(2.5) \qquad G'(t) = \int_0^{\infty} \omega(\lambda)\text{Cos}\lambda t\varphi_\lambda^Q(0)d\lambda = \tfrac{1}{2}\int_{-\infty}^{\infty} \varphi_\lambda^Q(0)\omega e^{i\lambda t}d\lambda =$$

$$= G_1(t) + G_1(-t)$$

$$(2.6)\qquad G_1(t) = (1/4\pi)\int_{-\infty}^{\infty} \Psi_{-\lambda}^{Q}(0)e^{i\lambda t}d\lambda = (1/4\pi)\int_{-\infty}^{\infty}\Psi_{\lambda}^{Q}(0)e^{-i\lambda t}d\lambda$$

where $G_1(t)$ vanishes for $t < 0$ (argue as before). Hence as in (2.3)

$$(2.7)\qquad \tfrac{1}{2}\Psi_{\lambda}^{Q}(0) = \tfrac{1}{2}\Phi_{\lambda}^{Q}(0)/c_Q(-\lambda) = \int_0^{\infty} G_1(t)e^{i\lambda t}dt$$

In general $\Phi_{\lambda}^{Q}(0)$ is not known but it is related to c_Q. For example from [9;10;31] we have (with the present normalization for Φ_{λ}^{Q}) a partial connection via $D\Phi_{-\lambda}^{Q}(0) = -2i\lambda c_Q(\lambda)$. In any event one can write

$$(2.8)\qquad G_1(t) = (1/4\pi)\int_{-\infty}^{\infty}\Phi_{\lambda}^{Q}(0)e^{-i\lambda t}d\lambda/c_Q(-\lambda) = \int_{\tilde{y}}^{\infty} H_1(\tau)K(t-\tau)d\tau =$$
$$(1/2\pi)\int_{-\infty}^{\infty}\Phi_{\lambda}^{Q}(0)e^{-i\lambda t}\{(1/\Phi_{\lambda}^{Q}(y))\int_{\tilde{y}}^{\infty}H_1(\tau)e^{i\lambda\tau}d\tau\}d\lambda$$

$$(2.9)\qquad K(t-\tau) = (A_{\infty}^{\frac{1}{2}}/2\pi)\int_{-\infty}^{\infty} e^{-i\lambda(t-\tau)}\Phi_{\lambda}^{Q}(0)e^{-i\lambda y}d\lambda$$

One notes by contour integration that formally $K(t-\tau) = 0$ for $\tau-t-\tilde{y} > 0$; since $\tau \geq \tilde{y}$ this means $K(t-\tau) = 0$ for $t < 0$ as desired and moreover $K(t-\tau) = 0$ for $\tau > t+\tilde{y}$. Consequently we obtain

$$(2.10)\qquad G_1(t) = \int_{\tilde{y}}^{\tilde{y}+t} H_1(\tau)K(t-\tau)d\tau$$

Theorem 2.4. Given $K(t-\tau)$ expressed as above (in (2.9)) it follows that (2.10) holds which gives a finite domain of dependence relation between H_1 and G_1.

3. Recovery of A and stability. The recovery of A via ω indicated in Corollary 2.2 by methods of [9;10;31] goes as follows. From (1.3)-(1.4) we have $G(t) = \int_0^{\infty} (\text{Sin}\lambda t/\lambda)\omega(\lambda)d\lambda$. Note that $\omega(\lambda)$ in [9-11;31] is written differently (with an A_{∞}^{-1}) but represents the same $\omega(\lambda)$ as we have here since the c_Q also changes with the different normalization of Jost solutions. Set now $d\sigma = d\omega - (2/\pi)d\lambda$ with

$$(3.1)\qquad T(y,x) = \int_0^{\infty} (\text{Sin}\lambda x/\lambda)\text{Cos}\lambda y d\lambda$$

Also let us write (cf. [9-11;31]) $G(t) = \int_0^{\infty} (\text{Sin}\lambda t/\lambda)\{d\sigma + (2/\pi)d\lambda\} = 1 + G_r(t)$ (the subscript r refers here to reflection data). Then depending on whether $y > x$ or $y < x$ one obtains $T(y,x) = \tfrac{1}{2}\{G_r(y+x) - G_r(y-x)\}$ or $T(y,x) = \tfrac{1}{2}\{G_r(y+x) + G_r(x-y)\}$. It follows that $T_y(y,x) =$

$\frac{1}{2}\{G_r'(y+x) - G_r'(|y-x|)\}$ and the G-L equation can be written $(x < y)$

$$(3.2)\qquad K(y,x) + \tfrac{1}{2}\{G_r(y+x) - G_r(y-x)\} = \tfrac{1}{2}\int_0^y K(y,s)\{G_r'(x+s) - G_r'(|x-s|)\}ds$$

We recall also that $A^{-\frac{1}{2}}(y) = 1 - K(y,y)$ and stability involves taking first approximate data $G_r'^*$ close enough to G_r' on $[0,2y]$ in L^1 norm and then $\|\Delta K(y,\cdot)\|_{\infty,y} \le c\{\|\varepsilon\|_{\infty,2y} + \|\varepsilon'\|_{L^1(2y)}\}$ where $\varepsilon = G_r^* - G_r$. In this context the stability question has also been investigated numerically in [32;33] with good results. First we state

Theorem 3.1. Given the spectral measure ω via Corollary 2.2 one can determine A(y) as in 9-11;31 from the unique solution of the G-L equation (3.2). Stability is estimated as indicated above.

Now for the stability question we first let H^*, G^*, etc. refer to the impedance A^*. Write $\Delta\omega = \omega^* - \omega$, $\Delta G = G^* - G$, etc. Let us write also $d\sigma = \sigma d\lambda$ and note that $\Delta\sigma = \Delta\omega$. Estimates on $\Delta\sigma$ are transmitted to ΔG_r by $\Delta G_r = \int_0^\infty \Delta\sigma(\mathrm{Sin}\lambda t/\lambda)d\lambda$ and $\Delta G_r' = \int_0^\infty \Delta\sigma \mathrm{Cos}\lambda t d\lambda$. Now estimates on ΔG_r and $\Delta G_r'$ on finite intervals are going to involve estimates on $\Delta\sigma$ in $L^1(0,\infty)$ and such estimates will be difficult to verify in practice (in terms of ΔH_1 say). Hence let us use the autocorrelation function $\mathcal{H}(t) = \int_{\tilde{y}}^\infty H'(t+\tau)H'(\tau)d\tau$ of Remark 2.3 ($F\mathcal{H} = (\pi/2A_\infty)\omega(\lambda) = |\hat{H}'|^2$, $H' = 0$ for $t < y$). From (2.5), with G' considered even because of the cosine representation, we obtain

$$(3.3)\qquad G'(t) = \int_0^\infty \omega \mathrm{Cos}\lambda t d\lambda = (A_\infty/\pi)\int_{-\infty}^\infty |\hat{H}'|^2 e^{-i\lambda t}d\lambda = A_\infty\mathcal{H}(t)$$

A factor of 2 (i.e. $2A_\infty\mathcal{H}(t)$ in (3.3)) arises because of the cosine representation and must be removed when considering G' via the full Fourier formula (cf. [9] and note the interplay between one and two sided delta functions - thus $(2/\pi)\int_0^\infty \mathrm{Cos}\lambda t d\lambda = \delta_+$ while $(1/\pi)\int_{-\infty}^\infty \exp(-i\lambda t)d\lambda = 2\delta$). We conclude that

Theorem 3.2. For $t > 0$ one has (3.3) or $G'(t) = A_\infty\mathcal{H}(t)$.

Remark 3.3. This is very nice in giving a direct relation between H' and G' so that stability estimates can be made directly via properties of H' and H without intervention of the spectral measure. Unfortunately it does not exhibit the nice dependence of G' on only a finite range of H' as in Theorem 2.4 (but of course Theorem 2.4 is not suited to calculation since $\Phi_\lambda^Q(0)$ is not determined).

Let us factor out the delta functions in (3.3) formally as follows. Again work with $G = 1 + G_r$, $A_\infty^{\frac{1}{2}}H_1 = \delta(t-\tilde{y}) + h_1$, etc. for $t > 0$ and one obtains formally (note $\tilde{y}-t < \tilde{y}$ for $t > 0$ and $h_1(\tilde{y}-t) = 0$)

$$G_r'(t) = h_1(\tilde{y}+t) + \int_{\tilde{y}}^{\infty} h_1(t+\xi)h_1(\xi)d\xi \tag{3.4}$$

To obtain estimates now on ε and ε' we assume first that for $t > \tilde{y}$, $A_\infty^{\frac{1}{2}}H = Y(t-\tilde{y}) + h(t)$, $h(t) = \int_{\tilde{y}}^t h_1(\tau)d\tau$ ($h_1 = h'$), and $G_r(t) = \int_0^t G_r'(\tau) d\tau$. Then from (3.4)

$$G_r(t) = \int_0^t h_1(\tau+\tilde{y})d\tau + \int_{\tilde{y}}^{\infty} h_1(\xi)\int_0^t h_1(\tau+\xi)d\tau d\xi = h(t+\tilde{y}) + \tag{3.5}$$

$$\int_{\tilde{y}}^{\infty} h_1(\xi)\{h(t+\xi) - h(\xi)\}d\xi = h(t+\tilde{y}) + \int_{\tilde{y}}^{\infty} h(t+\xi)h'(\xi)d\xi$$

since $-\int_{\tilde{y}}^{\infty} h_1(\xi)h(\xi)d\xi = -\frac{1}{2}h^2(\xi)|_{\tilde{y}}^{\infty} = \frac{1}{2}h^2(\tilde{y}) = 0$ if $h(\infty) = 0$. It should be no problem to assume h and $h_1 \in L^1 \cap L^\infty$ say and for $\varepsilon = G_r^* - G_r$ etc. as before

$$\Delta G_r' = \Delta h_1(t+\tilde{y}) + \int_{\tilde{y}}^{\infty} \{h_1^*(t+\xi)h_1^*(\xi) - h_1(t+\xi)h_1(\xi)\}d\xi; \tag{3.6}$$

$$\Delta G_r = \Delta h(t+\tilde{y}) + \int_{\tilde{y}}^{\infty} \{h^*(t+\xi)h_1^*(\xi) - h(t+\xi)h_1(\xi)\}d\xi$$

Let $\|h_1\|_\infty$, $\|h_1^*\|_\infty$, $\|h\|_\infty$, and $\|h^*\|_\infty$ be bounded by M ($\|\ \|_\infty$ means the sup norm over $[\tilde{y},\infty)$). Then ($\Delta h_1 = h_1^* - h_1$, etc.) $h_1^*(t+\xi)h_1^*(\xi) - h_1(t+\xi) h_1(\xi) = h_1^*(t+\xi)\Delta h_1(\xi) + h_1(\xi)\Delta h_1(t+\xi)$ and $h^*(t+\xi)h_1^*(\xi) - h(t+\xi)h_1(\xi) = h^*(t+\xi)\Delta h_1(\xi) + h_1(\xi)\Delta h(t+\xi)$. Consequently from (3.6)

$$|\varepsilon'| \le |\Delta h_1(t+\tilde{y})| + \int_{\tilde{y}}^{\infty} \{|h_1^*(t+\xi)||\Delta h_1(\xi)| + |h_1(\xi)||\Delta h_1(t+\xi)|\}d\xi \tag{3.7}$$

$$|\varepsilon| \le |\Delta h(t+\tilde{y})| + \int_{\tilde{y}}^{\infty} \{|h^*(t+\xi)||\Delta h_1(\xi)| + |h_1(\xi)||\Delta h(t+\xi)|\}d\xi$$

Theorem 3.4. Assume $\|h_1\|_\infty$, $\|h_1^*\|_\infty$, $\|h\|_\infty$, and $\|h^*\|_\infty \le M$ and that $\|\Delta h_1\|_{L^1}$ is suitably small. Then $|\Delta A|$ on $[0,\tilde{y}]$ can be estimated in terms of $\|\Delta h_1\|_{L^1}$, $\|\Delta h\|_{\infty,3\tilde{y}}$, and $\|\Delta h\|_{L^1}$ via

$$(3.8)\qquad \|\varepsilon'\|_{L^1(0,2T)} \le c\|\Delta h_1\|_{L^1(\tilde{y},\infty)};$$

$$\|\varepsilon\|_{\infty,2T} \le \|\Delta h\|_{\infty,\tilde{y}+2T} + M\{\|\Delta h_1\|_{L^1(\tilde{y},\infty)} + \|\Delta h\|_{L^1(\tilde{y},\infty)}\}$$

4. Complements. Let us go back to (1.6), multiply by $(2/\pi)\mathrm{Sin}\lambda\tau$, and integrate. We note first that $(2/\pi)\int_0^\infty \mathrm{Sin}\lambda\tau\mathrm{Sin}\lambda t d\lambda = \delta(t-\tau)$ and

$$(4.1)\qquad \varphi_\lambda^Q(\tilde{y}) = \mathrm{Cos}\lambda\tilde{y} + \int_0^{\tilde{y}} K(\tilde{y},\eta)\lambda\mathrm{Sin}\lambda\eta d\eta = \mathrm{Cos}\lambda\tilde{y} - K(\tilde{y},\eta)\Big|_0^{\tilde{y}} +$$

$$\int_0^{\tilde{y}} K_\eta(\tilde{y},\eta)\mathrm{Cos}\lambda\eta d\eta = \int_0^{\tilde{y}} K_\eta(\tilde{y},\eta)\mathrm{Cos}\lambda\eta d\eta + A_\infty^{-\frac{1}{2}}\mathrm{Cos}\lambda\tilde{y}$$

(cf. [9;10]). Here we recall that $1 - K(y,y) = A^{-\frac{1}{2}}(y)$, $A = A_\infty$ at $\tilde{y}$, $K(y,\eta) = 0$ for $\eta > y$, and $K(y,0) = 0$ (cf. [9], p. 282 for a representation of $K(y,\eta) = (2/\pi)\int_0^\infty \{\psi(\lambda,y)/2i\}\mathrm{Sin}\lambda\eta d\lambda$ to arrive at $K(y,0) = 0$ - see also (5.6)). Then from (1.6) it follows that (recall also $(2/\pi)\int_0^\infty \mathrm{Cos}\lambda\tilde{y}\mathrm{Cos}\lambda s d\lambda = \delta(\tilde{y}-s)$)

$$(4.2)\qquad H(\tau) = \int_0^\infty G(t)I(t,\tau,\tilde{y})dt;\; I = (2/\pi)\int_0^\infty \varphi_\lambda^Q(\tilde{y})\mathrm{Sin}\lambda t\mathrm{Sin}\lambda\tau d\lambda =$$

$$J + \tfrac{1}{2}A_\infty^{-\frac{1}{2}}(2/\pi)\int_0^\infty \mathrm{Cos}\lambda\tilde{y}\{\mathrm{Cos}\lambda|t-\tau| - \mathrm{Cos}\lambda(t+\tau)\}d\lambda =$$

$$J + \tfrac{1}{2}A_\infty^{-\frac{1}{2}}\{\delta(\tilde{y}-|t-\tau|) - \delta(\tilde{y}-t-\tau)\}$$

$$(4.3)\qquad J = (2/\pi)\int_0^\infty \tfrac{1}{2}\{\mathrm{Cos}\lambda|t-\tau| - \mathrm{Cos}\lambda(t+\tau)\}\int_0^{\tilde{y}} K_\eta(\tilde{y},\eta)\mathrm{Cos}\lambda\eta d\eta d\lambda =$$

$$\tfrac{1}{2}\int_0^{\hat{y}} K_\eta(\tilde{y},\eta)\{\delta(|t-\tau|-\eta) - \delta(t+\tau-\eta)\}d\eta =$$

$$= \tfrac{1}{2}\{K_2(\tilde{y},t-\tau) + K_2(\tilde{y},\tau-t) - K_2(\tilde{y},t+\tau)\}$$

where $K_2(\xi,\eta) = K_\eta(\xi,\eta)$ (note for $\tau > \tilde{y}$, $K_2(\tilde{y},t+\tau)$ does not arise). Consequently (4.2) becomes

$$(4.4)\qquad H(\tau) = \tfrac{1}{2}A_\infty^{-\frac{1}{2}}\{G(\tilde{y}+\tau) + G(\tau-\tilde{y}) - G(\tilde{y}-\tau)\} + $$

$$+ \tfrac{1}{2}\int_0^\infty G(t)\{K_2(\tilde{y},t-\tau) + K_2(\tilde{y},\tau-t) - K_2(\tilde{y},t+\tau)\}dt$$

Take now $\tau > \tilde{y}$ so $G(\tilde{y}-\tau) = 0$ and $K_2(\tilde{y},t+\tau) = 0$. We can write the integral term in (4.4) in the form (integrating by parts)

$$(4.5)\qquad \tfrac{1}{2}\int_\tau^{\tau+\tilde{y}} G(t)K_2(\tilde{y},t-\tau)dt + \tfrac{1}{2}\int_{\tau-\tilde{y}}^{\tau} G(t)K_2(\tilde{y},\tau-t)dt =$$

$$\tfrac{1}{2}K(\tilde{y},\tilde{y})\{G(\tilde{y}+\tau) + G(\tau-\tilde{y})\} - \tfrac{1}{2}\int_0^{\tilde{y}} G'(s+\tau)K(\tilde{y},s)ds + \tfrac{1}{2}\int_0^{\tilde{y}} G'(\tau-s)K(\tilde{y},s)ds$$

Now use $K(\tilde{y},\tilde{y}) = 1 - A_\infty^{-\frac{1}{2}}$ to obtain

<u>Theorem 4.1.</u> <u>For $\tau > \tilde{y}$</u>

$$(4.6)\qquad H(\tau) = \tfrac{1}{2}\{G(\tilde{y}+\tau) + G(\tau-\tilde{y})\} + \tfrac{1}{2}\int_0^{\tilde{y}} K(\tilde{y},s)\{G'(\tau-s) - G'(\tau+s)\}ds$$

Let us note in passing that for $\tau < \tilde{y}$ (where $H(\tau) = 0$) (4.4) reduces to the G-L equation (3.2). Indeed $G(\tau-\tilde{y}) = 0$ in (4.4) while $-G(\tilde{y}-\tau)$ remains, and in addition to (4.5) modified below, the integral terms contribute

$$(4.7)\qquad -\tfrac{1}{2}\int_0^{\tilde{y}-\tau} G(t)K_2(\tilde{y},t+\tau)dt = -\tfrac{1}{2}G(\tilde{y}-\tau)K(\tilde{y},\tilde{y}) +$$

$$+ \tfrac{1}{2}G(0)K(\tilde{y},\tau) + \tfrac{1}{2}\int_\tau^{\tilde{y}} G'(s-\tau)K(\tilde{y},s)ds$$

The modifications required in (4.5) involve

$$(4.8)\qquad \tfrac{1}{2}\int_0^\infty G(t)K_2(\tilde{y},\tau-t)dt = \tfrac{1}{2}G(0)K(\tilde{y},\tau) + \tfrac{1}{2}\int_0^\tau G'(\tau-s)K(\tilde{y},s)ds$$

Consequently we obtain from (4.4), (4.5), (4.7), and (4.8) ($G(0) = 1$)

$$(4.9)\qquad 0 = \tfrac{1}{2}A_\infty^{-\frac{1}{2}}\{G(\tilde{y}+\tau) - G(\tilde{y}-\tau)\} + \tfrac{1}{2}K(\tilde{y},\tilde{y})G(\tilde{y}+\tau) - \tfrac{1}{2}G(\tilde{y}-\tau)K(\tilde{y},\tilde{y})$$

$$+ K(\tilde{y},\tau) - \tfrac{1}{2}\int_0^{\tilde{y}} G'(s+\tau)K(\tilde{y},s)ds + \tfrac{1}{2}\int_0^{\tilde{y}} G'(|s-\tau|)K(\tilde{y},s)ds$$

Using again $K(\tilde{y},\tilde{y}) = 1 - A_{\infty}^{-\frac{1}{2}}$ we have (3.2).

Theorem 4.2. For $\tau < \tilde{y}$ (4.4) yields the G-L equation (3.2).

Remark 4.3. The dependence indicated in Theorem 4.1 between G and H again involves only finite intervals (but in a different manner than in Theorem 2.4). We note that the G-L equation involves G on $[0,2\tilde{y}]$ for $K(\tilde{y},\cdot)$ on $[0,\tilde{y}]$ while (4.6) plays off H on say $[\tilde{y},3\tilde{y}]$ against G on $[0,4\tilde{y}]$. Of course once G is known on $[0,2\tilde{y}]$, determining K and hence A on $[0,\tilde{y}]$, we know G on $[0,4\tilde{y}]$ by solving the direct problem. One hopes to use (4.6) and (3.2) = (4.9) in conjunction to develop a numerical scheme for example based on fixed point ideas and this is being investigated.

Let us think of G now as odd and G' as even (as is natural from the sine and cosine representations) and write (4.6) with (4.9) as follows. For $\tau > \tilde{y}$, $H(\tau) = \frac{1}{2}\{G(\tau+\tilde{y}) + G(\tau-\tilde{y})\} + \frac{1}{2}\int K(\tilde{y},s)\{G'(\tau-s) - G'(\tau+s)\}ds$ while for $\tau < \tilde{y}$, $-K(\tilde{y},\tau) = \frac{1}{2}\{G(\tau+\tilde{y}) + G(\tau-\tilde{y})\} + \frac{1}{2}\int K(\tilde{y},s)\{G'(\tau-s) - G'(\tau+s)\}ds$ (integrals $0 \to \tilde{y}$). Now treat $K(\tilde{y},\xi)$ as an odd function in ξ with $K(\tilde{y},\xi) = 0$ for $|\xi| > \tilde{y}$ and $K(\tilde{y},0) = 0$ (via the sine representation of K before (4.2)). Then by an easy calculation

$$(4.10) \qquad \{K(\tilde{y},\cdot) * G'\}(\tau) = \int_0^{\tilde{y}} K(\tilde{y},s)G'(\tau-s)ds - \int_0^{\tilde{y}} K(\tilde{y},s)G'(\tau+s)ds$$

Consequently, setting $\mathbb{G}(\tilde{y},\tau) = \frac{1}{2}\{G(\tau+\tilde{y}) + G(\tau-\tilde{y})\}$, we obtain $(\tau > 0)$

$$(4.11) \qquad H(\tau) = \mathbb{G}(\tilde{y},\tau) + \tfrac{1}{2}K(\tilde{y},\cdot) * G' \quad (\tau > \tilde{y});$$

$$-K(\tilde{y},\tau) = \mathbb{G}(\tilde{y},\tau) + \tfrac{1}{2}K(\tilde{y},\cdot) * G' \quad (\tau < \tilde{y})$$

Theorem 4.4. For $\tau > 0$ one can combine the equations in (4.11) to obtain $H(\tau) - K(\tilde{y},\tau) = \mathbb{G}(\tilde{y},\tau) + \frac{1}{2}K(\tilde{y},\cdot) * G'$.

5. Appendix. The derivation of the G-L equation (3.2) in [9;10;31] was largely ad hoc in nature. Let us give here a canonical derivation based on general transmutation procedures as in [9]. Thus the canonical G-L equation has the form

$$(5.1) \qquad \langle \beta(y,t), \mathbb{A}(t,x) \rangle = \tilde{\beta}(y,x)$$

where β and $\tilde{\beta}$ are the kernels of certain transmutations $D^2 \to Q$ and

$$(5.2) \qquad \mathbb{A}(t,x) = \int_0^{\infty} \omega(\lambda)\operatorname{Cos}\lambda x \operatorname{Cos}\lambda t\, d\lambda = \langle \operatorname{Cos}\lambda x, \operatorname{Cos}\lambda t \rangle_{\omega}$$

In fact $\tilde{\beta}(y,x) = \langle \operatorname{Cos}\lambda x, \varphi_{\lambda}^{Q}(y) \rangle_{\omega} = 0$ for $x < y$ and

(5.3) $$\beta(y,t) = (2/\pi)\int_0^\infty \varphi_\lambda^Q(y)\,\mathrm{Cos}\lambda t\, d\lambda$$

Now for $x < y$ we integrate in (5.1) formally to obtain (cf. (1.4)) $\langle \beta(y,t), A(t,x)\rangle = 0$ where

(5.4) $$A(t,x) = \int_0^x \mathbb{A}(t,\xi)d\xi = \langle \mathrm{Cos}\lambda t, \mathrm{Sin}\lambda x/\lambda\rangle_\omega = \tfrac{1}{2}\int_0^\infty \mathrm{Sin}\lambda(x+t)\omega d\lambda/\lambda$$

$$+\ \tfrac{1}{2}\int_0^\infty \mathrm{Sin}\lambda(x-t)\omega d\lambda/\lambda = \begin{cases} \tfrac{1}{2}\{G(x+t) + G(x-t)\}, & x > t \\ \tfrac{1}{2}\{G(x+t) - G(t-x)\}, & x < t \end{cases}$$

An analysis of kernels as in [9], pp. 332-333 allows us to write

(5.5) $$\beta(y,t) = A^{-\frac{1}{2}}(y)\delta(y-t) + K_t(y,t)$$

We will not repeat the material here from [9] leading to (5.5) but note that from [9;10;31] the kernel K arises in the form (integrate by parts and recall $K(y,y) = 1 - A^{-\frac{1}{2}}(y)$)

(5.6) $$\varphi_\lambda^Q(y) = \mathrm{Cos}\lambda y + \int_0^y K(y,\eta)\lambda\,\mathrm{Sin}\lambda\eta\, d\eta = A^{-\frac{1}{2}}(y)\,\mathrm{Cos}\lambda y + \int_0^y K_\eta(y,\eta)\,\mathrm{Cos}\lambda\eta\, d\eta$$

Consequently using (5.4) one obtains ($\beta(y,t) = 0$ for $t > y$)

(5.7) $$0 = \int_0^y \beta(y,t)A(t,x)dt = A^{-\frac{1}{2}}(y)\{G(x+y) - G(y-x)\} +$$

$$\int_0^x K_t(y,t)\{G(x+t) + G(x-t)\}dt + \int_x^y K_t(y,t)\{G(x+t) - G(t-x)\}dt$$

The last integrals in (5.7) are (recall $K(y,0) = 0$ and $G(0) = 1$)

(5.8) $$I = K(y,t)\{G(x+t) + G(x-t)\}\Big|_0^x + K(y,t)\{G(x+t) - G(t-x)\}\Big|_x^y -$$

$$- \int_0^x K(y,t)\{G'(x+t) - G'(x-t)\}dt - \int_x^y K(y,t)\{G'(x+t) - G'(t-x)\}dt =$$

$$2K(y,x) + K(y,y)\{G(x+y) - G(y-x)\} - \int_0^y K(y,t)\{G'(x+t) - G'(|x-t|)\}dt$$

Using $K(y,y) = 1 - A^{-\frac{1}{2}}(y)$, insert (5.8) in (5.7) to get (3.2). Hence

Theorem 5.1. The G-L equation (3.2) can be derived in a canonical manner as indicated above.

REFERENCES

[1] A. ALEKSEEV, Some inverse problems in the theory of wave propagation, I and II, Izv. Akad. Nauk SSSR, Ser. Geofiz., 11 (1962), pp. 1514-1531.

[2] A. ALEKSEEV, Inverse dynamical problems of seismology, in Some methods and algorithms for the interpertation of geophysical data, Izd. Nauka, Moscow, 1967, pp. 9-84.

[3] G. BAKER, Solution of an inverse elastic wave scattering problem, Jour. Acous. Soc. Amer., 71 (1982), pp. 785-789.

[4] A. BAMBERGER, G. CHAVENT, and P. LAILLY, About the stability of the inverse problem in one dimensional wave equations - application to the interpertation of seismic profiles, Appl. Math. Optim., 5 (1979), pp. 1-47.

[5] A. BLAGOVEŠČENSKIJ, The inverse problem in the theory of seismic wave propagation, Topics in Appl. Math., Ed. M. Birman, Vol. 3, 1969, pp. 55-67.

[6] A. BLAGOVEŠČENSKIJ, On a local method of solution of a nonstationary inverse problem for a nonhomogeneous string, Trudy Math. Inst. Steklov, 115 (1971), pp. 39-56.

[7] YU. BRYČKOV and A. PRUDNIKOV, Integral transforms of generalized functions, Moscow, 1977.

[8] R. BURRIDGE, The Gelfand-Levitan, the Marčenko, and the Gopinath-Sondhi integral operators of inverse scattering theory, regarded in the context of inverse impulse-response problems, Wave Motion, 2 (1980), pp. 305-323.

[9] R. CARROLL, Transmutation, scattering theory, and special functions, North-Holland, Amsterdam, 1982.

[10] R. CARROLL and F. SANTOSA, Scattering techniques for a one dimensional inverse problem in geophysics, Math. Meth. Appl. Sci., 3 (1981), pp. 145-171.

[11] R. CARROLL and F. SANTOSA, Stability for the one dimensional inverse problem via the Gelfand-Levitan equation, Applicable Anal., 13 (1982), pp. 271-277.

[12] R. CARROLL and F. SANTOSA, On some singular inverse problems, to appear.

13 D. COLTON and R. KRESS, The construction of solutions to acoustic scattering problems in a spherically stratified medium, I and II, Quart. Jour. Mech. Appl. Math., 31 (1978), pp. 9-17 and 32 (1979), pp. 53-62.

14 D. COLTON and W. WENDLAND, Constructive methods for solving the exterior Neumann problem for the reduced wave equation in a spherically symmetric medium, Proc. Royal Soc. Edinburgh, 75A (1975/76), pp. 97-107

15 H. DYM and H. McKEAN, Gaussian processes, function theory, and the inverse spectral problem, Academic Press, N.Y., 1976.

16 M. GERVER, The inverse problem for the one dimensional wave equation, Geophys. Jour. Royal Astr. Soc., 21 (1970), pp. 337-357.

17 M. GERVER, The inverse problem for the one dimensional wave equation with an unknown source of vibrations, Izd. Nauka, Moscow, 1974.

18 B. GOPINATH and M. SONDHI, Inversion of the telegraph equation and the synthesis of nonuniform lines, Proc. IEEE, 59 (1971), pp. 383-392.

19 M. HOWARD, Inverse scattering for a layered acoustic medium using the first order equations of motion, Geophysics, 48 (1983), pp. 163-170.

20 M. KREIN, On a method for the effective solution of the inverse boundary value problem, DAN SSSR, 94 (1854), pp. 987-990.

21 M. KREIN, On inverse problems for a nonhomogeneous string, DAN SSSR, 82 (1952), pp. 669-672

22 M. KREIN, On some cases of the effective determination of the density of a nonhomogeneous string from its spectral function, DAN SSSR, 93 (1953), pp. 617-620.

23 M. KREIN, On a fundamental approximation problem in the theory of extrapolation and filtration of stationary random processes, DAN SSSR, 94 (1954), pp. 13-16.

24 R. NEWTON, Inversion of reflection data for layered media: A review of exact methods, Geophys. Jour. Royal Astr. Soc., 65 (1981), pp. 191-215.

25 E. ROBINSON, Physical applications of stationary time series, MacMillan, N.Y., 1980.

26 P. SABATIER, On geophysical inverse problems and constraints, Jour. Geophysics, 43 (1977), pp. 115-137.

[27] P. SABATIER, Theoretical considerations for inverse scattering, Radioscience, to appear.

[28] P. SABATIER, Some topics on inversion theory applied to geophysics, in Inter. symp. on illposed problems - theory and practice, Reidel, 1980

[29] P. SABATIER, Spectral and scattering inverse problems, Jour. Math. Physics, 19 (1978), pp. 2410-2425.

[30] P. SABATIER, Problème direct et inverse de diffraction d'une onde élastique par une zone perturbée sphérique, CR Acad. Sci. Paris, 278 (1974), pp. 545-547 and 603-606.

[31] F. SANTOSA, Scattering techniques for the geophysical inverse problem, Thesis, Univ. Illinois, 1980.

[32] F. SANTOSA, Numerical scheme for the inversion of acoustical impedance profile based on the Gelfand-Levitan method, Geophys. Jour. Royal Astr. Soc., 70 (1982), pp. 229-243.

[33] F. SANTOSA and H. SCHWETLICK, The inversion of acoustical impedance profile by methods of characteristics, Wave Motion, 4 (1982), pp. 99-110.

[34] M. SILVIA and E. ROBINSON, Deconvolution of geophysical time series in the exploration for oil and natural gas, Elsevier-North-Holland, Amsterdam, 1979.

[35] W. SYMES, Inverse boundary value problems and a theorem of Gelfand and Levitan, Jour. Math. Anal. Appl., 71 (1979), pp. 379-402.

[36] W. SYMES, Impedance profile inversion via the first transport equation, to appear.

[37] W. SYMES, Stable solution of the inverse reflection problem for a smoothly stratified elastic medium, SIAM Jour. Math. Anal., 12 (1981), pp. 421-453.

[38] H. SZU, C. YANG, S. AHU, and C. CARROLL, Functional equation in the plasma inverse problem and solutions, Naval Res. Lab. Rept. 7946, 1975

[39] J. WARE and K. AKI, Continuous and discrete inverse scattering in a stratified elastic medium, Jour. Acous. Soc. Amer., 45 (1969), pp. 911-921.

[40] A. YAGLOM, An introduction to the theory of stationary random functions, Prentice-Hall, 1962.

Source Wavelet Deconvolution: A Linear Inverse Problem

Sven Treitel* and L. R. Lines*

Abstract. During the last couple of decades, seismic source wavelet deconvolution has served a useful role in enhancing the resolution of exploration seismic records. Seismic source wavelet deconvolution can be treated within the framework of the Backus-Gilbert (BG) inverse theory. A time shift invariant version of this theory in which the Euclidean norm is minimized, will create the Wiener shaping filter. The model of the BG theory is the ground impulse response, the BG mapping kernel is the source wavelet, and the BG resolving kernel is the convolution between the source wavelet and the Wiener shaping filter. BG inversion involves the minimization of an optimality criterion under a set of constraints. The application of the BG "filter energy" or "noise output power" constraint to Wiener filter design leads to the familiar prewhitening parameter that stabilizes the filter on the one hand, but degrades resolution on the other. These constraints provide novel insights into the performance of deconvolution filters.

1.0 Introduction. The following paper is an abbreviated and perturbed version of an earlier paper published in Geophysics by Treitel and Lines [1].

A common exploration problem involves the deconvolution of the seismic trace into a source generated wavelet and the impulse response of a layered earth. A review of many deconvolution methods making use of the least squares principle can be found in Robinson and Treitel [2].

An example of wavelet deconvolution is shown in Figures 1a,b. This example, provided by Seismograph Service Corporation, was discussed by Stone [3]. Figure 1a shows the original seismogram with a reef feature situated at about 0.950 seconds just slightly to the left of the center of the section. The arrivals are attenuated in

*Research Center, Amoco Production Co., Tulsa, OK 74102

amplitude at the top of the reef and delayed in time at the bottom of the reef and require some pulse compression. Figure 1b shows the effect of deconvolving the estimated wavelets (which are plotted at the bottom of the section of Figure 1b). Wavelet deconvolution produces pulse compression and dephasing, which acts as an aid in interpreting the reef feature.

Deconvolution may also be viewed as a linear inverse problem, in which the observations are the seismic trace values and the desired model is the medium's impulse response, see Oldenburg [4]. The Backus-Gilbert (BG) solution to the linear inverse problem is well known to earthquake seismologists, and has been treated in a series of papers by Backus and Gilbert [5], [6], [7]. A lucid description of the BG method has been given by Twomey [8].

In this paper we show that a specialized version of the BG approach reduces to the Wiener deconvolution problem familiar to exploration geophysicists.

2.0 Backus-Gilbert Inversion and Deconvolution. The BG formalism postulates that an observed time series $x(t)$ can be expressed in the form,

$$x(t) = \int k(t,\tau)\, f(\tau)\, d\tau \quad , \tag{2.1}$$

where t is the observation time and τ is a temporal integration variable. The time series $f(t)$ is the model we seek to identify, which by hypothesis is related to the observations $x(t)$ by the linear integral equation (2.1). The function $k(t,\tau)$ is called the mapping kernel of this integral equation, since it maps the model $f(t)$ into the observations $x(t)$. The mapping kernel $k(t,\tau)$ depends not only on the observation time, t, but also on the temporal integration variable, τ. In engineering language, $k(t,\tau)$ is a time-adaptive filter with an impulse response function depending explicitly on the observation time, t. We remark that (2.1) is a Fredholm integral equation of the first kind.

This description of $x(t)$ can be simplified if we may assume that the mapping kernel k is time shift-invariant, i.e., that the kernel remains unchanged for all observation time t. Then (2.1) can be written

$$x(t) = \int k(\tau)\, f(t-\tau)\, d\tau \quad , \tag{2.2}$$

which we recognize as the familiar convolutional model of the observed seismic trace, $x(t)$. We may then identify the mapping kernel $k(t)$ with the seismic source wavelet, or signature, and the model $f(t)$ with the subsurface impulse response.

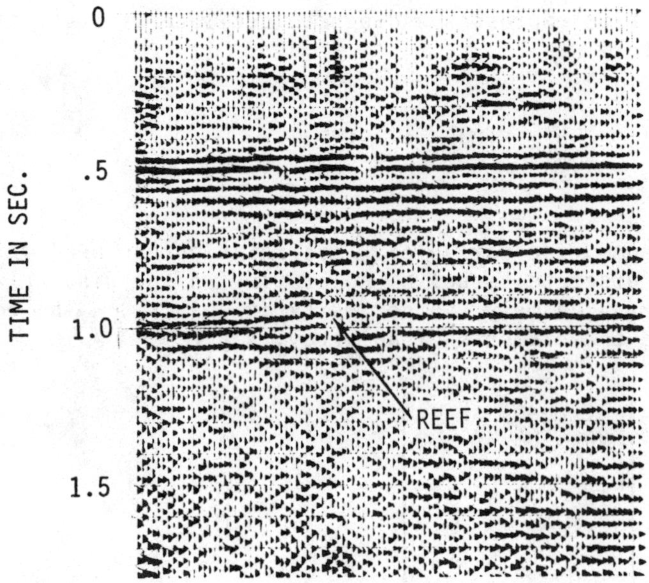

FIGURE 1a SEISMIC SECTION AFTER STANDARD PROCESSING (COURTESY SEISMOGRAPH SERVICE CO., STONE, 1976)

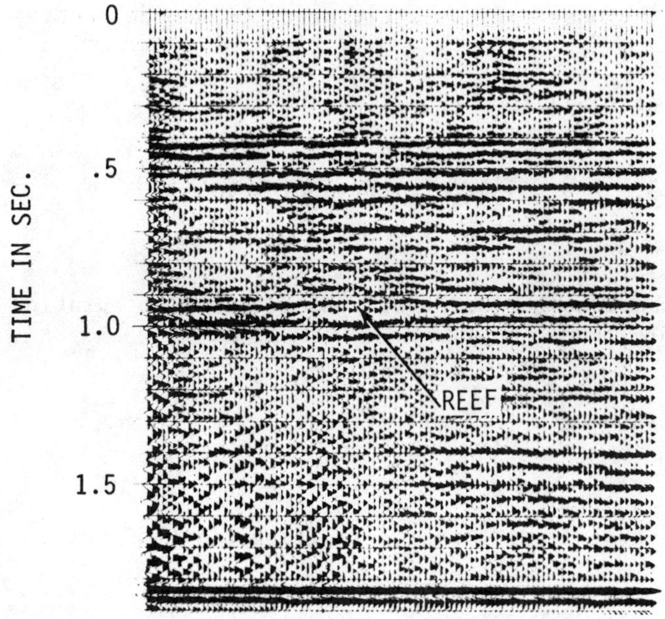

FIGURE 1b SEISMIC SECTION AFTER WAVELET DECONVOLUTION

Because it is impossible in practice to recover f(t) exactly, the BG formulation expresses a discrete estimate of f(t), namely $\hat{f}(t)$, in the form

$$(2.3) \qquad \hat{f}(t) = \sum_{\sigma} b_{t\sigma}\, x(\sigma) \quad , \quad t=0,1,\ldots \quad ,$$

where σ is a summation variable. This relation has been written in the form of a discrete kernel $b_{t\sigma}$ operating on the discretized observations x(t), namely the series $(x_0, x_1, \ldots, x_N)$. The coefficients $b_{t\sigma}$ are the elements of an array, say B,

$$B = \begin{bmatrix} b_{00} & b_{01} & \cdots \\ b_{10} & b_{11} & \cdots \\ & \cdots & \\ b_{N0} & b_{N1} & \cdots \end{bmatrix} ,$$

each row of which is the impulse response function of a filter yielding a model estimate at some particular time. In other words, the array B describes a discrete time-adaptive filter which, when operating on the observations x(t), produces a model estimate $\hat{f}(t)$.

Substituting (2.1) into (2.3), we obtain

$$\hat{f}(t) = \sum_{\sigma} b_{t\sigma} \int k\,(\sigma,\tau)\, f(\tau)\, d\tau \quad .$$

If we assume that the order of summation and integration is interchangeable, then

$$(2.4) \qquad \hat{f}(t) = \int \sum_{\sigma} b_{t\sigma}\, k(\sigma,\tau)\, f(\tau)\, d\tau \quad .$$

This expression leads to the definition of the function

$$(2.5) \qquad s(t,\tau) = \sum_{\sigma} b_{t\sigma}\, k(\sigma,\tau) \quad ,$$

so that the model estimate $\hat{f}(t)$ can be written

$$(2.6) \qquad \hat{f}(t) = \int s(t,\tau)\, f(\tau)\, d\tau \quad .$$

We see that $s(t,\tau)$ is a function whose deltaness determines the degree of resolution with which we can recover the model $f(t)$ from the data. In particular, if $s(t,\tau) = \delta(t-\tau)$, then the model estimate is identically equal to the model. More generally, if $s(t,\tau)$ is a broader function of τ, then the model estimate will be an averaged version of $f(t)$. Accordingly $s(t,\tau)$ is called the scanning function, or resolving kernel; the closer $s(t,\tau)$ is to $\delta(t-\tau)$, the better is the resolution obtainable.

Let us return to the case for which the mapping kernel, or wavelet $k(t)$ is time shift-invariant. Further, we assume that all processes are discrete with a uniform time increment $\Delta t=1$. Hence the continuous functions $x(t)$, $k(t)$, $f(t)$, $\hat{f}(t)$, and $s(t)$ are replaced by the corresponding discrete sequences x_t, k_t, f_t, $\hat{f}_t$, and s_t. Now equation (2.2) becomes

$$(2.7) \qquad x_t = \sum_{\tau=0}^{m} k_\tau\, f_{t-\tau} \quad ,$$

where k_t is a discrete (m+1)-length mapping kernel or wavelet. The model estimate (2.3) can now be written as the convolution

$$(2.8) \qquad \hat{f}_t = \sum_{\sigma} b_{t-\sigma}\, x_\sigma = \sum_{\sigma=0}^{n} b_\sigma\, x_{t-\sigma} \quad ,$$

where b_t is the (n+1)-length time shift-invariant filter $b_t=(b_0,b_1,\ldots,b_n)$. Just as before, we substitute the observed time series [Eq. (2.7)] into the relation for the model estimate [Eq. (2.8)],

$$(2.9) \qquad \hat{f}_t = \sum_{\sigma=0}^{n} b_\sigma \sum_{\tau=0}^{m} k_\tau\, f_{t-\tau-\sigma} \quad .$$

Letting $\tau+\sigma=\mu$, we obtain

$$s_\mu = \sum_\tau b_{\mu-\tau} k_\tau \quad , \tag{2.10}$$

in analogy to Eq. (2.5). Then (2.9) becomes

$$\hat{f}_t = \sum_\mu s_\mu f_{t-\mu} \quad , \tag{2.11}$$

where s_t is the discrete scanning function, or resolving kernel. If now s_t is a unit spike at t=0 then we recognize from (2.10) that b_t is the exact inverse filter for the seismic source wavelet k_t, and in this instance, the model would then be recoverable exactly from the observations. We have just expressed a classic problem in exploration seismology, in which an estimate of the time-invariant source wavelet is used to deconvolve it from the recorded seismic trace. We can easily see this by expressing the convolutions (2.7), (2.8), (2.10), and (2.11) in "shorthand" form. Thus,

$$x_t = k_t * f_t \quad , \tag{2.12}$$

where the symbol (*) denotes convolution. Then

$$\begin{aligned} b_t * x_t &= b_t * k_t * f_t \\ &= s_t * f_t \\ &= \hat{f}_t \end{aligned} \tag{2.13}$$

where the resolving kernel or filter output is

$$s_t = b_t * k_t \quad .$$

In practice, s_t cannot be infinitely sharp, but only approximately so. Accordingly, the BG formalism introduces several measures of sharpness, or "deltaness", namely Q, toward which s_t should tend in accordance with a particular optimality criterion. Two of them are

$$(2.14a) \quad Q = \sum_t (d_t - s_t)^2 \quad ,$$

and

$$(2.14b) \quad Q = \sum_t (t - t_0)^2 \, s_t^2 \quad .$$

The first of these criteria is the square, or Euclidean norm, while the second is known as the second moment norm. In both cases, the objective is to minimize Q subject to a set of constraints which will be described in detail below. In (2.14a), d_t is a sharp, yet not infinitely sharp, pulse while in (2.14b) t_0 is a particular value of the observation time about which the energy in s_t is to be concentrated. The second moment norm criterion has not enjoyed widespread use in exploration seismology, but it does have several interesting features. Digital filters designed with the second moment norm (SMN) criterion are treated by the present authors in a separate paper (Lines and Treitel [9]). Our experience suggests that the SMN filters are inferior to Wiener filters for noisy data.

Returning to the square norm (2.14a), we observe that because $s_t = b_t * k_t$,

$$(2.15) \quad Q = \sum_t (d_t - b_t * k_t)^2 \quad .$$

In the absence of any constraints, the minimization of Q yields the filter which operates on the known mapping kernel, or source wavelet. We thus obtain a least squares approximation to a desired sharply peaked output sequence. What we have just described are the design specifications for the familiar Wiener shaping filter operating on the known input sequence. This filter produces the actual output which approximates the desired output in the least squares sense (Robinson and Treitel [2]). The design is pictured in Figure 1c. In other words, the BG inversion formalism leads directly to the Wiener shaping filter if the known mapping kernel is time shift-invariant and the minimization of the square norm Q [Eq. (2.15)] is unconstrained.

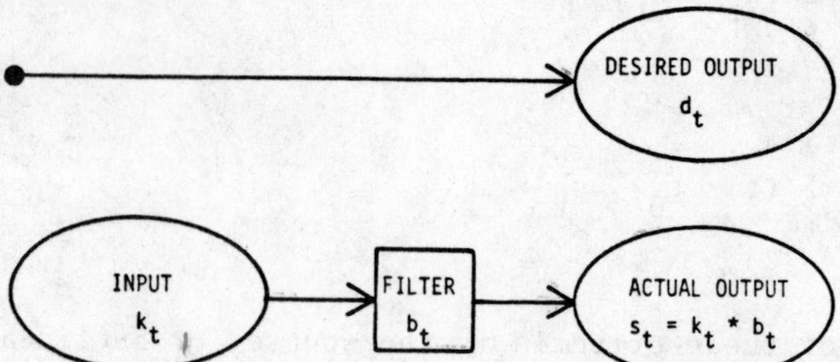

Figure 1c). Design diagram for the unconstrained Wiener Shaping Filter (from Geophysics, V. 47, p. 1155)

The parallelism between BG inversion and Wiener shaping deconvolution is pictured in Table 1, where we show the correspondence in terminology.

TABLE 1
The Parallelism Between BG Inversion and Wiener Shaping Deconvolution

Wiener Shaping Deconvolution	Backus-Gilbert Inversion
Source Wavelet	Mapping Kernel
Impulse Response	Model
Shaping Filter	Weighting Coefficients
(Sharp) Desired Output	Deltaness
Actual Output	Resolving Kernel or Scanning Function

Thus the Wiener shaping filter b_t can operate on the observed seismic trace x_t to produce the model, or impulse response estimate $\hat{f}_t$, as the relations (2.13) indicate. It is often possible to improve filter performance by determining the optimum lag value of the desired output pulse relative to the input wavelet k_t (Robinson and Treitel [2]), a property that has not yet been exploited within the BG formalism.

We have demonstrated the close connection between BG inversion and Wiener shaping deconvolution. In the next section we shall investigate a number of modified Wiener filters which result when the constraints introduced by the BG formalism are included in the filter design.

3.0 The Constrained Wiener Filter. The absence of any constraints on the minimization of the square norm (2.15) can cause poor filter performance, particularly in the case of noisy observations x_t. The BG approach thus minimizes the square norm subject to a constraint condition on the filter energy:

$$(3.1a) \qquad \sum_t b_t^2 = \text{constant} \quad .$$

As we shall see, this constraint contributes to filter stability and leads to what engineers and statisticians call "prewhitening". The original BG inversion applied the "unimodular constraint" to prevent scale distortions. However, because constant scale factors are usually unimportant in the interpretation of relative seismic amplitudes, we will not discuss this constraint.

It will be convenient to introduce vector and matrix notation. Let:

$$k = \text{col}\ (k_0, k_1, \ldots, k_m) \quad = \text{source wavelet}$$

$$b = \text{col}\ (b_0, b_1, \ldots, b_n) \quad = \text{shaping filter}$$

$$s = \text{col}\ (s_0, s_1, \ldots, s_{m+n}) = \text{actual output}$$

$$d = \text{col}\ (d_0, d_1, \ldots, d_{m+n}) = \text{desired output}$$

$$e = \text{col}\ (e_0, e_1, \ldots, e_{m+n}) = d-s = \text{error vector}$$

be column vectors of length as shown, and let K be the (m+n+1) by (n+1) rectangular matrix

$$K = \begin{bmatrix} k_0 & 0 & \cdots & 0 \\ k_1 & k_0 & \cdots & \cdot \\ \cdot & k_1 & & \\ \cdot & \cdot & & \\ k_m & \cdot & & k_0 \\ 0 & k_m & & k_1 \\ \cdot & 0 & & \cdot \\ \cdot & & & \cdot \\ \cdot & \cdot & & k_m \\ & \cdot & & \end{bmatrix}$$

Then the convolution $s_t = k_t * b_t$ becomes

$$\text{(3.2)} \qquad s = K\,b \quad .$$

Since e=d-s, the unconstrained square norm (2.14a) can now be written

$$\text{(3.3)} \qquad \begin{aligned} Q &= (d - s)^T(d - s) \\ &= e^T e \quad . \end{aligned}$$

The filter energy constraint (3.1a) can now be written

$$b^T b = \text{constant} = c \quad ,$$

and we therefore seek to minimize Q subject to $b^T b$=const=c. We use the method of Lagrange multipliers (see e.g., Hildebrand [10]) and minimize

$$\text{(3.4)} \qquad Q = e^T e + \lambda\,(b^T b - c) \quad ,$$

where c is a suitable real and positive constant, and where λ is the Lagrange multiplier. Then

$$\begin{aligned} Q &= (d - s)^T(d - s) + \lambda(b^Tb - c) \\ &= (d - Kb)^T(d - Kb) + \lambda(b^Tb - c) \\ &= d^Td - 2d^TKb + b^TK^TKb + \lambda(b^Tb - c) \quad . \end{aligned}$$

Next we compute $\partial Q/\partial b$ and set the result to zero*,

$$\frac{\partial Q}{\partial b} = -2d^TK + 2b^TK^TK + 2\lambda b^T = 0 \quad ,$$

which is

$$b^T (K^TK + \lambda I) = d^TK \quad ,$$

where I is the identity matrix. Transposing both sides,

$$(K^TK + \lambda I)\ b = K^Td \quad .$$

But

(3.5) $$K^TK = R \quad \text{and} \quad K^Td = g \quad ,$$

where R is the (n+1) by (n+1) input autocorrelation matrix, and where g is the (n+1) by 1 column vector of the crosscorrelation between the input k_t and the desired output d_t. The autocorrelation matrix R is symmetric and Toeplitz (Robinson and Treitel [2]). We thus have the system of normal equations

(3.6) $$(R + \lambda I)\ b = g \quad ,$$

---

*Note that the differentiation is carried out with respect to the vector b (see e.g. Graybill [11]).

whose solution is

$$(3.7)\qquad b = (R + \lambda I)^{-1} g \quad .$$

Without the filter energy constraint $b^T b$ = constant, (3.7) yields the well-known solution for the unconstrained Wiener shaping filter,

$$(3.8)\qquad b = R^{-1} g \quad .$$

We can now recognize that the Lagrange multiplier λ plays the role of what engineers and statisticians term the "prewhitening parameter" (Treitel and Wang [12]). Rather than solving for λ by substitution of (3.7) into the constraining relation in (3.1a), it is sufficient to require merely that λ be a real and positive number whose magnitude is a few percent or less of the principal diagonal element r_0 of R. This element is the zeroth lag value of the autocorrelation and hence is positive. The addition of a matrix λI (λ real and positive) to R tends to stabilize the calculation of R^{-1} because the small eigenvalues β of R (which are real and positive because R is an autocorrelation matrix) are increased to the corresponding larger eigenvalues $(\beta+\lambda)$ of $R+\lambda I$. These matters are treated in detail by Jackson [13] and by Wiggins [14]. We can see intuitively why the constraint in (3.1a) leads to prewhitening: if R^{-1} blows up, so will the filter b, and hence filter energy becomes infinite. By forcing filter energy to remain finite, we achieve a stable inversion at the price of a small perturbation of the principal diagonal element r_0 of the autocorrelation matrix R.

At this point it is instructive to deal with a related problem, in which we assume that the known input wavelet is corrupted by additive uncorrelated white noise ε_t. We now seek to find the Wiener shaping filter producing a least squares approximation to the desired output d_t, but under the constraint that its response to an input of pure uncorrelated noise ε_t remain bounded. This noise has mean zero and variance, or noise power σ_0^2, that is

$$(3.9)\qquad E\{\varepsilon_t\} = 0 \quad \text{and} \quad E\{\varepsilon_t^2\} = \sigma_0^2 \quad .$$

The analysis of noisy data leads to another system of normal equations

$$(R + [1 + \lambda]\, \sigma_0^2 I)\, b = g \quad ,$$

whose solution is

$$(3.10) \qquad b = (R + [1 + \lambda]\, \sigma_0^2 I)^{-1}\, g \quad ,$$

where once again we assume that λ is a small positive number. This filter has several interesting properties. If we set λ=0 in (3.12), we have

$$(3.11) \qquad b = (R + \sigma_0^2 I)^{-1}\, g \quad ,$$

which is the Wiener shaping filter in the presence of additive white noise ε, but with no constraint on the output noise power. If we set σ_0^2=0 in (3.10), we have

$$(3.12) \qquad b = R^{-1}\, g \quad ,$$

which again yields the unconstrained Wiener shaping filter (3.8), since now there is no additive noise in the input. If we compare (3.11) with (3.7), we observe that the stabilization of the wavelet autocorrelation matrix R can be achieved formally by the expedient of adding white noise to the input wavelet. This, of course, is the origin of the term "prewhitening".

The imposition of the noise output power constraint increases the magnitude of all eigenvalues of the associated autocorrelation matrix, so that the autocorrelation matrix will be nonsingular and will be better conditioned for inversion.

The performance of the filter (3.10) is illustrated in Figure 2. Part A shows the noise-free case: k_t is shaped into an excellent approximation of the desired output spike [Eq. (3.14)]. In Part B, white noise ε_t was added to k_t, such that the ratio of noise variance to signal variance, became equal to 0.20. Eq. (3.11) now holds, and we observe the expected degradation in the actual output: there is a strong spurious event at about t=22. In Part 3, the filter was computed with (3.10) by setting λ=0.20. The spurious event at t=22 has now been attenuated, but at the expense of a broader approximation to the desired output spike at t=0. We observe that the parameter λ determines the trade-off between resolution and noise suppression, as has been pointed out by Jackson [13] and by Wiggins [14]. This trade-off can be examined in greater detail by plotting the squared error, Q, versus the sum of squares of the filter coefficients, as a function of λ. Figure 3 shows this curve for the noisy example of Figure 2(B). A small

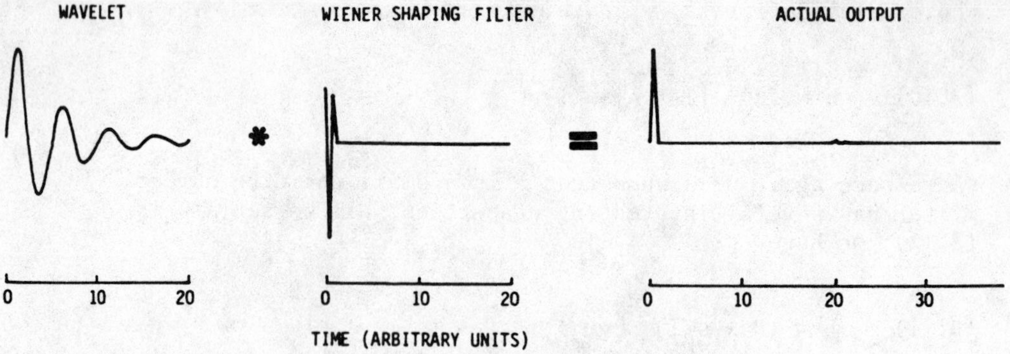

FIG. 2a. The unconstrained Wiener shaping filter in the absence of noise

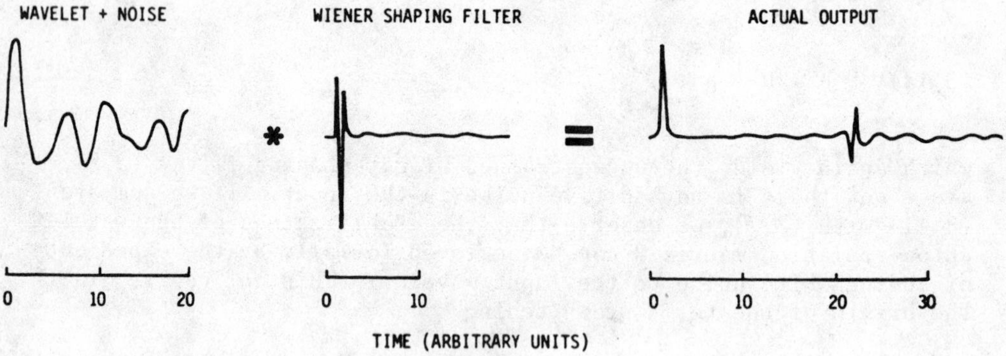

FIG. 2b. The unconstrained Wiener shaping filter in the presence of noise

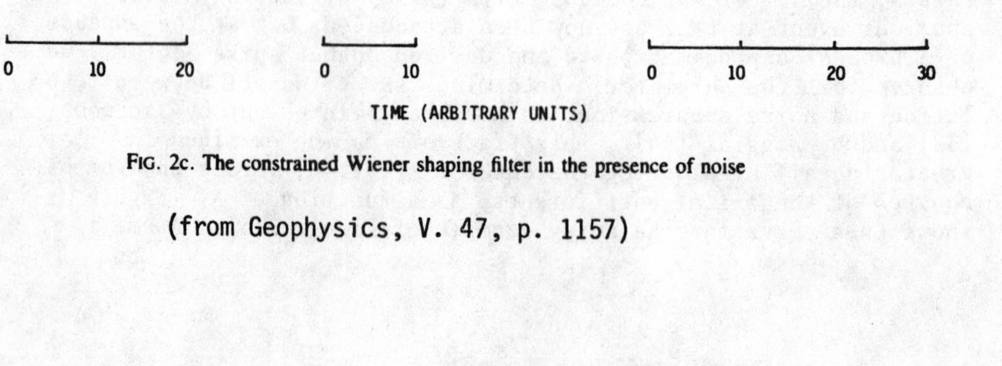

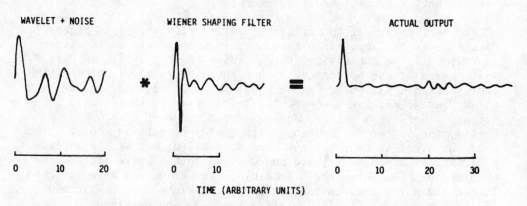

FIG. 2c. The constrained Wiener shaping filter in the presence of noise

(from Geophysics, V. 47, p. 1157)

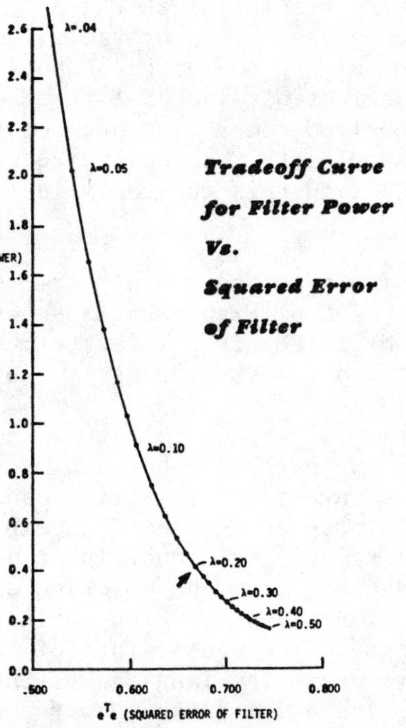

Figure 3. The variation of the filter power and the squared error for different values of λ, for the wavelet of Figures 2b),c). The arrow indicates the value of λ used in Figure 2c. (from Geophysics, V. 47, p. 1158)

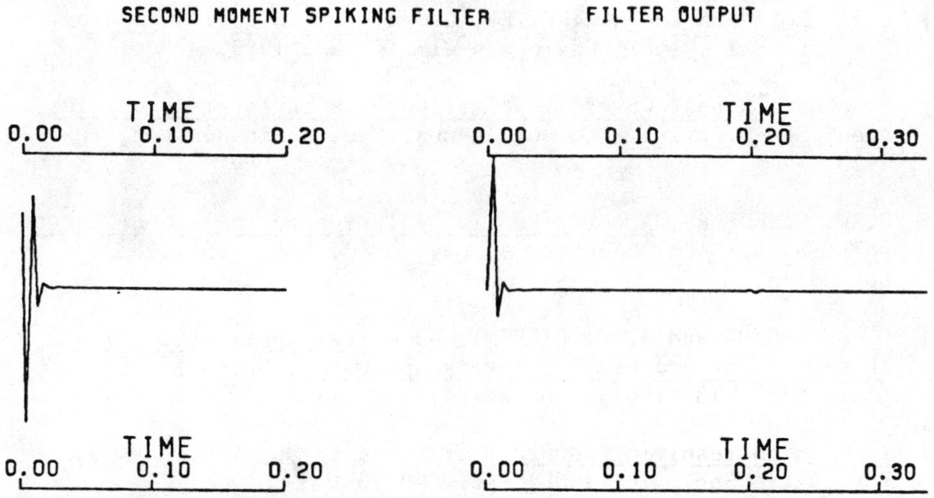

Figure 4. Second moment norm spiking filter for wavelet in Figure 2a with filter output. (from Geophysics, V. 48, p. 509)

value of Q yields sharp resolution at the price of poor uncorrelated noise suppression. Conversely, good noise suppressions are achievable only at the price of poor resolution. In practice, one would select a value of λ from such a trade-off curve corresponding to a desired compromise between resolution and noise suppression. For example, the choice $\lambda=0.20$ was made for the filter of Figure 2(C), and this choice is indicated by an arrow on Figure 3.

The performance of the second moment norm spiking (SMN) filter for the noiseless wavelet of Figure 2a is shown in Figure 4. The performance of the SMN filter is similar to the Wiener filter for the noiseless case but degrades severely in noisy environments (Lines and Treitel [9]).

4.0 Conclusions. We have seen how a time shift invariant specialization of the BG inversion formalism leads to the familiar convolutional model of the seismogram. In exploration seismology we generally wish to remove, or deconvolve the known mapping kernel, or source wavelet, from the observed seismogram in order to produce an estimate of the model, which in this case is the subsurface's impulse response. The constraints of the BG approach have familiar interpretations in the language of the linear shift invariant Wiener filter: the noise output power constraint yields the classical prewhitening criterion for filter stabilization.

REFERENCES

[1] S. TREITEL and L. R. LINES, Linear inverse theory and deconvolution, Geophysics, v. 47 (1982), pp. 1153-1159.

[2] E. A. ROBINSON and S. TREITEL, Geophysical Signal Analysis, Prentice-Hall, Inc., Englewood Cliffs, NJ, 1980.

[3] D. STONE, Robust wavelet estimation by structural deconvolution, SEG preprint from 46th Annual Meeting in Houston, Texas, 1976.

[4] D. W. OLDENBURG, A comprehensive solution to the linear deconvolution problem, Geophys. J. Roy. Astr. Soc., 65 (1981), pp. 331-358.

[5] G. E. BACKUS and J. F. GILBERT, Numerical application of a formalism for geophysical inverse problems, Geoph. J. Roy. Astr. Soc., 13 (1967), pp. 247-276.

[6] _____, The resolving power of gross earth data, Geophy. J. Roy. Astr. Soc., 16 (1968), pp. 169-205.

[7] ____, Uniqueness in the inversion of inaccurate gross earth data, Phil. Trans. Roy. Soc. London, A, 266 (1970), pp. 123-192.

[8] S. TWOMEY, Introduction to the Mathematics of Inversion in Remote Sensing and Indirect Measurements, Elsevier Scientific Publ. Co., Amsterdam, 1977.

[9] L. R. LINES and S. TREITEL, Digital filtering with the second moment norm, Geophysics, 48 (1983), pp. 505-514.

[10] F. B. HILDEBRAND, Advanced Calculus for Applications, Prentice-Hall, Inc., Englewood Cliffs, NJ, 1962.

[11] F. A. GRAYBILL, Introduction to Matrices with Applications in Statistics, Wadsworth Publishing Co., Inc., Belmont, CA, 1969.

[12] S. TREITEL and R. J. WANG, The determination of digital Wiener filters from an ill-conditioned system of normal equations, Geoph. Prosp., 24 (1976), pp. 317-327.

[13] D. D. JACKSON, Interpretation of inaccurate, insufficient, and inconsistent data, Geophys. J. Roy. Astr. Soc., 28 (1972), pp. 97-109.

[14] R. A. WIGGINS, The general linear inverse problem: Implication of surface waves and free oscillations for earth structures, Reviews of Geophysics and Space Physics, 10 (1972), pp. 251-285.

Acknowledgments. We thank Amoco Production Company for permission to publish this manuscript and we thank Dale Stone of SSC for providing us with a good real data example. We are also grateful to Geophysics Editor, Professor Gerald Gardner, who has given us permission to use material from our papers in Geophysics.

Geophysical Inversion by Least-Squares Deconvolution

Enders A. Robinson*

Abstract. Oil and natural gas are found in traps located deep within the sedimentary layers of the earth's crust. The reflection seismic method is by far the most important geophysical technique used to map the underground interfaces between the geological strata. These seismic maps together with other geological information are used to locate favorable drilling sites for exploratory wells. The seismic method involves the transmission of man-made seismic disturbances into the earth, and the recording of the resulting echos (or reflections) from the geologic interfaces. These recordings (or traces) are in the form of time series, one time series for each source and receiver pair. However various types of noise interfere with the desired reflections, and so the interpretation of the data presents a formidable problem in time series analysis. A whole branch of geophysics, called geophysical data processing, has grown up in the past twenty years to provide the people, equipment, and methods to analyze these time series. The present paper describes the practical inversion methods in everyday use. These methods are deconvolution techniques based upon statistical models and implemented by the principle of least squares. The deconvolution methods convert the observed seismic data into pictures of the subsurface structure of the earth.

1. Introduction to Deconvolution. Seismic inversion methods treat the structure of the entire seismic reflection trace x_k, and in particular how multiple reflections build up and influence the results which we see on the trace. It is the aim of seismic inversion theory to unravel this structure and give us the reflection coefficients of the layered earth system which produced this trace. A prototype of such seismic inversion methods is dynamic deconvolution. However, all seismic inversion methods that deal with the whole reflection seismogram as one unit are fraught with difficulties. The impediments which obstruct one-dimensional inversion methods are largely due to the three-dimensional nature of the seismic experiment. A one-dimensional seismic field trace receives energy from a three-dimensional subsurface geometry. However, any one-dimensional inversion of the trace is working within the context

*University of Tulsa, Tulsa, OK 74104

of a one-dimensional geometry. Thus the inverse method tries to ascribe energy which originates in three-dimensions to a one-dimensional model, and this represents a serious specification error which is often fatal.

One solution to this problem is to make use of earlier, more direct, and less complex inversion techniques as the deconvolution methods in Robinson (1954). The essence of these deconvolution approaches, as opposed to general inversion, is that they utilize only a segment of the seismic trace, say the part of the trace that lies within a time gate from time index m to time index m+n. By choosing successive time gates, which may overlap to various extents, we can cover the entire trace in a step-wise time-varying manner. The advanage of working within selected time gates one at a time, and not with the entire trace at once, is that the deconvolution method only has to cope with a limited amount of information in any given instance. As a result the method can be intrinsically more simple, direct, and resilient, and consequently more robust and resistent to both random noise and signal-generated (organized) noise, including energy coming from other dimensions.

These simple and direct inversion methods were originally referred to as predictive decomposition. However the word "decomposition" gave way to the word "deconvolution", so they are now called predictive deconvolution methods. Predictive deconvolution is usually divided into two types. Predictive deconvolution with unit prediction distance is called spike deconvolution, whereas predictive deconvolution with greater prediction distance is called gapped deconvolution. Predictive deconvolution makes use of one-sided (i.e., causal) least-square operators, and so represents a subset of what may be called least squares deconvolution methods. For example, other least squares deconvolution methods are in use, which involve the design of two-sided (i.e., noncausal) least squares filters. Such filters are applied for signature deconvolution and wavelet processing. Signature deconvolution is used to remove source and near-surface effects from the seismogram. Wavelet processing represents one of the last processing operations to be applied to the seismic data. The purpose of wavelet processing is to convert the trace into a form which clearly delineates the subsurface layering for seismic interpretation.

Let us now speak in general terms. Let us consider a physical system that is linear and time-invariant. The system can be described by its impulse response function. The impulse response function is defined as the output (response) to a spike input (impulse). As input, we feed into the system a white noise process, that is, a process whose autocorrelation is a spike. What is the output? This result is basic. The output is a stationary random process. This process lies in that large interior region between the two extremes, that is, between the extreme of a white noise process, and the other extreme of a periodic process. This basic result can be depicted as:

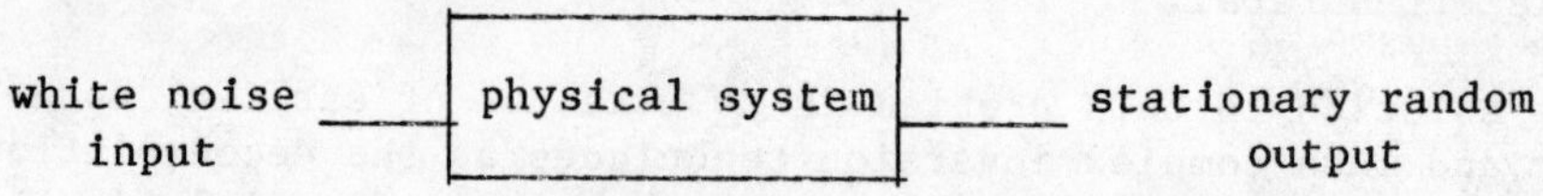

Let us represent the white noise input as the time series ε_k and the stationary random output as the time series x_k. Let the impulse response be w_k. Our basic result can now be written as

$$\varepsilon_k * w_k = x_k$$

That is, the output is the convolution of the input with the impulse response function.

What is the autocorrelation of the stationary time series x_k? We know that the autocorrelation of the white noise is a spike, so the autocorrelation must be related in some simple way to the autocorrelation of the impulse response function. What is this relationship? We make use of the fact that the unnormalized autocorrelation of a signal is equal to the convolution of the signal with its time reverse. Thus the autocorrelation of x_k is

$$x_k * x_{-k} = [\varepsilon_k * w_k] * [\varepsilon_{-k} * w_{-k}]$$

Since convolution is commutative we can rearrange the right hand side as

$$x_k * x_{-k} = [\varepsilon_k * \varepsilon_{-k}] * [w_k * w_{-k}]$$

The first expression in brackets on the right hand side is the autocorrelation of the white noise. This autocorrelation is a spike, and a unit spike acts as unity in convolution. Hence we have the important theorem that:

$$x_k * x_{-k} = \sigma^2 \, w_k * w_{-k}$$

where σ^2 is a scale factor which represents the power (energy) of the white noise. This result says that the autocorrelation of the stationary time series is equal to the autocorrelation of the impulse response function, except for the scale factor σ^2. In words, the white noise does not (and cannot) influence the resonances of the system. If we let $\phi_{xx}(k)$ and $\phi_{ww}(k)$ represent the autocorrelations of the stationary time series x_k and the impulse response function w_k respectively, then the above equation is

$$\phi_{xx}(k) = \sigma^2 \phi_{ww}(k)$$

As we will see this equation represents one of the basic theorems utilized in the theory of predictive deconvolution.

2. White Reflectivity Model. The seismic trace can be visualized as the response of the earth to a seismic source, such as an explosion. The convolutional model represents the received trace x_k as the convolution of a seismic wavelet w_k with the reflectivity function ε_k. The reflectivity function is defined as the sequence of reflection coefficients of the subsurface interfaces. The term "reflection coefficient" is used here to refer to the local (or Fresnel) reflection coefficient of the interface in question. For computational purposes we must use a discrete model, so we pick some sampling time interval, say 4 milliseconds, as the spacing (in two-way time) of the (mathematically defined) interfaces represented by the ε_k.

We now come to the white reflectivity hypothesis. An hypothesis is an assertion subject to verification. It is a conjecture that accounts, within a theory or ideational framework, for a set of facts and that can be used as a basis for further investigation. It is a proposition stated as a basis for argument and reasoning. The white reflection hypothesis represents a working proposition. It does not represent absolute truth. However, the white reflection hypothesis does represent a picture that is supported by the data in enough cases so that it is useful. The white reflection hypothesis is a bench mark as to the statistical distribution of the reflection coefficients used as a reference point in a seismic survey of a completely unknown region.

The white reflectivity hypothesis states that the reflectivity function is a sample from a white noise process. In other words, the reflection coefficients ε_k form a sequence of uncorrelated random variables. This hypothesis would be expected to hold in those areas where the various sediments were laid down over geologic time in a non-predictable random manner. As a result the reflection coefficients would be unrelated to each other, and thus they would form a random white noise sequence.

When we say that a reflectivity function is white, we do not mean that its autocorrelation values for non-zero shifts are identically zero, but that they more or less lie in a band given by the probable range. Of course some will lie outside this range, but most should lie within. An actual reflectivity function can be computed from the well logs from an oil well, and then the autocorrelation of the empirical reflectivity function within a time gate can be computed. We would plot this autocorrelation and see how much it deviates from the theoretical spike autocorrelation. If the deviation is within statistical limits, then we say that the white reflectivity hypothesis is upheld for the geologic sedimentary column corresponding to that time gate. This computation has been done for oil wells in many different oil fields, and the results show that white reflectivity represents a good working hypothesis for the explorationist working in an unexplored area. The situation corresponds to playing cards. A good working hypothesis for card games is that the card shuffle is random. The shuffling mixes the playing cards together to change their order of arrangement. The shuffled deck of cards lays on the table before us, even as the layers of an unknown sedimentary basin appear as cards in a shuffled deck. If we drew the cards one by one and found them black, red, black, red, black, red, all the way to the last, we would be surprised, even as we would be if the reflection coefficients were plus, minus, plus, minus, plus, minus, all the way to the deepest interface.

In playing with a particular dealer, or in exploring a particular basin, as more experience is gained certain idiosyncrasies might come out, as significant definite biases. For such a dealer we would then want to modify our hypothesis. In the same way, as the explorationist learns more about an area, he would want to modify the hypothesis in accord with what he has learned about the actual reflection coefficient distribution present in the sedimentary column.

In exploration we are always working against time. Time is money. We must start with a noncommittal hypothesis and then modify it only to the amount that time and money will allow. The white reflectivity hypothesis is the best such initial hypothesis to use within selected time gates.

The white-reflectivity convolutional model is

$$x_k = w_k * \varepsilon_k$$

where the reflectivity function ε_k is white noise. Thus the trace is a realization of a stationary random process, and in particular, the autocorrelation of the trace is approximately equal to the autocorrelation of the seismic wavelet. This result is important, because from the received trace we cannot directly measure the wavelet, due to the mutual overlapping of wavelets and resulting interference with each other. Although we cannot measure the wavelet directly we can obtain its autocorrelation, for as we have shown in the preceding section the autocorrelation of the received seismic trace is equal to the autocorrelation of the wavelet, except for a scale factor. Of course this determination of its autocorrelation does not determine the wavelet as there are many wavelets having the same autocorrelation. However, we have made an important first step in the determination of the seismic wavelet.

Let us now summarize. The white-reflectivity convolutional model states that a given discrete finite-length seismic trace is additively composed of wavelets with random white amplitudes.

Because of this randomness, the autocorrelation of the trace is equal to the autocorrelation of the wavelet, within a scale factor. Of course, this equality is only approximate due to statistical fluctuations, especially for large time shifts where the number of cross-products are few. Hence we have the basic result that we can find the autocorrelation of a wavelet, at least approximately, without any direct measurement of wavelet. This result is one of the basic building blocks of the statistical use of deconvolution (Robinson, 1954).

The fact that autocorrelation of trace gives the autocorrelation of basic wavelet should seem reasonable as the trace is assumed to be generated by the convolution of a white reflectivity function with the wavelet. The autocorrelation of white noise is zero at all shifts except shift zero, and hence the contributions to the autocorrelation of trace must be due to the wavelet.

Many great oilfields in Texas and Oklahoma discovered in the early days of seismic prospecting were in areas which produced textbook-type (i.e., archetypal) seismograms. These seismograms as recorded in the field showed beautiful primary reflections which accurately represented the sedimentary structure. The reason is that in these particular areas the sedimentary layers give rise to a sequence of reflection coefficients (i.e., the reflectivity function) which is of a white-noise nature. Due to this randomness of the entire sedimentary column, the multiples cancel each other out, except at the times of the primaries, where they build up and actually enhance the primary reflections.

When there are one or more strong reflecting layers in the sedimentary column, then the multiples from these layers can build up and mask the primary events. For example, in marine exploration the water layer represents a nonattenuating medium bounded by two strong reflecting interfaces and hence represents an energy trap. A seismic pulse generated in this energy trap will be successively reflected between the two interfaces. Consequently, reflections from deep horizons below the water layer will be obscured by the water reverberations. As another example, a limestone layer at depth with strong reflecting interfaces can also produce multiple reflections which interfere with primary information on the seismogram.

Despite the presence of strong reflecting interfaces interspersed in the geologic column, there often remain significant sections where the interfaces are characterized by reflection coefficients that are small and white. In such cases, we can pick time gates on the reflection seismogram inside of which the reflectivity function may be considered to be white. Thus by carefully selecting time gates on a reflection seismogram, we are able to pick out sections where we may assume the reflectivity function is a white-noise series. The small reflection coefficient over-extended (SRCOE) convolutional model (Robinson, 1983b) states that the reflection seismogram due to a spike source is the output of a minimum-delay system. This system has impulse response given by the multiple-train of the entire sedimentary section and input given by the reflectivity function. Often we can select a time gate on the field trace so that the corresponding gate in the reflectivity function may be considered to be a white noise series. At this point, we should state an important qualification; we do not demand pure whiteness, but only off-color white.

In this way we have specialized the convolutional model so that it can form the basis for a method to determine the required deconvolution operator. The specialization states that

(1) the earth acts as a minimum-delay system in producing the train of multiple events that appear on the reflection seismogram.

(2) the reflectivity function over a selected gate of the sedimentary column is a white-noise series.

Because of these special features, this seismic model can be used as a basis for determining the deconvolution operator. In brief, the seismic model is a minimum-delay-wavelet, white-reflectivity-input convolutional model.

Deeper reflections have a higher percent of low frequency energy than shallow reflections because of the greater attenuation of the higher frequencies as a result of absorption and other filtering mechanisms; hence time-variant filtering is required in which the pass band moves toward low frequencies as record time increases. One method of achieving time-variant filtering is to use separate gates (for example, shallow and deep) so that the deconvolution operator varies with record time. The proper use of predictive deconvolution requires this time-varying approach. We design the operator and carry out the deconvolution on only one gate at a time. Several gates are required for each field trace.

In using any convolutional model of the seismic trace we must always take this into consideration. Information about the subsurface reflectivity is necessarily lost due to sampling and filtering effects. The series of reflection coefficients may be operated upon by harmonic analysis techniques to obtain the Fourier transform. The transform will produce the magnitude and phase spectrum of the sampled continuous function which is represented by the reflection coefficients. The reflectivity function sampled at two milliseconds has a Nyquist frequency of 250 Hertz. Convolving the reflectivity with a wavelet which is band limited to say 20 to 70 Hertz, will produce an output which is also band limited to 20 to 70 Hertz, since the output can contain only frequencies common to the input and to the wavelet. The immediate result of the convolutional model is that some of the definition of the sedimentary section has been irrevocably lost. The definition is limited by the highest frequency present in the signal. Definition in this case is now limited to the bed thickness traversed by one wavelength or period of 70 Hertz information, or roughly 0.014 seconds. The minimum bed thickness that can be defined by the reflection coefficients is determined by the sampling interval of 0.002 seconds.

3. Convolutional Model as the Basis for Deconvolution. The basic components of the convolutional model used to study the seismic reflection process consist of a seismic wavelet w_k and a series of reflection coefficients ε_k (the reflectivity series) representing the layering of the earth. Their convolution represents the seismic recording (the field trace) x_k. The model is

$$x_k = w_k * \varepsilon_k$$

An asterisk is the accepted mathematical sign to denote convolution. Thus the entire system is simulated by a single seismic wavelet which transforms the reflectivity into a reasonable duplicate of the signal x_k received by a field recorder. Of course, this time-invariant model is assumed to be valid only over a portion of the entire seismic trace, because as we know a more exact model would require a time-varying wavelet.

In the convolutional model we can think of the reflectivity as the input, the wavelet as the unit impulse response function, and the field trace as the output. The basic equation of the model of the process is

$$\text{(input)} * \text{(wavelet)} = \text{(output)}$$

The synthetic seismogram is an example of the practical use of the convolutional model. A series of reflection coefficients, which form a string of pulses representing the earth reflectivity sequence, is fed into the system as input. Convolution of the seismic wavelet with the input produces the output, a synthetic seismogram.

The operation can be reversed, due to the fact that the process of convolution is analogous to multiplication. Thus, if the input convolved with the seismic wavelet equals the output, the output can be "divided" (deconvolved) by the seismic wavelet to equal the input. But although convolution follows the same commutative rule as multiplication, convolution is not multiplication, and the reverse process, deconvolution, is not division.

The field wavelet w_k has the s.a.m.i. representation

$$w_k = s_k * a_k * m_k * i_k$$

where s_k is the source signature, a_k the absorption, m_k the multiples, and i_k the instruments. We assume that source signature deconvolution has been performed, or else that a minimum-delay source has been employed. In any case we will assume that the wavelet is minimum delay, so we will write the minimum delay wavelet as b_k instead of w_k. The field trace now has the representation

$$x_k = b_k * \varepsilon_k$$

where b_k is minimum-delay. This equation represents a minimum-delay convolutional model of the seismic trace. We generally assume that the leading coefficient b_0 of the wavelet is one.

If we transform to the frequency domain, the convolutional model becomes

$$X(\omega) = B(\omega)\, E(\omega)$$

where $X(\omega)$, $B(\omega)$, and $E(\omega)$ are respectively the discrete Fourier transform of the trace x_k, the wavelet b_k, and the reflectivity ε_k. Thus, convolution in the time domain corresponds to multiplication in the frequency domain. We can solve for $E(\omega)$ by the equation

$$E(\omega) = \frac{X(\omega)}{B(\omega)}$$

This equation is the frequency-domain counterpart of deconvolution. Thus deconvolution in the time domain corresponds to division in the frequency domain. The inverse Fourier transform of $1/B(\omega)$ gives the <u>inverse wavelet</u> $a_k = (a_0, a_1, a_2, a_3, \cdots)$. Because b_k is minimum delay its inverse a_k is also minimum delay (i.e., causal, stable, and minimum-phase). Also because we assume that $b_0 = 1$, it follows that $a_0 = 1$.

Practical application of deconvolution is the process whereby the output signal (the field trace), is convolved with the inverse wavelet (the deconvolution operator) to determine the input signal (the reflectivity):

$$(\text{output}) * (\text{inverse wavelet}) = (\text{input})$$

This equation gives the essence of deconvolution. It represents a method of finding the input signal that produced a known output. As such, deconvolution represents a type of seismic inversion.

All deconvolution procedures may be related to some model of the process which develops the recorded seismic field trace. We have made several basic assumptions in developing the convolutional model, and the success of the deconvolution process is dependent upon the validity of these assumptions under real conditions. For example, the reliability of the noise-free model may be degraded by the effect of actual noise. If theoretical noise is added to the model, then the quality of deconvolution will depend upon whether or not the actual noise meets the assumptions regarding the theoretical noise which is assumed to be present.

The fact exists that there are a large number of discrepancies between theory and practice. However, many ingenious techniques have been developed to handle some of the problems, and the remainder often fit the assumptions well enough to achieve considerable success. A salient point is that geologic conditions vary. Thus the interpreter must recognize the situation existing for a particular area, and know what computer processes are available and their effects on the data. All of the most commonly used method of deconvolution assume a model in which a given portion of the lithologic section is represented by a completely random and uncorrelated series of reflection coefficients which has a completely white spectrum. A seismic shot initiates a pulse which almost immediately degenerates into a damped wavelet. This wavelet travels through the earth layers where it suffers reflections and refractions. The resulting field trace recorded by detectors at the surface of the earth represents the output. The convolutional model states that the field trace (within the given time gate) is composed of the sum of a multitude of overlapping wavelets, each wavelet weighted by the corresponding reflection coefficient.

In the application of predictive decomposition, it is assumed that the wavelet is unknown, but is minimum delay, that the frequency content of the lithologic section is completely white, and that the additive noise is white or absent. The frequency content of the wavelet on the field trace can be derived by taking the autocorrelation of the field trace. The reason is that the power spectrum of a white signal (i.e., the reflection coefficient series) is completely flat, so the colored frequency content of the wavelet is the same as that of the field trace. The known quantities in the normal equations are these computed autocorrelation coefficients, and the unknown quantities are the coefficients of the required deconvolution filter. By solving the normal equations, we obtain the deconvolution filter. It can be shown that, depending on how we construct the normal equations, we can obtain either of two types of predictive deconvolution filter. One is called the spike deconvolution filter and the other the gapped deconvolution filter. Both types of predictive deconvolution filters are required to be causal (one-sided). The deconvolution operation actually is done by convolution, that is, by the convolution of the deconvolution filter with the field trace.

In the case of spike deconvolution, the filter is a least-squares approximation to the inverse of the seismic wavelet. It is for this reason that the spike deconvolution filter is called an inverse filter. When the spike deconvolution filter (or operator) is convolved with the field trace it is, in fact, convolved in turn with all of the wavelets which make up the field trace. The operator converts each of these wavelets, as well as possible, into a spike, greatly improving seismic resolution. The amplitude of each output spike will be proportional to the wavelet amplitude (i.e., the reflection coefficient), and the sharpness will be a function of the frequency bandwidth. The spike can be no sharper than the best approximation possible with the available bandwidth.

Accepting the basic white-reflectivity, minimum-delay-wavelet convolutional model as correct, the major contribution to the effectiveness of this operation lies in the method used to design the operator. In common practice the operators are designed to a finite length by the least-squares criterion. It can be shown that the least-squares inverse operator may or may not converge rapidly to the exact theoretical inverse (Robinson and Treitel, 1980). If it does not converge rapidly then the finite-length least-squares operator may cause serious specification errors and hence not do an effective job of deconvolution. However, the use of the least squares method assures that within the limits of the length of the operator defined, the convolution of the spike deconvolution operator with the field wavelet will produce the best possible least-squares approximation to the desired spike output function.

The effectiveness of deconvolution is dependent upon the applicability of the basic assumptions. In some cases the assumptions can be modified to fit the actual conditions. In other cases there is no easy remedy for the divergence between model and reality. For instance, one basic assumption is that the lithologic section is indeed completely white. Unfortunately, this assumption is not always true. In fact, it is rarely exactly true and the deviation between the white assumption and the actual lithologic spectrum will determine a measure of effectiveness of the deconvolution process.

The white-reflectivity, minimum-delay-wavelet convolutional model, upon which predictive deconvolution theory depends, assumes the approximate validity of the following conditions (Robinson, 1954, 1957):

1. The seismic wavelet is well-defined.
2. The seismic wavelet is a minimum delay time function (i.e., a stable causal time function with minimum-phase spectrum).
3. The additive noise is absent or small.
4. The spectrum of the reflectivity function (i.e., reflection coefficient series) is white.
5. The field trace is stationary, i.e., does not change with time, over a given time gate.
6. The field trace is broad band.

In reality the following conditions probably exist:

1. The seismic wavelet is not well defined.
2. The wavelet is stable and causal, but is mixed phase.
3. The additive noise may be great.
4. The spectrum of the reflectivity is not white.
5. The field trace is time-variant over the given time gate.
6. The field trace is narrow band.

The seismic wavelet may be a very narrow band signal of some length, whereas the reflectivity is completely sharp and broad band. Evidently, the reflectivity is modified extensively in nature's production of the field trace. The earth and seismic instruments invariably produce frequency filtering and phase delay. The resulting time shifting spreads the response due to a given interface over several milliseconds of record time, smearing the detail and interfering with the resolving powers of the observed field trace. Complete deconvolution must therefore restore both the amplitude spectrum and the phase spectrum to that of the reflectivity, but this goal often is not possible to attain. The problem becomes one of determining the required parameters. The filtering effect of the seismic experiment can nearly completely eliminate some of the frequency components present in the actual reflectivity function. As a result perfect deconvolution is not possible. Because of this and other reasons, the problem is attacked from a statistical standpoint and uses least squares methods to derive the best possible deconvolution operator (in a mathematical sense). The tremendous advantage of this procedure is that the best possible answer, in the least squares sense, is always obtained. Other procedures may provide completely invalid output when there is any deviation from the basic assumption, or may require information that is not available. The statistical least squares approach will provide the minimum mean square error of implementation, but again this is in the mathematical sense in regard to the specified model, and any specification errors may still be large.

4. The Practical Problem of Geophysical Inversion. In order to fix ideas, let us consider in general terms the problem of seismic exploration for oil in the earth's sedimentary strata. The source is an explosion or another form of energy which is introduced into the ground at the surface. The reflection seismogram x_k is the seismic reflection record (or trace or time series) which is digitally recorded at the surface. The reflection coefficient sequence ε_k is a digitized representation of the reflectivity of the earth as a function of depth. As a result, knowledge of the ε_k sequences for various geographic locations on the surface allows the seismic interpreter to make contour maps of the earth's sedimentary structure at depth. In other words, the reflection seismic method is a method of obtaining a picture of what the earth looks like thousands of feet below the surface from an experiment (i.e., a surface source of energy and a surface recording of the resulting reflection response to that source) carried out on the surface.

The nature of the geophysicist's problem can be visualized by imagining that the earth's crust is a stack of Plexiglas sheets, all opaque with different properties and thicknesses, each having irregular surfaces, some of the plates being tilted, bent or deformed, and some containing pockets or traps of varying shapes and sizes. Some of these traps may contain accumulations of oil and natural gas. Now, the geophysicist taps the surface of this medium and he analyzes the resulting response at the surface to determine the thickness and physical properties of each plate, details of the interfaces between plates, and the locations and shapes of the traps in the plates. With this analogy in mind, the earth's crust may be described as an acoustically translucent, heterogeneous, multi-layered medium. The traps for oil and natural gas may have an areal extent of only a half of a square mile, and be as much as four miles deep within the earth, with no geologic evidence at the surface that there is a trap deep below.

In order to discover more oil and gas to replace the amount consumed, the oil exploration industry records about two million seismic traces x_k each and every day, year after year. Each of these two million time series has about 1500 data points (i.e., $k = 0, 1, 2, \ldots, 1500$). These field traces must be analyzed to yield a picture of the subsurface structure.

Up to about 1960, the recorded analog trace (subject to only some electric filtering) was analyzed by eye in order to detect reflected events from the subsurface interfaces. From these observations, the seismic interpreter was able to draw subsurface contour maps. In many geographical areas of the world the method worked well; the interpretations on the whole were correct, and great oil fields were discovered. The question is why did the method work? But the question "why" is not important in comparison to the fact that the method did work; the seismic interpreter was able to detect primary reflected events by eye. The primary reflected event from interface k is defined as the pulse that travels directly down from the source to interface k and then directly back to the surface; its generating function is

$$\sigma_{k-1}^2 \, \varepsilon_k \, s^k$$

where σ_{k-1}^2 is the product of the two-way transmission coefficients of the interfaces from the surface through interface k-1, c_k is the reflection coefficient of interface k, and s is the unit delay operator.

However, for each primary reflected event, there are many multiple reflected events, and from a strictly mathematical point of view, these multiple events should overwhelm the primary events on the recorded trace x_k. That is, from a strictly mathematical point of view, the reverberations of this complex stratified system we call the earth should overwhelm our ability to pick distinct primary reflections on the seismic records.

As the search for oil extended into new areas all over the world, it was realized that there were many geographical areas where seismic record quality was poor, or in other words, the multiple reflections were overwhelming the primary reflections. In particular, in water-covered areas such as Lake Maracaibo in Venezuela and in the Persian Gulf, strong multiple waves in the water layer gave the observed seismic trace a ringing character which made it impossible to detect the primary reflections coming up from the deep interfaces. Strong reverberations from surface layers masked the desired primary events in many land areas of exploration. In fact, as exploration pushed into more difficult geographical areas, all types of multiple reflected energy began to be recognized on the traces and made conventional visual interpretation difficult to impossible. Moreover, conventional methods of electric filtering and field techniques could not overcome these difficulties.

5. The Statistical Basis for Geophysical Inversion. From a theoretical point of view, it is important to develop models of the earth. In classical science, a great many models are known in which the behavior of the system is fully determined by a precisely fixed mathematical structure subject to idealized boundary-value or initial-value conditions. Such is the case for the earth model first treated in a classic paper of Lamb in 1904 on the propagation of seismic waves in an elastic solid. Classical geophysics is concerned with the develop- of such deterministic models. However, because of the mathematical complexity of these models, only a very few simple geometric configurations within the earth are susceptible to analytic solutions. Because the field geophysicist historically was faced with a large number of different physical configurations, each of a complicated nature, the methods of classical geophysics were of no direct use and could only serve as a guide. The situation in exploration seismology in the early 1950's was summarized by one of the leading field geophysicists with this statement: "We have sharpened our tools as much as we can; what we need now are some new tools".

The new tool was soon in coming. It was the digital computer which made possible the digital processing of seismic data, and in particular deconvolution. In turn, these new digital methods were based on more sophisticated mathematical models than the classic deterministic seismic models of Rayleigh, Lamb, and Jeffreys.

The digital revolution in seismology as well as in other sciences is based on statistical (or data-oriented) models which make possible the unraveling (or deconvolution) of the observed time series. The essence of this statistical approach is that, in addition to its physical structure, a system has a structure of behavior within which the system operates. This structure of behavior can be deduced from field observations. Experiments with the statistical approach have confirmed the existence of this behavior and have brought us closer to understanding the workings of nature. The basis of this approach lies within the behavior of the physical media and in the interaction of their components. The underlying permanence is in the rules by which energy is exchanged between components, and in this respect the concept of the minimum-delay of energy becomes a central concept. We see that there is a subtle shift of emphasis here between the deterministic and the statistical approach. The statistical approach is concerned about the transactions rather than the things; that is it deals with the dynamics of what happens rather than with characteristics of the system as an object. The field data in the form of time series are the keys to this approach, for the analysis of the time series tells us what happens and in this way depicts the structure of the system. For example, in the statistical approach, we are interested in the correlation among reflection coefficients in a sequence of strata, and with the flow of energy within this structure. In other words, the statistical approach looks at the relationship between things rather than the things themselves.

Predictive deconvolution is based on an extremely sophisticated yet highly robust statistical model. This statistical model can explain how seismic waves propagate in certain kinds of sedimentary layering, and this propagation can in no way be easily accounted for by a deterministic model. This situation is entirely analogous to the work of Maxwell, Boltzmann, and Gibbs in thermodynamics and statistical physics in which they introduced statistical methods to describe processes which were beyond the reach of deterministic physics. With the great computer capacity that soon will be available, it is conceivable that it may be possible to bypass the statistics in some cases and return to deterministic models. But still the human mind can comprehend and understand only a limited amount of data, and we need the discipline and the order of statistics to ease our task. Most of the great innovations in physics for over a century have been statistical, from the concept of entropy to quantum physics.

In the same spirit, seismic wave propagation as experienced in the field can only be understood in a statistical sense. The reason why seismic data processing works, and works quite successfully in most instances, is that the basic data have been generated by a statistical process within the earth.

In those cases in which the reflection coefficients of the interfaces are small, the reflection response is equal to the convolution of a minimum-delay reverberation wavelet with the reflection coefficient sequence. In many physical problems in which large amounts of data are handled, the reflection coefficient sequence may be considered as a realization of a random process, in which case the reflection response is the corresponding realization of a time series generated by a statistical minimum-delay model. In the seismic exploration for petroleum and natural gas, the reflection coefficient series represents the reflectivity of the earth's crust and so can be used to make contour maps of the earth's structure at depth. Empirically, it is known that various intervals within the earth's crust have uncorrelated reflection coefficient sequences, and as a result the reflectivity of the deep earth's crust can be obtained by the predictive deconvolution of reflection seismograms recorded on the surface.

Let us now further explain the statistical minimum-delay model. The earth's crust is made out of a large number of strata in complex configurations. In the analysis of seismic waves from a physical point of view, we try to understand why the various waves that propagate through these strata behave the way they do. It is apparent that this is a difficult subject, and so we have to deal with it differently than with simpler situations. One way to analyze the properties of the strata is to start from a physical point of view, namely the point of view acquired over the years by the field geophysicists who analyze and interpret the seismic records. These geophysicists have a rough idea where the waves are going and they begin by making the right kind of approximations, knowing what is big and what is small in a given complicated situation. These interpretation problems are so complex that even an elementary understanding, although inaccurate and incomplete, is worth having. One of the things learned by these field geophysicists is that the analysis requires an understanding of the theory of probability. We do not want to know where every wave is actually moving, but rather how many move here and there on the average and the mutual buildup or cancelling of effects. Large numbers of seismic reflection records are needed to carry out an exploration program over a geographic area. The quantity of data necessarily requires the consideration of each record as a member of a larger group or ensemble of records. Thus, the reliability of a single record is considerably less than the reliability of the ensemble average in connection with the description of the geological conditions existing in that area. Also, from an economic standpoint, the amount of control in such an exploration program must be kept at a bare minimum consistent with worthwhile results. As a result, the working geophysicist must proceed to fit his empirical data into the larger overall framework from a statistical point of view. A major justification for using the statistical approach in seismology is due to the fact that large amounts of data must be processed; any data in large enough quantities takes on a statistical character, even though each individual piece of data is of a deterministic nature. Thus, the field geophysicist in working with the physical properties of the earth is faced with a situation which is essentially statistical. For example, a reflection which may be followed from trace to trace, record to record, usually has more value to the seismic interpreter, and hence is statistically more significant, than a reflection which appears only on a few traces.

6. Critique of the White Reflectivity Hypothesis. Let us now consider a critical aspect of the statistical model, namely when and why can the reflectivity be regarded as a realization of a

stochastic process. As discussed in Robinson (1983b), the answer to this question must be deferred to when more complete statistical studies on seismic reflectivity are available. With the great computer capacities and storage facilities now available, these important works will not be long in forthcoming.

At one extreme, we have a reflectivity with small reflection coefficients which are completely unpredictible, i.e., the small white reflection coefficient (SWRC) hypothesis. At the other extreme, we have a reflectivity with large reflection coefficients which are completely predictable. Such a case is realized by a large cyclic reflection coefficient (LCRC) series.

When we speak of a white reflection coefficient sequence, we must consider such a reflectivity as a mathematical ideal which may or may not adequately describe reality in any given application. The fact is that sedimentary rocks usually do not give a spectrum which is completely white. There are definite dominant frequency components and periodic elements in the geologic column which provide the amplitude and character contrasts of reflections and which are coherent across several traces to provide the continuity used to carry reflection horizons. The character and frequency content of the amplitude spectrum of the reflection coefficient series varies widely, closely meeting the description of white signal in some areas and being far removed in others. According to Lindseth (1970), generally a completely random sand-shale sequence will come very close to meeting the white assumption. On the other hand a section made up of definite lithologic units and sharp velocity contrasts similar to that which exists over much of Western Canada may have strong periodic elements. This of course causes both the amplitude spectrum and the autocorrelation to have character which differs markedly from a white spectrum. Should the inverse operator in spike deconvolution be designed on the assumption that the only character present in the field trace is that of the seismic wavelet, the net effect of the deconvolution may be to actually eliminate some of the reflection coefficients (events) rather than enhance them.

A computational way to check the white hypothesis is to take the series of reflection coefficients developed for a synthetic seismogram in the same area as the field work and examine the amplitude spectrum. If the amplitude spectrum is completely white then obviously the process is completely random and the reflectivity is similar to pure white noise. However, if strong dominant peaks exist on the spectrum they represent dominant frequency components which cause some periodic influence on the record. When such a situation occurs the method of handling the data should be different but the means may not be readily obtainable.

For the convolutional model $x_k = w_k * \varepsilon_k$, the autocorrelation of the trace x_k is equal to the convolution of the autocorrelation of the wavelet w_k with the autocorrelation of the reflectivity ε_k. Because the autocorrelation of a white series is a spike, it follows that under the white reflectivity hypothesis the autocorrelation of the trace is simply proportional to the autocorrelation of the wavelet. This result is one of the basic theorems upon which the method of predictive deconvolution depends. In the case of a non-white reflectivity, the autocorrelation of the wavelet is not given by the autocorrelation of the reflectivity alone. In other words, in the non-white case, the power spectrum of the trace is the product of two non-flat spectra, namely the energy spectrum of the wavelet and the power spectrum of the reflectivity. If the normal procedures are used to develop the operator for the deconvolution process, the operator will endeavour to produce a completely white spectrum in the output (i.e., deconvolved) trace. When such a situation occurs, desired elements present in the reflectivity may be suppressed, and the net result is to actually suppress or diminish the amplitude of actual reflecting events.

The white-reflectivity model assumes any irregularities in the amplitude spectrum of the field trace and are caused strictly by the spectrum of the seismic wavelet. In the non-white model the spectrum of the field trace is the product of the irregular spectrum of the wavelet and the irregular spectrum of the reflectivity. This may be carried to the extreme case where the spectrum irregularity is entirely due to the reflectivity of the earth and the wavelet spectrum is uniform. Such is the basic assumption made for simple Vibroseis processing. The Vibroseis operation crosscorrelates the recorded trace with a flat or smooth amplitude spectrum wavelet merely to restore the phase of the reflectivity spectrum without appreciably modifying the shape of the amplitude spectrum of the reflectivity. (Lindseth, 1970).

7. Critique of Predictive Deconvolution. Reflectivity spectra are often not completely white, but they are close enough so that in many cases the statistical approach embodied in predictive deconvolution works very well indeed. In the white-reflectivity case, the power spectrum of the trace, which is equal to the product to the reflectivity power spectrum and the wavelet energy spectrum, is approximately proportional to the energy spectrum of the wavelet. Thus the white-reflectivity model, if applicable, provides a method of obtaining the amplitude spectrum of the unknown wavelet from the known amplitude spectrum of the field trace. The white reflectivity model is usually used over short intervals (time gates) on the recorded field trace. The reason is that the physical field trace as generated by the earth is a time-varying phenomenon, whereas all of the usual mathematical convolutional models are time-invariant. The approximations implicit in the convolutional model therefore can only apply over some restricted time interval. However, it is much more difficult to verify statistically that a short interval of a stochastic series is white as compared to a long interval of the series. It is well known that random processes can develop run series which may have

definite non-statistical characteristics when the sample being examined is only a short segment, such as a thin lithologic motif. A long signal is required to verify that the series has a truly random distribution. However, when predictive deconvolution is used within such a restricted time gate on the field trace, and it is indeed used many millions of times each and every day by the oil industry, it is implicitly assumed that the reflectivity function within that time gate is white. Let us now enlarge upon this theme.

The part of the seismic trace within a given time gate contains the primary reflections from the interfaces within a certain section of the earth's crust. If we assume that the reflection coefficients ε_k within this earth section are mutually uncorrelated (i.e., that these ε_k represent a realization from a white-noise process), then the classical method of predictive deconvolution becomes applicable. At this point, let us note that the terms "minimum-delay" and "minimum-phase" are the same so they may be used interchangeably. Also, the terms "predictive deconvolution" and "predictive decomposition" may be used interchangeably.

Predictive deconvolution requires a white minimum-delay model. To emphasize that the seismic wavelet is minimum delay, we use the symbol b_k instead of the general symbol w_k. The convolutional model becomes $x_k = b_k * \varepsilon_k$. The method of predictive deconvolution may be described as follows. Within the time gate, the ε_k are white; hence, all the spectral shape of the trace x_k within the time gate is due to b_k. As a result, computation of the autocorrelation of x_k within the gate averages out the white-noise elements ε_k and, therefore, gives us the autocorrelation of b_k. Since b_k is minimum-delay, its inverse a_k can be computed directly from its autocorrelation by solving the normal equations. The inverse operator a_k is the required spike deconvolution operator. Spike deconvolution is the process of convolving the inverse operator a_k with the trace x_k. The result of the deconvolution is the reflection coefficient sequence ε_k which is called the deconvolved trace. The deconvolved trace ε_k represents the earth's reflectivity as a function of depth within the earth section being analyzed. In practice, of course, many variations of the basic deconvolution method described here can be used. For example, the inverse operator a_k represents an autoregressive operator, that is, a prediction error operator with unit prediction distance; prediction error operators for other prediction distances also can be used. When the prediction distance is equal to one, predictive deconvolution is called spike deconvolution. If the prediction distance is greater than one, predictive deconvolution is called gapped deconvolution. Adaptive and time-varying deconvolution methods as well as multitrace methods may be used also.

One of the basic assumptions of predictive deconvolution is that within a selected gate the reflection coefficient sequence ε_k is white, that is, the assumption that the power spectrum of ε_k is flat within the given gate and that the shape of the power spectrum of the reflected trace within the given gate is due solely to the wavelet b_k. This is a crucial assumption. An investigation of reflection spike sequences estimated from well-log data has shown that within selected gates it is usually valid to the degree required for the successful application of predictive deconvolution. Often a departure from a flat spectrum at low frequencies is indicated. This loss of low frequencies represents a type of deviation which is user-friendly. That is, this deviation is relatively harmless with respect to deconvolution, as compared to more harmful types of deviations which can occur, but fortunately do so much less often. The study of sonic logs from oil wells shows that the assumption of a white reflection sequence is a good one for usually one or several depth intervals (gates) in an oil well, but can break down for certain intervals where a few strong reflections dominate.

Let us now look at the minimum-phase assumption. The fact that reverberating seismic energy is minimum-phase is well established; that is, the multiple reflection wave trains are minimum delay. We must also consider the source waveform which for an explosion is relatively narrow although it cannot be considered as narrow as a spike. Many studies have been made on source pulses. These have shown that the pulse radiated by an explosion is minimum-phase or very close to it. It is usual for underwater sources to emit non-minimum-phase signals but, under good design and proper operational conditions, the non-minimum-phase components can be minimized. In any case, the non-minimum-phase source wavelet should be recorded and removed from the field trace by signature deconvolution. Absorption in the earth is generally held to be minimum-phase, and so too is the response of most recording systems. Minimum-phase then is likely to be satisfied in practice. As a result, all these minimum-phase effects can be included in the minimum-delay wavelet b_k in the convolutional model.

Let us now consider the non-white convolutional model. A non-white model which may be used is one in which the lithologic section is not considered to be the result of purely random process but rather has some periodic or cyclical components. The spectrum is not completely white. Whereas the white model may be treated by purely statistical and or probabilistic methods, the non-white model is a deterministic model which requires that the actual separate components of the spectrum be determined. If the spectrum of the reflectivity is not white problems arise as far as predictive deconvolution is concerned, and deconvolution techniques must be changed or adapted as conditions warrant. Although the non-white model may be a more reliable description of the actual situation, it is also one which is more difficult to work with. Deconvolution operations must be directed to determining the individual contribution of the wavelet and reflectivity components separately, whereas the white minimum-delay model, if applicable, can derive the wavelet from the autocorrelation of the trace. Lindseth (1970) observes that a compromise between the pure statistical approach and the deterministic approach may be visualized as one of the reasons that white noise is added to the spectrum before a deconvolution operator is determined. Apart from purely mathematical reasons concerning stability, white noise is sometimes added to the autocorrelation of the signal in order to develop a deconvolution operator which provides a more satisfying or more useful output. In summary, the process of simple inverse deconvolution by the statistical approach leans heavily on several assumptions in the development of the operator. When the assumptions are valid good results may be expected, but poor results probably are symptomatic of an invalid assumption. Current research is directed to the determination of the problem and the selection of alternative methods to provide better results.

Although the physical theory of wave propagation is straightforward and well understood, its consequences within a system of many layers can be surprisingly elaborate, even as a palette of primary colors (the reflection coefficients) offers little glimpse of the infinite variety of tones that may be obtained by repeated blending (the seismic trace). The prediction of such complex behavior of observed traces has been a longstanding problem in geophysics, with applications ranging from ideal (archetype) situations to ones which cannot be interpreted. To the student of wave dynamics, nature could give no better specimens than the many variations of reflectivity encountered in geophysical surveys. For many years our grasp of the dynamics of seismic traces was limited to theoretical calculations. However, with the large scale processing of digital seismic data, patterns have emerged, and it is now realized that the success of digital methods rests on a statistical interpretation of the geologic processes which produced the sedimentary rock layers. No longer can the geophysical processes of wave propagation be separated from the geological processes of sedimentation. Not quite trusting of the previous rough-and-ready theory, exploration geophysicists in the past few decades began simulating the propagation dynamics of wave motion in layered media on computers and from this infer the raypaths and traveltime of seismic events. This simulation is made meaningful by the excellent measurements which are now taken in oil wells (boreholes), namely, the various logs which give us acoustic impedance (and hence the reflectivity), and the vertical seismic profile (VSP). By shooting a vertical seismic profile (VSP) in an oil well, the actual downgoing and upgoing waves within the sedimentary layers can be directly recorded and compared with those obtained by simulation. The VSP data together with the well log data (velocity log and density log) make possible a new era in seismic exploration. The well log data give a direct measure of the seismic reflectivity (reflection coefficient series), the VSP data give a direct measure of the wave motion within the earth, and finally the seismic field traces give the recorded seismic motion on the surface of the earth. Thus all aspects of the seismic experiment can be measured and cross-verified where boreholes are available. The knowledge gained from such studies can be used to make geophysical methods more reliable in new prospects, where there are no oil wells and we must rely on the field traces alone. The general approach, now, is to use the observed field traces to identify patterns of reflections and thus establish the conditions under which the sedimentary rocks were deposited, and even to establish the history of the sedimentary basin. This approach makes up the discipline of seismic stratigraphy.

In Robinson (1983b) we examine the small white reflection coefficient (SWRC) hypothesis at length, and have called it the archetypal situation. It serves as a benchmark at one end of an infinite range of possibilities, and thus establishes a basis from which we can measure and compare other types of situations which may be encountered in the geologic column. We are also indebted to the imaginative work of Morlet, Arens, Fourgeau, and Giard (1982). They gave us another benchmark, namely the large cyclic reflection coefficient (LCRC) hypothesis. One benchmark is the antithesis of the other, and yet both situations, or approximations to them, can be found within the earth. In one, the reflection coefficients are small; in the other, they are large. In one, the reflection coefficients are white (that is, completely unpredictable); in the other, they are cyclic or periodic (that is, completely predictable). It is interesting that actual geologic situations can fall anywhere between these two extremes. It is even more interesting that at these two extremes, deconvolution of the seismic traces is not required, essentially because we understand the make-up of the seismic trace in such cases. Deconvolution is used, and used successfully, on field traces which correspond to reflectivity functions that lie in that great area between the archetypal (SWRC) case and the Morlet (LCRC) case.

According to the statistical point of view, the reflection coefficient sequence ε_k may be considered as a realization of a random (or stochastic) process. The random minimum-delay convolutional model represents the reflection seismic trace as the composition of a minimum-delay wavelet and a random (but not necessarily white) reflection coefficient series. In theory, the approximation upon which this time-invariant model is based can usually hold with moderate errors only over relatively short time intervals on the seismic trace. In practice, it is usually not feasible to analyze the whole trace in its entirety, and so instead the trace x_k is cut up into time intervals (i.e., time gates) and then is analyzed gate by gate. Often these gates overlap to some extent, and then the results from the several gates are blended together so as to give a time-varying character to the overall analysis. Although this model was introduced in the geophysical literature thirty years ago, it is still the subject of extensive research and spirited discussion. Its underlying structure is extremely recondite despite its simple appearance.

The statistical minimum-delay model is one-dimensional, so it can only be regarded as a prototype of more extensive statistical models that will be possible to construct because of increased data acquisition and data processing capacity. The 1D convolutional model serves to provide us with insight on how statistical wave propagation takes place. It should not be regarded as a final or definitive model in any sense. Higher dimensional models (1.5D, 2D, 2.5D, or 3D) which serve as the basis for stacking and migration also require a statistical basis (Robinson, 1983a).

Let us now examine the statistical minimum-delay model for n interfaces under the hypothesis that the reflection coefficients ε_1, $\varepsilon_2, \cdots, \varepsilon_n$ are small but not white. Then the unnormalized autocorrelation coefficients $\gamma_1, \gamma_2, \cdots, \gamma_{n-1}$ of the reflection coefficients series will not vanish, so the right-half autocorrelation generating function

$$G(s) = \gamma_1 s + \gamma_2 s^2 + \cdots + \gamma_{n-1} s^n$$

will not be zero. Because the reflection coefficients are small, the fundamental polynomials P and Q are approximately

$$P(s) = 1 + G(s)$$
$$Q(s) = -E(s)$$

where E(s) is the reflectivity generating function

$$E(s) = \varepsilon_1 s + \varepsilon_2 s^2 + \cdots + \varepsilon_n s^n$$

Thus the generating function

$$T(s) = \frac{\sigma_n s^{0.5n}}{P(s)}$$

of the seismic transmission response is approximately

$$T(s) = \sigma_n s^{0.5n} [1 - G(s)]$$

where σ_n is the one-way transmission factor

$$\sigma_n = [(1 - c_1^2)(1 - c_2^2) \cdots (1 - c_n^2)]^{1/2}$$

The generating function

$$R(s) = \frac{-Q(s)}{P(s)}$$

of the seismic reflectivity is approximately

$$R(s) = E(s)\ [1 - G(s)]$$

All of the input energy must either come out of the system as part of either T(s) or R(s). The transmission response represents the energy which escapes down into the basement, and R(s) that which escapes up into the air.

In many exploration prospects, the random reflectivity appears to be a realization of a locally correlated process. In simple terms, this effect generally exhibits itself as a negative value for the first-lag autocorrelation coefficient γ_1, and approximately zero values for the autocorrelation coefficients of greater lags. Thus the power spectrum of the reflectivity has the form

$$\Gamma(\omega) = \gamma_0 + 2\gamma_1 \cos \omega$$

where γ_1 is negative. This power spectrum is therefore deficient in low frequencies, and builds up as frequency increases (to the Nyquist frequency $\omega = \pi$). The transmission response generating function becomes simply

$$T(s) = \sigma_n s^{0.5n} (1 - \gamma_1 s)$$

so the transmission response is the wavelet $(\sigma_n, -\gamma_1 \sigma_n)$ where the first coefficient occurs at time 0.5n. Thus the transmission response is a short wavelet with two positive coefficients, which certainly represents a benign situation. Likewise, we have

$$R(s) = E(s) [1 - \gamma_1 s]$$

so the reflection response is

$$(0, \varepsilon_1, \varepsilon_2, \cdots, \varepsilon_n) * (1, -\gamma_1)$$

That is, the reflection response is given by the reflectivity function convolved with the relatively harmless two-term wavelet with positive coefficients. It would be the job of deconvolution to remove this wavelet. We see that in this case, at least, a non-white reflectivity function does not have to be devastating, but instead can be handled with appropriate deconvolution and other data processing techniques.

Let us now answer the question we posed earlier, namely why did the seismic method work in so many areas before the advent of deconvolution and other forms of digital processing? The answer is that in these good seismic areas, the reflection coefficient sequence ε_k is made up of predominantly small coefficients with a white (or nearly white) spectrum for the entire crustal sedimentary column. Thus, the autocorrelations γ_i of the reflection coefficient sequence are approximately zero. Thus, under the small white reflection coefficient (SWRC) hypothesis, we have G(s) = 0, so

$$T(s) = \sigma_n s^{0.5n}$$
$$R(s) = E(s)$$

These equations say that the transmission response is a spike of amplitude σ_n occurring at 0.5n, and that the reflection response is the reflection coefficient series $(0, \varepsilon_1, \varepsilon_2, \cdots, \varepsilon_n)$. This is the archetypal seismogram. In other words, in those areas where the reflection coefficients are small and uncorrelated, the reflection response (i.e., the field trace stripped of the source wavelet, absorption effects and instrument response) reduces simply to the sequence of reflection coefficients ε_k. The net effect of the white nature of the subsurface reflection coefficients is to cancel out all the multiples and to amplify all the primaries so they have amplitude ε_k instead of amplitude $\sigma^2_{k-1}\,\varepsilon_k$. Here is a case in nature where randomness has taken a very complex physical situation and made it extremely simple and beautiful.

If the entire lithology is white, then we have an archetypal (i.e., multiple-free) field trace, so only such things as signature deconvolution and wavelet processing are required. On the other hand, if the lithology is not white, then the field trace has multiples which have to be removed by deconvolution. However, successful application of predictive deconvolution requires that we can find gates in which the lithology is either white or else known.

The archetypal case is interesting for this reason. It helps explain what we mean by the term "completely random". The autocorrelation is a second-order statistic, so it only measures randomness between pairs of variables. In the small white reflection coefficient (SWRC) case, the "small" wipes out all the higher order moments, so we are left with the autocorrelation coefficients, and then the "white" wipes out these second order moments, so the fundamental polynomial P(s) becomes one. When P(s) = 1, only a spike is transmitted into the basement, and all the rest of the energy is displayed as the reflection seismogram. We are thus led to questions like this: Is there a form of randomness where P(s) is approximately one even for large reflection coefficients, and physically what does this mean?

The SWRC case says that a completely unpredictable (i.e., white) reflectivity gives a reflection response which is completely predictable (i.e., the reflection response is equal to the reflectivity). Thus the SWRC case says that the trace is an accurate reflection of the depth function; the source completely and accurately illuminates each and every interface and we see them all in an undistorted way by perfect reflection. The LCRC case says that a completely predictible (i.e., periodic) reflectivity gives a reflection response which does not sort out the individual layers. For a low frequency source, everything is beamed through the layers, so we can see nothing by reflection. For a high frequency source, everything is superreflected from the first interface, and we see nothing below this interface.

What then is the final test for the statistical minimum-delay model and the associated method of predictive decomposition or deconvolution? The answer lies in the fact that today as well as in all years since 1965, virtually every single seismogram taken in the exploration of oil and natural gas has been processed according to this model. These 15 billion or more seismic traces from every part of the world must speak for themselves, and they say the statistical minimum-delay model and the method of predictive deconvolution are physically valid within the economic limits set by the seismic method of petroleum exploration.

In conclusion of this paper let us quote Professor W. A. Schneider (1977): "The work horse of statistical wavelet deconvolution for the past one and one half decades has been the predictive decomposition approach, which assumes the reflectivity function is statistically white and the convolutional wavelet to be minimum phase. To say that this has not been an effective tool is to condemn hundreds of thousands of miles of seismic processing and to deny untold millions of barrels of oil discovered from these data. It would be equally incorrect to say predictive deconvolution, with its restrictive assumptions on the wavelet and reflectivity function, has always been applied intelligently".

REFERENCES

M. M. Backus, 1959, Water reverberations, their nature and elimination, Geophysics, v. 24, pp. 233-262.

M. M. Backus, and R. Chen, 1975, Flat spot exploration, Geophysical Prospecting, v. 23, pp. 533-577.

E. K. Darby, and N. S. Neidell, 1966, Application of dynamic programming to the problem of plane wave propagation in a layered medium: Geophysics, v. 31, no. 6, pp. 1037-1048.

M. Foster, R. Sengbush, and R. Watson, 1968, Use of Monte Carlo techniques in optimum design of the deconvolution process: Geophysics, v. 23, no. 6.

J. N. Galbraith, 1971, Prediction error as a criterion for operator length, Geophysics 36, pp. 261-265.

J. W. J. Hoskin, 1980, A stochastic model of seismic reflections, 50th Annual Meeting, Society of Exploration Geophysicists, Tulsa, OK.

R. O. Lindseth, 1970, Recent advances in digital processing of geophysical data, Society of Exploration Geophysicists, Tulsa, OK.

J. P. Lindsey, 1960, Elimination of seismic ghost reflections by means of a linear filter: Geophysics, v. 25, no. 1, pp. 130-141.

J. Makhoul, 1975, Linear Prediction: A Tutorial Review, IEEE Proc. 63, pp. 561-580.

J. M. Mendel, 1977, "White noise estimators for seismic data processing in oil exploration", IEEE Trans. on Automatic Control, v. AC-22, no. 5, pp. 694-706.

J. M. Mendel, and J. Kormylo, 1978, Single channel white noise estimators for deconvolution, Geophysics, v. 43, pp. 102-124.

R. F. Mereu, 1976, Exact wave-shaping with a time-domain digital filter of finite length, Geophysics 41, pp. 659-672.

J. Morlet, G. Arens, E. Fourgeau, and D. Giard, 1982, Wave propagation and sampling theory, Geophysics, v. 47, pp. 203-236.

J. G. Negi, and V. P. Dimri, 1979, On Wiener filter and maximum entropy method for multichannel complex systems, Geophys. Prospect. 27, pp. 156-167.

K. L. Peacock, and S. Treitel, 1969, Predictive Deconvolution: Theory and Practice, Geophysics, v. 34, no. 2, pp. 155-169.

W. K. Pratt, 1972, Generalized Wiener filtering computation techniques, IEEE Trans. Computers C-21, pp. 636-641.

E. A. Robinson, 1954, Predictive decomposition of seismic traces with applications to seismic exploration. Ph.D. Thesis, M.I.T., Cambridge, MA. (Reprinted in Geophysics, v. 32, pp. 418-484, 1967).

E. A. Robinson, 1957, Predictive decomposition of seismic traces, Geophysics, v. 22, no. 4, pp. 767-778.

E. A. Robinson, 1966, Multichannel z-transforms and minimum-delay, Geophysics, v. 31, pp. 482-500.

E. A. Robinson, 1968, Basic equations for synthetic seismograms using the z-transform approach, Geophysics, v. 33, pp. 521-523.

E. A. Robinson, 1978, Iterative identification of non-invertible autoregressive moving averge systems with seismic applications, Geoexploration, v. 16, pp. 1-19.

E. A. Robinson, 1983a, Migration of Geophysical Data, IHRDC Publishing Co., Boston, MA.

E. A. Robinson, 1983b, Seismic Inversion and Deconvolution, Geophysical Press, Amsterdam.

E. A. Robinson, and S. Treitel, 1980, Geophysical Signal Analysis, Prentice Hall, Englewood Cliffs, NJ.

J. C. Robinson, 1972, Computer-designed Wiener filters for seismic data, Geophysics 37, pp. 235-259.

W. A. Schneider, 1977, Wavelet processing. In: The Stationary Convolutional Model of the Reflection Seismogram, Society of Exploration Geophysicists, Tulsa, OK.

W. A. Schneider, K. L. Larner, J. P. Burg, and M. M. Backus, 1964, A new data-processing technique for the elimination of ghost arrivals on reflection seismograms: Geophysics, v. 29, no. 5, pp. 783-805.

C. J. Sicking, 1980, Windowing and estimation variance in deconvolution, paper presented at the 50th Annual International Meeting of SEG, Houston, TX.

S. Treitel, and E. A. Robinson, Deconvolution - homomorphic or predictive? IEEE Trans. on Geoscience Electronics, v. GE-15, no. 1, pp. 11-13, Jan. 1977.

S. Treitel, and R. J. Wang, 1976, The determination of digital Wiener filters from an ill-conditioned system of normal equations, Geophys. Prospect. 24, pp. 317-327.

T. J. Ulrych, D. E. Smylie, O. G. Jenson, and G. K. C. Clarke, 1973, Predictive filtering and smoothing of short records by using maximum entropy, J. Geophys. Res 78, pp. 4959-4964.

G. P. Wadsworth, E. A. Robinson, J. G. Bryan, and P. M. Hurley, 1953, Detection of reflections on seismic records by linear operators, Geophysics 18, pp. 539-586.

R. J. Wang, 1977, Adaptive predictive deconvolution of seismic data, Geophysical Prospecting, v. 25, pp. 342-381.

R. J. Wang, and S. Treitel, 1973, The determination of digital Wiener filters by means of gradient methods, Geophysics 38, pp. 310-326.

G. M. Webster, 1978, Deconvolution, v. 1, Geophysics Reprint Series. SEG, Tulsa, OK.

R. E. White, and P. N. S. O'Brien, 1974, Estimation of the primary seismic pulse, Geophysical Prospecting, v. 22, no. 4, pp. 627-651.

N. Wiener, 1949, The extrapolation, interpolation and smoothing of stationary time series with engineering applications, M.I.T. Press, Cambridge, MA.

R. A. Wiggins, and E. A. Robinson, 1965, Recursive solution to the multichannel filering problem, J. Geophys. Res. 70, pp. 1885-1891.